W9-AQN-995

DISCOVERIES AND OPINIONS OF GALILEO

Stillman Drake was born in 1910 in California, and received his A.B. from the University of California in 1932. His interest in the history and biography of science centers in seventeenth-century physics and astronomy. Beginning with the *Dialogue Concerning the Two World Systems*, published in 1953, he has translated into English virtually all the scientific works of Galileo. Mr. Drake is a member of the History of Science Society and the History of Science Dinner Club of the University of California. Previously employed by Blyth & Co., Inc. in San Francisco, Mr. Drake is now Professor of the History of Science at the University of Toronto.

DISCOVERIES AND OPINIONS OF GALILEO

Including

The Starry Messenger (1610)

Letter to the Grand Duchess Christina (1615)

And Excerpts from

Letters on Sunspots (1613)

The Assayer (1623)

Translated
with an Introduction and Notes
by Stillman Drake

DOUBLEDAY ANCHOR BOOKS
DOUBLEDAY & COMPANY, INC., GARDEN CITY, NEW YORK

COVER BY ANTONIO FRASCONI

TYPOGRAPHY BY EDWARD GOREY

The Anchor Books edition is the first publication of
Discoveries and Opinions of Galileo.

Anchor Books edition: 1957

)

To
FRANK DE BELLIS
*dauntless in the cause
of Italian culture*

PREFACE

The purpose of this book is to present in substantially Galileo's own words both the astronomical discoveries that made him famous and the philosophical opinions that cost him his freedom.

Four short works of Galileo's have been selected. Two have never before appeared in English, while two have been previously translated but are practically unobtainable. Free translations have been made and mathematical sections have been omitted, with the interests of the general reader principally in mind. Other technical passages have been left intact in the hope that students also will make use of this volume. The casual reader may skip such portions without serious loss of continuity, and his indulgence is accordingly requested. Brief explanatory notes are included.

The introductory material is divided into four sections, one being placed before each of the translations. These sections proceed chronologically and may be read as a continuous essay if desired. They are designed to sketch the general background of Galileo's significance to our time, the conditions which preceded his work, and the effect upon it of certain crucial events which occurred during the middle years of his life. Anything like a complete biography lies far beyond the scope of this volume, but for those who may wish to pursue further reading a short chronology of principal events in Galileo's life and a bibliography of books in English have been provided as an appendix.

Translations of the *Letters on Sunspots* and excerpts from *The Assayer* have been made directly from the Italian texts as presented in the definitive edition of Galileo's works compiled under the supervision of Professor Antonio Favaro. Translations of *The Starry Messenger* and the

Letter to the Grand Duchess are based upon earlier English versions cited in the appendix, corrected and modernized after comparison with the texts in the above edition and with translations into other languages. The chief abridgments are indicated by rows of dots, placed between paragraphs when the material omitted is of considerable length. Many condensations or short deletions have been made without indication.

Grateful acknowledgment is rendered to Mr. Eric Bentley for having suggested this undertaking, to Mr. Jason Epstein for encouraging it, to Mr. Jon Cornin for his friendly assistance and suggestions, and to Miss Katharine Coggins for help in preparing the manuscript. Mr. Victor di Suvero was most helpful in reviewing and correcting the translations of extracts from *The Assayer*. Professor Antonio Banfi has kindly consented to the use of a passage from his superb biography of Galileo, and Professor Erwin Panofsky to a quotation from one of his letters.

CONTENTS

CONTENTS

DISCOVERIES AND OPINIONS OF GALILEO

INTRODUCTION: FIRST PART

I

A century ago Giacomo Leopardi, in an essay on fame, re-marked that continual progress in science obscures the achievements of men who have devoted their lives to it. He took Galileo as an example. "Who reads the works of Galileo any more?" he asked. "Certainly they were quite remarkable in their time, yet any average physicist of our age is far superior to Galileo in his science."[1]

We may let Galileo retort in his own words. Writing in praise of William Gilbert, his great predecessor in the study of magnetism, he said: "I do not doubt that in the course of time this new science will be improved by further obser-vations, and still more by true and conclusive proofs. But this need not diminish the glory of the first observer. My regard for the inventor of the harp is not made less by knowing that his instrument was very crudely constructed and still more crudely played. Rather, I admire him more than I do the hundreds of craftsmen who in ensuing cen-turies have brought this art to the highest perfection. . . . To apply oneself to great inventions, starting from the smallest beginnings, is no task for ordinary minds; to divine that wonderful arts lie hid behind trivial and childish things is a conception for superhuman talents."[2]

If modern physicists care nothing for the works of Ga-lileo, that is a matter of taste and not merely one of progress. Modern poets still read Homer, and modern philosophers Plato, not only because those works are excellently written

[1] Quoted from Enrico Persico, *Galileo e la fisica* (Milan, 1942). Cf. Leopardi, *Parini's Discourse on Glory*, ch. 11.
[2] *Dialogue Concerning the Two Chief World Systems* (Berke-ley, 1953) pp. 406-7. (Cited hereafter as *Dialogue*.)

but also because they throw light upon the origins of poetry and philosophy—matters of special interest to poets and philosophers, and not without a certain value and attraction to the rest of us. Similarly the works of Galileo are well written, and throw light upon the origins of modern science; hence, even if few physicists are interested in them today, it does not necessarily follow that no one else ought to be.

Leopardi was an Italian man of letters, and it was natural that he should choose an Italian scientist to illustrate his idea. Unfortunately his reasoning implies that Galileo's books were intended to be read only, or at least primarily, by physicists. This is as if one were to suppose that Homer wrote only for poets, or Plato primarily for philosophers. But the fact is that Galileo scarcely ever got around to writing for physicists at all. Nearly without exception he wrote and published for the benefit of his countrymen in every walk of life who happened to share his insatiable curiosity about the universe and his ardent wish to discover the laws of nature. Indeed, there were no physicists in his day except philosophers, and these soon became his principal opponents. During most of his life Galileo ignored his professorial colleagues abroad by refusing to write in Latin. The readers he especially cultivated at home lived outside the universities, as we shall presently learn from his own words. And they were delighted by his barbed attacks against pedantry as well as by the colloquial fashion in which he presented his own discoveries and opinions.

For the sake of argument we may grant that if in Leopardi's time the physicists had little reason to read the works of Galileo, they have still less reason now. But what about the rest of us? Science now dominates every phase of our culture to a degree that can hardly be exaggerated. It follows that we ought to have an interest in every truly significant phase of this phenomenon which so profoundly affects our lives and thoughts. To the most recent developments in science we are indeed almost obliged to pay some attention, but these are not necessarily its most significant aspects in a cultural sense. So far as scientific facts are con-

cerned, no layman can hope to acquire more than the most
superficial smattering; it is a commonplace that today even
the best-informed man is not fully in touch with the latest
developments in more than a few specialized fields. Facts,
however, constitute only a part of what science has to teach
us, and they make up neither the most interesting nor the
most significant part in relation to the age in which we
live. The truly influential and pervasive aspects of modern
science are not its facts at all, but rather its method of
inquiry and its criterion of truth.

Now those are precisely the things whose introduction
created modern science. They were, moreover, first made
clear in the writings of Galileo, and perhaps even today
there is no other source from which they may be obtained
more easily, more clearly, or more entertainingly by the
nonscientific reader. It was to the man of general interests
that Galileo originally addressed his works, and his remarkable success in explaining his method and revealing his
criterion of truth is attested by the prompt and vigorous
opposition which he inspired, led by professors who regarded the new method as injurious to philosophy and by
priests who believed the new criterion of truth to be inimical to religion. All later attempts to explain scientific
method and define scientific truth, however much more
logical and thorough, have been considerably less effective.

We may be inclined to take it for granted that we fully
understand the implications of scientific method; that we
can easily tell whether or not any given statement may
properly be called scientific. But the things we take for
granted are not always those which we best understand.
Thoughtful men of our time are often disturbed to hear the
term "scientific" carelessly applied. Some say that it is a
term not truly comprehended by anyone unless he has personally confronted laboratory problems or conscientiously
designed experiments of his own. No doubt the best way to
find out all that is implied by the word "scientific" is to
become a scientist, but that is a course not open to everyone. A quite reasonable alternative is to read the writings

of a man who was obliged to work out for himself, step by step, all the required procedures. Such a man was Galileo. If we wish to capture the true and living spirit of scientific inquiry without seeking this in the laboratory ourselves, then we cannot do better than to read his works.

II

The true originators of new lines of thought speak perforce not to specialists but to all who will listen. Hence it is not to Galileo, who wrote for laymen, so much as to Newton, who wrote for physicists, that Leopardi's explanation of neglect might truly apply. By 1687, when Newton published his monumental *Mathematical Principles of Natural Philosophy,* the educated layman for whom Galileo had written was left far behind. Newton's work had to be interpreted to the public by popularizers, and ever since his time we have depended upon such intermediaries for news of scientific advances and explanations of their significance to us. But Galileo was his own popularizer. He had to be, for he wanted both the methods and the rudiments of the new sciences he was founding to be understood by everyone who could read. Because his literary talents were considerable he was able to present his discoveries attractively and his opinions persuasively. The purely scientific material in his books was enlivened for the reader by the devastating sarcasm with which he was accustomed to puncture his pompous opponents. This sort of thing went out of fashion in physical science as rapidly as the old criteria of truth gave way to those which Galileo himself introduced. Thus Galileo's polemics in science rendered polemics in science obsolete. But at the same time they make his work eminently readable, and moreover they contribute substantially to our understanding of the origin and essential nature of modern scientific thought by giving us a glimpse of what preceded it.

Less than fifty years elapsed between Galileo's last book and Newton's first, but the changes that had taken place during that interval were enormous. The focus of intellectual interest had moved; the thin edge of the wedge which now separates the scientist from the public had been driven. Since we shall not have occasion to explore the changes that took place after Galileo's time, we may suggest them here by contrasting the two men themselves. Each spent a period as professor in a prominent university and then entered a sort of government service. But there all resemblance ends. Galileo's work had gone counter to every accepted tradition of his age; Newton's fitted intimately into the spirit of his time. Newton shrank from controversy and declined even to answer ignorant critics; Galileo was nothing if not combative, and used his most obstinate opponents as foils for his own purposes. Newton cared little for society, particularly that of women. Galileo thrived on companionship, and his mistress bore him three children. Newton tended to be abstemious, while Galileo delighted in wine—which he called "light held together by moisture"—and even when under close arrest he insisted on having a well-stocked cellar. Whenever he could find time he diverted himself by gardening, and he loved to observe the growth of plants; Newton, though he took an occasional turn in his garden, could not abide the sight of a weed there. Galileo took pleasure in conversing with artisans and applying his science to their practical problems; Newton preferred the precisely designed experiment and the deductive application of scientific laws. While Newton spent much of his life in alchemical pursuits and theological speculations, Galileo (almost alone in his age) ridiculed the alchemists, and ventured into theology only when it encroached upon his science. Galileo was personally skilled in art, talented in music, and devoted to literature; to Newton these appear to have remained passive enjoyments. In Galileo it is hard to say whether the qualities of the man of the Renaissance were dominant, or those of our own scientific age. Of Newton this question cannot even be asked.

III

The spirit of modern science, the conditions of its origin, and the reasons for its eventual triumph shine through the vestiges of older thought in the works of Galileo. But that is not all. The very issues for which Galileo fought are by no means settled, though for a long time they appeared to be. Now, after a period of quiescence, they have once again come vividly to life.

Science has afforded man an unprecedented mastery over nature. But to those who do not regard the conquest of nature as a proper end in itself, science has never appeared as an unmixed blessing. In the beginning, men who viewed it with distrust were very numerous and influential, and wherever they held power scientific thought was quickly subordinated to their authority. Gradually their number and influence diminished as the value to mankind of free scientific inquiry became apparent, and the effectiveness with which they could enforce their authority weakened. A final attempt to subordinate science to religion was made a century ago when the doctrine of organic evolution was propounded, and that attempt merely added to the prestige of science. As a result we became accustomed to seeing the protests of the antiscientific treated with impatience if not contempt.

But within the last decade events have created a new alarm concerning the unchecked progress of scientific knowledge. This time it is not the church but the state which feels morally obliged to impose external limitations upon the freedom of scientific inquiry and the communication of knowledge and opinion. This time the universities are impelled by public opinion and governmental policies to reconsider the scope of academic freedom, rather than by philosophical opinion and theological policies. But it is not the issues which are new, nor even the forms in which they confront us; only the center around which antiscientific forces rally has been changed. The issues are very similar to those which were fought out in the time of Galileo; the stakes are not much higher now than they were then, and the balance of power between the two sides is about the same as before.

Whether or not the fears of those who would now save us from science are any better grounded than were those of the men who opposed its unrestrained advance at the very beginning remains to be seen. Meanwhile it is instructive to reconsider the first battle that was waged in this long war of ideas—a battle which began with skirmishes between Galileo and his adversaries, and ended with their official but brief victory and his punishment. We shall be concerned only with those first skirmishes and the uneasy armistice that preceded the pitched battle; his ultimate defeat has been much discussed in other books, where these early but significant thrusts and parries of opinion have been relatively neglected.

Even in those early stages the forces that came into play were many and varied. It is of course impossible to do justice here to many of the factors that historically were involved, or even to avoid misrepresenting them to some extent by necessarily arbitrary selection and emphasis. Nevertheless a brief sketch of the background of the age will be attempted in the hope of making clearer the impact of Galileo's discoveries and opinions upon his contemporaries.

IV

European life in the Middle Ages displays even to the casual student a unifying web of religious beliefs and aspirations. Despite the myriad political sovereignties, despite the limited contact between men of different lands, despite the barriers of caste and a host of other conditions of daily life which tended to divide and separate men, all shared a common faith that dominated the intellectual spirit of the time. Scholarship was possible only through patronage except in rare and unusual cases, and it therefore tended to center upon the interests of the church that in return provided its chief support. The study and interpretation of texts occupied a high place among scholarly pursuits, and next after purely religious texts those of a philosophical nature received the most attention. Hence it appears that few practical problems of a physical nature were presented to scholars for consideration and solution, or indeed came to their attention in any way. Philosophical problems of physics were the subject of much discussion, but the method employed was that of logical argument as applied to the opinions of ancient writers, rather than direct observation and investigation. Not the laws of nature, but the divine will which underlay them, was considered the proper object of inquiry.

The pursuit of learning during the Middle Ages brought students into association around teachers of great reputation in many European cities. These associations, which at first were informal congregations of mature men in quest of specific instruction, gradually evolved into formal universities with recognized civil jurisdictions and having the power to confer degrees and to accredit teachers. As repositories of accumulated knowledge and as establishments responsible for the continuance of authoritative instruction, the universities necessarily became conservative institutions in every sense of the term. Although not controlled by the church, they were predominantly peopled by churchmen and every teacher was imbued with church doctrines. Because scholars came to them from every land and migrated continually from one university to another, all instruction was given in Latin. Thus the universities had great influence in preserving the religious emphasis of scholarly researches, in resisting the intrusion of unorthodox doctrines, and in maintaining a separation of language between scholars and men in other walks of life.

With the opening of the Renaissance, rifts appeared in the unity of medieval intellectual life. Preoccupation with religious matters began to give way before the wonders of reported explorations and discoveries. Intellectual interests and the desire for knowledge commenced to spread beyond the circles of professional scholarship into those of the nobility and the rising merchant class. Texts of works from classical antiquity and from oriental lands became available in much greater number and variety. While these were distracting some of the scholars from their traditional hair-splitting disputes, men of culture generally became curious about the origins of familiar things and the nature of alien ones. Even before any open split occurred within the church itself, a diversion of intellectual interest from God and his word into man and his works had taken place in the ranks of scholars. This humanist movement was originally neither hostile to, nor irreconcilable with, Christian theology; it was at first simply the opening of a new outlet for intellectual energy. Yet with its advent the monopoly of theology and philosophy upon the minds of men, so to speak, was broken. Humanism captured the imagination of a large proportion of the liveliest geniuses of the time, and though its intention was not to weaken religious institutions, its effect was to undermine their power.

V

Italy was pre-eminently the land of the Renaissance and the home of the humanist movement in its greatest vitality. Of the many ways in which this manifested itself, two are of primary interest here—the cultivation of the colloquial language and the spontaneous appearance of informal academies. Both these phenomena are inextricably linked with the origin of modern science and do much to explain its astonishingly rapid progress and its characteristic points of emphasis.

The origin of Italian literature and emergence of the Tuscan dialect as the literary language considerably ante-dates the Renaissance; in this the works of Dante, Petrarch and Boccaccio had been decisive. During the early Renaissance there was in fact a definite return to Latin, largely as a result of excessive admiration for and imitation of classical works. The scholarly language was also preferred for translations of newly discovered Greek texts. But before long the previous literary movement was resumed, and great pride came to be taken in the power and expressiveness of the native tongue. During the sixteenth century a large number of classic works were translated into Italian. The center of this movement was Florence, and a guiding spirit in it was the *Accademia degli Umidi*—the "Academy of Moistures." The founders of this organization were literary men who at first met merely to enjoy the pleasure of mutual discussion; as it grew in size and influence the society gained the patronage of the Grand Duke and was transformed into the Florentine Academy. In the cultivation of their mother tongue the academicians not only translated many classics but composed popular books of philosophy and science, and proposed the compilation of a complete dictionary of spoken Italian. This latter project was eventually carried out by an offshoot of the Florentine Academy which called itself the *Accademia della Crusca*—the "Academy of Chaff."

These fanciful names, and others adopted by many of the academies founded during this period everywhere in Italy, bespeak the half-serious, half-deprecatory attitude of men who pursued their studies outside the universities and who concentrated their attention upon subjects not recognized in orthodox and conservative curricula. Anything related to man was considered by them a legitimate object of research —his artistic as well as his philosophical, his literary as well as his political history. Music, architecture, sculpture, and painting found new vigor in activities independent of the requirements of the church, while their origins and history were eagerly traced among ruins and relics of the past and in allusions by classical authors. Often enough the men who undertook these tasks had been trained in the universities, but were not associated with them in any other way. Applying their education in the directions and fashions that best suited their own tastes, they in turn formed associations in order to communicate their ideas and spread their interests, yet without quite daring to represent themselves seriously as organizations of learned men in competition with or in opposition to the universities. The modest and sometimes even abject names which they therefore applied to their academies tend to hide the enormous importance of those institutions in the development of new fields of scholarship and the transmission of new knowledge to the public.

VI

We must next consider, though briefly, the state of astronomy prior to the time of Galileo. Although it was a good deal more scientific in its approach than was physics, still it bore little resemblance to the astronomy with which we are familiar today. Heavenly bodies were not regarded as physical objects made of ordinary matter. They were supposed instead to consist of some superior kind of substance free from all change. Their motions were investigated geometrically, but there was no thought of reducing their behavior to mechanical laws. Ancient Greek astronomers had adopted perfectly circular motion of all heavenly bodies as axiomatic. Philosophers supported this idea by asserting that only perfectly circular motion was appropriate to these perfect and unchanging bodies. Yet observation had revealed many difficulties in allowing simple circular motion around the earth to all the planets, among which the sun and moon were included at that time. Various devices had been invented to "save the appearances." In the Ptolemaic system[3] there were two. First, the centers of planetary orbits were placed at some distance from the center of the earth, and such orbits were called *eccentric*. Second, most planets were given small circular orbits around centers which moved in large circles around the earth, and these smaller circles were called *epicycles*. The latter were of special value in accounting for the fact that planets appear

[3] This system took its name from Claudius Ptolemy, who brought it to completion about 150 A.D. It had been set forth by Hipparchus about three centuries earlier. Although the Ptolemaic system was defended by the followers of Aristotle, in reality it was the much older astronomy of Eudoxus (ca. 408–355 B.C.) to which Aristotle's statements were originally intended to apply.

from time to time to slow down, stop, and temporarily reverse their motion among the fixed stars.[4]

With the passage of time and the accumulation of more accurate observations, a great number of eccentrics and epicycles had to be introduced in order to account for various irregularities. As a result, astronomical computations had become very complex. Even worse, in the eyes of mathematicians, was the increasing departure of the entire astronomical system from that symmetry and elegance which they and the philosophers expected of it. Early in the sixteenth century the Polish astronomer Copernicus, impelled by distaste for this inelegance, suggested placing the sun at or near the center of the heavens and giving the earth an orbit equivalent to that which had previously been assigned to the sun. This reduced the complexity of the calculations relatively little, but it had the very great advantage of introducing greater order and symmetry into man's conception of the heavens. At the same time it had the objectionable feature of removing the earth from its unique and distinguished situation at the center of the universe—a result which could not fail to antagonize the philosophers and above all the theologians, who taught that the heavenly bodies were created especially for the use and service of man, and that man was the subject of God's principal care and concern. The Copernican system had the further disadvantage of requiring vast and rapid motions of the earth, which seemed to contradict all common sense and everyday experience. Fully aware of the controversy this would create, Copernicus long refrained from publishing his ideas, though they circulated among other scholars in manuscript form and in a brief published description by one of his pupils. Eventually he was persuaded to publish them in full in the great book *De revolutionibus orbium coelestium,* the first copy of which was placed in his hands while he lay on his deathbed in 1543. Unknown to Copernicus a preface had been anonymously added to his book

---

[4] This happens, for example, when the earth in its annual course about the sun overtakes and passes (so to speak) one of the slower-moving outer planets.

by an officious clergyman, advising readers that the ideas in it were to be construed not literally but merely as hypotheses useful in simplifying the work of astronomers.

The storm of controversy which might have been expected did not take place at once. Most writers on astronomy continued to accept the arguments Ptolemy had set forth against any motion of the earth and against its being situated anywhere except at the center of the universe. A few adhered to the new system but made little effort to popularize it.

In 1572 a supernova and in 1577 an exceptionally conspicuous comet appeared and were carefully observed by the Danish astronomer, Tycho Brahe, who determined that both these phenomena were located in the celestial regions; that is, beyond the moon. The motion of the comet destroyed for him the possibility of solid crystalline spheres in the heavens such as were generally assumed to carry the stars and planets in their courses, for the comet would necessarily have penetrated them. These and other considerations induced him to forsake the Ptolemaic system, though he did not accept that of Copernicus. Instead he proposed a third alternative in which the earth remained fixed at the center of the universe while the moon and sun went around it, the planets revolving about the sun as it went around the earth.

This system offered a convenient escape for those who were aware of the untenability of the Ptolemaic view but could not accept a motion of the earth. It seems absurd to us, because we think of the planetary motions in terms of the laws of mechanics, but from a strictly geometrical point of view such as was taken by astronomers of that period the Tychonic system was equivalent to its rivals. Some well-informed astronomers connected with the Catholic Church, particularly among the Jesuits, supported Tycho, while those associated with the universities generally adhered to Ptolemy in deference to the philosophers who had linked his views with those of Aristotle. Hence the system of Copernicus was not widely discussed, and the great controversy over its merits was to await the time when it first came to the attention of large numbers of people with evidence in support of it that had not been known to its author.

VII

The old and distinguished Florentine family from which Galileo[5] was descended had originally been called Bonajuti. His great-great-grandfather had changed the family name to Galilei in honor of a brother, a noted physician of the fifteenth century whose given name was Galileo. Vincenzio Galilei, the father of the great scientist, was by trade a cloth merchant. He had moved the family from Florence to Pisa in the hope of improving its fortunes, and it was there that Galileo was born on February 15, 1564, about the same time as Shakespeare. Vincenzio was an accomplished musician, composer, and music theorist who wrote several books on these subjects that reveal some traits later characteristic of his son—a good knowledge of mathematics, distrust and even contempt of reliance upon authority, and a pugnacious temper. From him Galileo received instruction not only in music but probably in drawing, a field in which his skill is said to have been noteworthy and his judgment to have been such as to have enjoyed the respect of several noted artists. His love for music endured all his life, and he found solace in his years of adversity by playing on the lute.

Galileo's unusual abilities soon became sufficiently evident to justify his enrollment at the University of Pisa despite the family's meager funds. His father wished him to study medicine, but at that time university instruction in this subject consisted largely in lecturing from the texts of Galen and Aristotle and inculcating respect for those authors. This Galileo found very tiresome. He frequently disputed the doctrines thus handed down, and acquired a reputation among his professors as obstinate and argumentative. Meanwhile his own interest turned to mathematics, in which his first instruction is said to have come from out-

[5] With the exception of rulers, Galileo is the last of the great Italians to enjoy the distinction of being known almost universally by his given name.

side the university at the hands of a teacher attached to the Tuscan court, Ostilio Ricci by name. Ricci was a practical rather than an academic mathematician, and it is probably significant that Galileo's introduction to mathematics came from such a source, as his ultimate great contributions to physics consisted in the application of mathematical concepts to observed phenomena—something that has never had much appeal to pure mathematicians.

At the age of twenty-five, with assistance from Guidobaldo dal Monte, a nobleman of great scientific talent, Galileo secured the chair of mathematics at the University of Pisa. It was a miserably paid post, but one that enabled him to pursue his real interests. During his professorship at Pisa he is said to have proved the incorrectness of Aristotle's ideas about the speeds of falling bodies by dropping unequal weights from the Leaning Tower. Such demonstrations, however conclusive they would be for us, had little effect upon the professors of philosophy, who felt an antipathy in any case toward this former pupil of theirs who had so often set himself up against the authority of the ancients. Either because of this mutual dislike or because of political pressure used against Galileo by an illegitimate son of the Grand Duke whom he had offended, the appointment at Pisa did not last long. In the summer of 1592, being then twenty-eight years old, Galileo left his native Tuscany for the Republic of Venice, having obtained the long-vacant chair of mathematics at the University of Padua.

VIII

Galileo remained at Padua for eighteen years. There he accomplished most of the work in mechanics which lies at the basis of modern physics, though he did not publish this until long afterward. It appears that he taught only conventional courses in mathematics and astronomy, but that he went somewhat beyond these in the private instruction which he gave to many students in order to supplement his salary. Several of these private pupils became lifelong friends who were able later to give him valuable support. At Padua he lived for several years with a Venetian woman named Marina Gamba, who bore him two daughters (in 1600 and 1601) and a son (in 1606). The years he spent at Padua were later recalled by Galileo as the happiest of his life. Yet while there he seems never to have abandoned the idea of returning to Tuscany, and when he succeeded in doing so he never revisited Padua or Venice despite many promises that he would.

Around the year 1597 Galileo devised a mathematical instrument which he called the "geometric and military compass."[6] This was not unlike the proportional compass already in use elsewhere in Europe, though Galileo's model was an improvement in several respects and bore a number of additional scales of his own invention. The instrument enabled its user to solve a wide variety of problems, and in this period before the invention of logarithms it was invaluable to engineers and military men. There was sufficient demand for it to justify Galileo in employing a craftsman to produce his compasses in quantity for sale. A dispute originating over this invention first precipitated Galileo into the realm of polemic writing—a field in which he must have enjoyed himself a good deal, as he never again left it. This first literary feud arose as follows.

As early as 1601 Galileo had applied to the reigning family at Florence, the Medici, for appointment as tutor in mathematics to the heir apparent, Cosimo. This action was part of his quiet campaign to remain in the minds of the Tuscan rulers in the hope of returning there in a position of distinction. When Cosimo was old enough to benefit from such instruction, which was not until the summer vacation of 1605, Galileo was invited to give him private lessons. The course included instruction in the use of his compass. When Galileo returned to Padua he prepared his first book, published at his own house in 1606. It was in effect a handbook of instructions for buyers of the compass, and he

[6] This instrument, later called the "sector," served among other purposes that of today's proportional compass or proportional divider.

dedicated it to the young prince. He wrote it in the Tuscan dialect partly to gratify his noble pupil and partly in order to assure its usefulness to practical men. For the use of scholars, especially those outside Italy, a Latin work on the same subject was promptly published by a student at Padua named Baldassar Capra. To Galileo's irritation a large part of Capra's production was merely a translation (or rather a Latin paraphrase) of Galileo's book; moreover, Capra practically accused Galileo of having stolen the invention from him. This combination of plagiarism and effrontery was too much for Galileo, who brought charges against the author before the university officials and had the book suppressed and Capra severely censured. But since not all copies were recovered, and Galileo feared that Capra's insolent charges might have damaged his reputation both in Italy and abroad, he published in 1607 a *Defense against the Calumnies and Impostures of Baldassar Capra*. In this very entertaining book Galileo first displayed those polemic talents which were soon to be brought to bear in much more serious subjects upon far more formidable opponents.

IX

The year 1609 was a turning point in the history of astronomy and in Galileo's own career. In that year the great German astronomer Johannes Kepler, with whom Galileo had been in correspondence intermittently for many years, published a momentous book called *Astronomia Nova*—the New Astronomy. This book contained the key to the true description of the planetary motions and foreshadowed their explanation decades later by Sir Isaac Newton. Kepler had been an assistant to Tycho, upon whose death in 1601 he acquired the Danish astronomer's incomparably accurate observations of the orbit of Mars. After many years of painstaking analysis applied to these data, Kepler had finally succeeded in discovering the source of confusion and error which had existed in all previous theories of the planets. His discovery was that the shape of a planetary orbit is not circular, but elliptical, and that the sun is not at the center but at one focus of the ellipse. This discovery cleared the path to the elimination of the eccentric circles and epicycles which had beset all previous astronomy.

The importance of Kepler's work was not immediately recognized, even by Galileo; in fact it was not fully appreciated until the time of Newton, who showed that Kepler's findings could be mathematically deduced from the law of universal gravitation. The *Astronomia Nova* was an enormous volume in which the crucial proof was buried amid a long description of Kepler's researches, including all the wrong leads and blind alleys which he took an unaccountable interest in relating. Moreover, Kepler's Latin was not always clear even to his contemporaries, and relatively few really studied his work. Even among those who did, there were not many men open-minded enough to consider seriously the possibility of noncircular orbits in the heavens. Hence, although Kepler's greatest contribution to astronomy belongs to the year 1609, it remained almost unknown until much later.

In the same year that Kepler in Germany was publishing his great but unappreciated contribution to theoretical astronomy, Galileo in Italy was preparing a contribution to observational astronomy which was destined to have a very different fate. In June or July of 1609 word reached him that a curious optical device had been invented in Holland, by means of which distant objects could be made to appear closer. The details were unknown to Galileo, but he promptly set to work to figure them out for himself if he could. His own account of the events which followed will be found in the first and last of the works here translated. Whether or not he was the first to apply the telescope to celestial objects (a matter of perennial debate among historians of science), Galileo was certainly the first to publish the results of that momentous event.

The book describing Galileo's observations appeared in March 1610. Unlike Kepler's massive tome it was scarcely more than a pamphlet. There was no doubt in Galileo's mind of the authenticity and importance of the discoveries

he announced, and since he wished to have them reach astronomers and philosophers all over Europe as quickly as
possible he addressed his book to them and wrote it in
Latin. He called it the *Sidereus Nuncius*, which was generally taken to mean "the messenger of the stars," not only
by Galileo's contemporaries but by translators in succeeding generations.[7] Several booklets appeared in reply with
titles referring to this "messenger," and there were allusions to this idea in many poems and literary works. Galileo did not correct these authors, but he may not have
meant the title to be so interpreted. Several years later a
Jesuit critic assailed him for having represented himself as
the ambassador of heaven; in the margin of his copy of
this attack Galileo noted that the word *nuncius* means
"message" as well as "messenger," and asserted that he had
intended only the humbler meaning. On the basis of this
and other evidence, modern scholars have suggested that
the word in question has always been mistranslated in this
title. But it is now too late to change that, and perhaps
even if the established tradition is incorrect it ought to be
preserved. *Se non è vero, è ben trovato;* from a literary
standpoint there can hardly be a question which word is
preferable. And if "starry" is not quite synonymous with
"sidereal," it may be excused as rather more intelligible.

[7] A previous English translation was published in 1880 by
Edward Stafford Carlos. Other published translations include
one into French by the Abbé Alexandre Tinelis, *Le Mesager
Céleste* (Paris, 1681) and two into Italian; *Annunzio Siderio*
(Florence, 1948, tr. Maria Timpanaro Cardini) and *Nunzio
Siderio* (Milan, 1953, tr. Luisa Lanzillotta, in vol. 34 of *La
Letteratura Italiana.*)

lileo's failure to publish anything showed clearly that he had nothing to say worth printing. If his two minor works had failed to impress those who shared that opinion, *The Starry Messenger* certainly succeeded.

THE
STARRY MESSENGER

Revealing great, unusual, and remarkable spectacles, opening these
to the consideration of every man,
and especially of philosophers and
astronomers;
AS OBSERVED BY GALILEO GALILEI
Gentleman of Florence
Professor of Mathematics in the
University of Padua,
WITH THE AID OF A
SPYGLASS
lately invented by him,
In the surface of the Moon, in innumerable
Fixed Stars, in Nebulae, and above all
in FOUR PLANETS
swiftly revolving about Jupiter at
differing distances and periods,
and known to no one before the
Author recently perceived them
and decided that they should
be named
THE MEDICEAN STARS

Venice
1610

Surely a distinguished public service has been rendered by
those who have protected from envy the noble achievements of men who have excelled in virtue, and have thus
preserved from oblivion and neglect those names which deserve immortality. In this way images sculptured in marble
or cast in bronze have been handed down to posterity; to
this we owe our statues, both pedestrian and equestrian;
thus have we those columns and pyramids whose expense
(as the poet says)[1] reaches to the stars; finally, thus cities
have been built to bear the names of men deemed worthy
by posterity of commendation to all the ages. For the nature
of the human mind is such that unless it is stimulated by
images of things acting upon it from without, all remem-
brance of them passes easily away.

Looking to things even more stable and enduring, others
have entrusted the immortal fame of illustrious men not to
marble and metal but to the custody of the Muses and to
imperishable literary monuments. But why dwell upon
these things as though human wit were satisfied with
earthly regions and had not dared advance beyond? For,
seeking further, and well understanding that all human
monuments ultimately perish through the violence of the
elements or by old age, ingenuity has in fact found still
more incorruptible monuments over which voracious time
and envious age have been unable to assert any rights. Thus
turning to the sky, man's wit has inscribed on the familiar
and everlasting orbs of most bright stars the names of those

---

[1] Propertius iii, 2, 17.

whose eminent and godlike deeds have caused them to be
accounted worthy of eternity in the company of the stars.
And so the fame of Jupiter, of Mars, of Mercury, Hercules,
and other heroes by whose names the stars are called, will
not fade before the extinction of the stars themselves.

Yet this invention of human ingenuity, noble and admirable as it is, has for many centuries been out of style.
Primeval heroes are in possession of those bright abodes,
and hold them in their own right. In vain did the piety of
Augustus attempt to elect Julius Caesar into their number,
for when he tried to give the name of "Julian" to a star
which appeared in his time (one of those bodies which the
Greeks call "comets" and which the Romans likewise named
for their hairy appearance), it vanished in a brief time and
mocked his too ambitious wish. But we are able, most serene Prince, to read Your Highness in the heavens far more
accurately and auspiciously. For scarce have the immortal
graces of your spirit begun to shine on earth when in the
heavens bright stars appear as tongues to tell and celebrate
your exceeding virtues to all time. Behold, then, four stars
reserved to bear your famous name; bodies which belong
not to the inconspicuous multitude of fixed stars, but to the
bright ranks of the planets. Variously moving about most
noble Jupiter as children of his own, they complete their
orbits with marvelous velocity—at the same time executing
with one harmonious accord mighty revolutions every
dozen years about the center of the universe; that is, the
sun.[2]

Indeed, the Maker of the stars himself has seemed by
clear indications to direct that I assign to these new planets
Your Highness's famous name in preference to all others.
For just as these stars, like children worthy of their sire,
never leave the side of Jupiter by any appreciable distance,
so (as indeed who does not know?) clemency, kindness of

[2] This is the first published intimation by Galileo that he accepted the Copernican system. Tycho had made Jupiter revolve
about the sun, but considered the earth to be the center of the
universe. It was not until 1613, however, that Galileo unequivocally supported Copernicus in print.

heart, gentleness of manner, splendor of royal blood, nobility in public affairs, and excellency of authority and rule have all fixed their abode and habitation in Your Highness. And who, I ask once more, does not know that all these virtues emanate from the benign star of Jupiter, next after God as the source of all things good? Jupiter; Jupiter, I say, at the instant of Your Highness's birth, having already emerged from the turbid mists of the horizon and occupied the midst of the heavens, illuminating the eastern sky from his own royal house, looked out from that exalted throne upon your auspicious birth and poured forth all his splendor and majesty in order that your tender body and your mind (already adorned by God with the most noble ornaments) might imbibe with their first breath that universal influence and power.

But why should I employ mere plausible arguments, when I may prove my conclusion absolutely? It pleased Almighty God that I should instruct Your Highness in mathematics, which I did four years ago at that time of year when it is customary to rest from the most exacting studies. And since clearly it was mine by divine will to serve Your Highness and thus to receive from near at hand the rays of your surpassing clemency and beneficence, what wonder is it that my heart is so inflamed as to think both day and night of little else than how I, who am indeed your subject not only by choice but by birth and lineage, may become known to you as most grateful and most anxious for your glory? And so, most serene Cosimo, having discovered under your patronage these stars unknown to every astronomer before me, I have with good right decided to designate them by the august name of your family. And if I am first to have investigated them, who can justly blame me if I likewise name them, calling them the Medicean Stars, in the hope that this name will bring as much honor to them as the names of other heroes have bestowed on other stars? For, to say nothing of Your Highness's most serene ancestors, whose everlasting glory is testified by the monuments of all history, your virtue alone, most worthy Sire, can confer upon these stars an immortal name. No one can doubt that you will fulfill those expectations, high though they are, which you have aroused by the auspicious beginning of your reign, and will not only meet but far surpass them. Thus when you have conquered your equals you may still vie with yourself, and you and your greatness will become greater every day.

Accept then, most clement Prince, this gentle glory reserved by the stars for you. May you long enjoy those blessings which are sent to you not so much from the stars as from God, their Maker and their Governor.

Your Highness's most devoted servant,

GALILEO GALILEI

PADUA, March 12, 1610

ASTRONOMICAL MESSAGE

Which contains and explains recent observations
made with the aid of a new spyglass[3]
concerning the surface of the moon,
the Milky Way, nebulous stars, and
innumerable fixed stars,
as well as four planets never before seen, and
now named

THE MEDICEAN STARS

Great indeed are the things which in this brief treatise I
propose for observation and consideration by all students of
nature. I say great, because of the excellence of the subject
itself, the entirely unexpected and novel character of these
things, and finally because of the instrument by means of
which they have been revealed to our senses.

Surely it is a great thing to increase the numerous host
of fixed stars previously visible to the unaided vision, adding
countless more which have never before been seen, exposing
these plainly to the eye in numbers ten times exceeding the
old and familiar stars.

It is a very beautiful thing, and most gratifying to the
sight, to behold the body of the moon, distant from us almost sixty earthly radii,[4] as if it were no farther away than

---

[3] The word "telescope" was not coined until 1611. A detailed
account of its origin is given by Edward Rosen in *The Naming
of the Telescope* (New York, 1947). In the present translation
the modern term has been introduced for the sake of dignity
and ease of reading, but only after the passage in which Galileo
describes the circumstances which led him to construct the instrument (pp. 28–29).

[4] The original text reads "diameters" here and in another
place. That this error was Galileo's and not the printer's has
been convincingly shown by Edward Rosen (*Isis*, 1952, pp.

two such measures—so that its diameter appears almost thirty times larger, its surface nearly nine hundred times, and its volume twenty-seven thousand times as large as when viewed with the naked eye. In this way one may learn with all the certainty of sense evidence that the moon is not robed in a smooth and polished surface but is in fact rough and uneven, covered everywhere, just like the earth's surface, with huge prominences, deep valleys, and chasms.

Again, it seems to me a matter of no small importance to have ended the dispute about the Milky Way by making its nature manifest to the very senses as well as to the intellect. Similarly it will be a pleasant and elegant thing to demonstrate that the nature of those stars which astronomers have previously called "nebulous" is far different from what has been believed hitherto. But what surpasses all wonders by far, and what particularly moves us to seek the attention of all astronomers and philosophers, is the discovery of four wandering stars not known or observed by any man before us. Like Venus and Mercury, which have their own periods about the sun, these have theirs about a certain star that is conspicuous among those already known, which they sometimes precede and sometimes follow, without ever departing from it beyond certain limits. All these facts were discovered and observed by me not many days ago with the aid of a spyglass which I devised, after first being illuminated by divine grace. Perhaps other things, still more remarkable, will in time be discovered by me or by other observers with the aid of such an instrument, the form and construction of which I shall first briefly explain, as well as the occasion of its having been devised. Afterwards I shall relate the story of the observations I have made.

About ten months ago a report reached my ears that a

---

344 ff.). The slip was a curious one, as astronomers of all schools had long agreed that the maximum distance of the moon was approximately sixty terrestrial radii. Still more curious is the fact that neither Kepler nor any other correspondent appears to have called Galileo's attention to this error; not even a friend who ventured to criticize the calculations in this very passage.

certain Fleming[5] had constructed a spyglass by means of which visible objects, though very distant from the eye of the observer, were distinctly seen as if nearby. Of this truly remarkable effect several experiences were related, to which some persons gave credence while others denied them. A few days later the report was confirmed to me in a letter from a noble Frenchman at Paris, Jacques Badovere,[6] which caused me to apply myself wholeheartedly to inquire into the means by which I might arrive at the invention of a similar instrument. This I did shortly afterwards, my basis being the theory of refraction. First I prepared a tube of lead, at the ends of which I fitted two glass lenses, both plane on one side while on the other side one was spherically convex and the other concave. Then placing my eye near the concave lens I perceived objects satisfactorily large and near, for they appeared three times closer and nine times larger than when seen with the naked eye alone. Next I constructed another one, more accurate, which represented objects as enlarged more than sixty times. Finally, sparing neither labor nor expense, I succeeded in constructing for myself so excellent an instrument that objects seen by means of it appeared nearly one thousand times larger and over thirty times closer than when regarded with our natural vision.

It would be superfluous to enumerate the number and importance of the advantages of such an instrument at sea as well as on land. But forsaking terrestrial observations, I turned to celestial ones, and first I saw the moon from as near at hand as if it were scarcely two terrestrial radii away. After that I observed often with wondering delight both the planets and the fixed stars, and since I saw these latter to be very crowded, I began to seek (and eventually found)

[5] Credit for the original invention is generally assigned to Hans Lipperhey, a lens grinder in Holland who chanced upon this property of combined lenses and applied for a patent on it in 1608.

[6] Badovere studied in Italy toward the close of the sixteenth century and is said to have been a pupil of Galileo's about 1598. When he wrote concerning the new instrument in 1609 he was in the French diplomatic service at Paris, where he died in 1620.

a method by which I might measure their distances apart.

Here it is appropriate to convey certain cautions to all who intend to undertake observations of this sort, for in the first place it is necessary to prepare quite a perfect telescope, which will show all objects bright, distinct, and free from any haziness, while magnifying them at least four hundred times and thus showing them twenty times closer. Unless the instrument is of this kind it will be vain to attempt to observe all the things which I have seen in the heavens, and which will presently be set forth. Now in order to determine without much trouble the magnifying power of an instrument, trace on paper the contour of two circles or two squares of which one is four hundred times as large as the other, as it will be when the diameter of one is twenty times that of the other. Then, with both these figures attached to the same wall, observe them simultaneously from a distance, looking at the smaller one through the telescope and at the larger one with the other eye unaided. This may be done without inconvenience while holding both eyes open at the same time; the two figures will appear to be of the same size if the instrument magnifies objects in the desired proportion.

Such an instrument having been prepared, we seek a method of measuring distances apart. This we shall accomplish by the following contrivance.

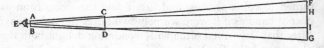

Let ABCD be the tube and E be the eye of the observer. Then if there were no lenses in the tube, the rays would reach the object FG along the straight lines ECF and EDG. But when the lenses have been inserted, the rays go along the refracted lines ECH and EDI; thus they are brought closer together, and those which were previously directed freely to the object FG now include only the portion of it HI. The ratio of the distance EH to the line HI then being

found, one may by means of a table of sines determine the
size of the angle formed at the eye by the object HI, which
we shall find to be but a few minutes of arc. Now, if to the
lens CD we fit thin plates, some pierced with larger and
some with smaller apertures, putting now one plate and now
another over the lens as required, we may form at pleasure different angles subtending more or fewer minutes of
arc, and by this means we may easily measure the intervals
between stars which are but a few minutes apart, with no
greater error than one or two minutes. And for the present
let it suffice that we have touched lightly on these matters
and scarcely more than mentioned them, as on some other
occasion we shall explain the entire theory of this instrument.

Now let us review the observations made during the past
two months, once more inviting the attention of all who are
eager for true philosophy to the first steps of such important
contemplations. Let us speak first of that surface of the
moon which faces us. For greater clarity I distinguish two
parts of this surface, a lighter and a darker; the lighter part
seems to surround and to pervade the whole hemisphere,
while the darker part discolors the moon's surface like a
kind of cloud, and makes it appear covered with spots. Now
those spots which are fairly dark and rather large are plain
to everyone and have been seen throughout the ages; these
I shall call the "large" or "ancient" spots, distinguishing
them from others that are smaller in size but so numerous
as to occur all over the lunar surface, and especially the
lighter part. The latter spots had never been seen by anyone before me. From observations of these spots repeated
many times I have been led to the opinion and conviction
that the surface of the moon is not smooth, uniform, and
precisely spherical as a great number of philosophers believe
it (and the other heavenly bodies) to be, but is uneven,
rough, and full of cavities and prominences, being not unlike the face of the earth, relieved by chains of mountains
and deep valleys. The things I have seen by which I was
enabled to draw this conclusion are as follows.

On the fourth or fifth day after new moon, when the moon is seen with brilliant horns, the boundary which divides the dark part from the light does not extend uniformly in an oval line as would happen on a perfectly spherical solid, but traces out an uneven, rough, and very wavy line as shown in the figure below. Indeed, many luminous excrescences extend beyond the boundary into the darker portion, while on the other hand some dark patches invade the illuminated part. Moreover a great quantity of small blackish spots, entirely separated from the dark region, are scattered almost all over the area illuminated by the sun with the exception only of that part which is occupied by the large and ancient spots. Let us note, however, that the said small spots always agree in having their blackened parts directed toward the sun, while on the side opposite the sun they are crowned with bright contours, like shining summits. There is a similar sight on earth about sunrise, when we behold the valleys not yet flooded with light though the mountains surrounding them are already ablaze with glowing splendor on the side opposite the sun. And just as the shadows in the hollows on earth diminish in size as the sun rises higher, so these spots on the moon lose their blackness as the illuminated region grows larger and larger.

Again, not only are the boundaries of shadow and light in the moon seen to be uneven and wavy, but still more

astonishingly many bright points appear within the dark-
ened portion of the moon, completely divided and separated
from the illuminated part and at a considerable distance
from it. After a time these gradually increase in size and
brightness, and an hour or two later they become joined
with the rest of the lighted part which has now increased
in size. Meanwhile more and more peaks shoot up as if
sprouting now here, now there, lighting up within the
shadowed portion; these become larger, and finally they
too are united with that same luminous surface which extends ever further. An illustration of this is to be seen in the
figure above. And on the earth, before the rising of the sun,
are not the highest peaks of the mountains illuminated by
the sun's rays while the plains remain in shadow? Does not
the light go on spreading while the larger central parts of
those mountains are becoming illuminated? And when the
sun has finally risen, does not the illumination of plains and
hills finally become one? But on the moon the variety of
elevations and depressions appears to surpass in every way
the roughness of the terrestrial surface, as we shall demonstrate further on.

At present I cannot pass over in silence something
worthy of consideration which I observed when the moon
was approaching first quarter, as shown in the previous
figure. Into the luminous part there extended a great dark
gulf in the neighborhood of the lower cusp. When I had
observed it for a long time and had seen it completely dark,
a bright peak began to emerge, a little below its center, after
about two hours. Gradually growing, this presented itself
in a triangular shape, remaining completely detached and
separated from the lighted surface. Around it three other
small points soon began to shine, and finally, when the moon
was about to set, this triangular shape (which had meanwhile become more widely extended) joined with the rest
of the illuminated region and suddenly burst into the gulf
of shadow like a vast promontory of light, surrounded still
by the three bright peaks already mentioned. Beyond the
ends of the cusps, both above and below, certain bright

points emerged which were quite detached from the remaining lighted part, as may be seen depicted in the same figure. There were also a great number of dark spots in both the horns, especially in the lower one; those nearest the boundary of light and shadow appeared larger and darker, while those more distant from the boundary were not so dark and distinct. But in all cases, as we have mentioned earlier, the blackish portion of each spot is turned toward the source of the sun's radiance, while a bright rim surrounds the spot on the side away from the sun in the direction of the shadowy region of the moon. This part of the moon's surface, where it is spotted as the tail of a peacock is sprinkled with azure eyes, resembles those glass vases which have been plunged while still hot into cold water and have thus acquired a crackled and wavy surface, from which they receive their common name of "ice-cups."

As to the large lunar spots, these are not seen to be broken in the above manner and full of cavities and prominences; rather, they are even and uniform, and brighter patches crop up only here and there. Hence if anyone wished to revive the old Pythagorean[7] opinion that the moon is like another earth, its brighter part might very fitly represent the surface of the land and its darker region that of the water. I have never doubted that if our globe were seen from afar when flooded with sunlight, the land regions would appear brighter and the watery regions darker.[8] The large spots in the moon are also seen to be less elevated

---

[7] Pythagoras was a mathematician and philosopher of the sixth century B.C., a semilegendary figure whose followers were credited at Galileo's time with having anticipated the Copernican system. This tradition was based upon a misunderstanding. The Pythagoreans made the earth revolve about a "central fire" whose light and heat were reflected to the earth by the sun.

[8] Leonardo da Vinci had previously suggested that the dark and light regions of the moon were bodies of land and water, though Galileo probably did not know this. Da Vinci, however, had mistakenly supposed that the water would appear brighter than the land.

than the brighter tracts, for whether the moon is waxing or waning there are always seen, here and there along its boundary of light and shadow, certain ridges of brighter hue around the large spots (and we have attended to this in preparing the diagrams); the edges of these spots are not only lower, but also more uniform, being uninterrupted by peaks or ruggedness.

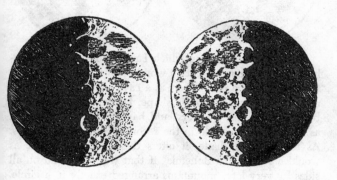

Near the large spots the brighter part stands out particularly in such a way that before first quarter and toward last quarter, in the vicinity of a certain spot in the upper (or northern) region of the moon, some vast prominences arise both above and below as shown in the figures reproduced below. Before last quarter this same spot is seen to be walled about with certain blacker contours which, like the loftiest mountaintops, appear darker on the side away from the sun and brighter on that which faces the sun. (This is the opposite of what happens in the cavities, for there the part away from the sun appears brilliant, while that which is turned toward the sun is dark and in shadow.) After a time, when the lighted portion of the moon's surface has diminished in size and when all (or nearly all) the said spot is covered with shadow, the brighter ridges of the mountains gradually emerge from the shade. This double aspect of the spot is illustrated in the ensuing figures.

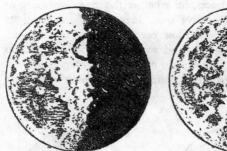

There is another thing which I must not omit, for I beheld it not without a certain wonder; this is that almost in the center of the moon there is a cavity larger than all the rest, and perfectly round in shape. I have observed it near both first and last quarters, and have tried to represent it as correctly as possible in the second of the above figures. As to light and shade, it offers the same appearance as would a region like Bohemia[9] if that were enclosed on all sides by very lofty mountains arranged exactly in a circle. Indeed, this area on the moon is surrounded by such enormous peaks that the bounding edge adjacent to the dark portion of the moon is seen to be bathed in sunlight before the boundary of light and shadow reaches halfway across the same space. As in other spots, its shaded portion faces the sun while its lighted part is toward the dark side of the moon; and for a third time I draw attention to this as a very cogent proof of the ruggedness and unevenness that pervades all the bright region of the moon. Of these spots, moreover, those are always darkest which touch the boundary line between light and shadow, while those farther off

[9] This casual comparison between a part of the moon and a specific region on earth was later the basis of much trouble for Galileo; see the letter of G. Ciampoli, p. 158. Even in antiquity the idea that the moon (or any other heavenly body) was of the same nature as the earth had been dangerous to hold. The Athenians banished the philosopher Anaxagoras for teaching such notions, and charged Socrates with blasphemy for repeating them.

appear both smaller and less dark, so that when the moon ultimately becomes full (at opposition[10] to the sun), the shade of the cavities is distinguished from the light of the places in relief by a subdued and very tenuous separation.

The things we have reviewed are to be seen in the brighter region of the moon. In the large spots, no such contrast of depressions and prominences is perceived as that which we are compelled to recognize in the brighter parts by the changes of aspect that occur under varying illumination by the sun's rays throughout the multiplicity of positions from which the latter reach the moon. In the large spots there exist some holes rather darker than the rest, as we have shown in the illustrations. Yet these present always the same appearance, and their darkness is neither intensified nor diminished, although with some minute difference they appear sometimes a little more shaded and sometimes a little lighter according as the rays of the sun fall on them more or less obliquely. Moreover, they join with the neighboring regions of the spots in a gentle linkage, the boundaries mixing and mingling. It is quite different with the spots which occupy the brighter surface of the moon; these, like precipitous crags having rough and jagged peaks, stand out starkly in sharp contrasts of light and shade. And inside the large spots there are observed certain other zones that are brighter, some of them very bright indeed. Still, both these and the darker parts present always the same appearance; there is no change either of shape or of light and shadow; hence one may affirm beyond any doubt that they owe their appearance to some real dissimilarity of parts. They cannot be attributed merely to irregularity of shape, wherein shadows move in consequence of varied illuminations from the sun, as indeed is the case with the other, smaller, spots which occupy the brighter part of the moon and which change, grow, shrink,

[10] Opposition of the sun and moon occurs when they are in line with the earth between them (full moon, or lunar eclipse); conjunction, when they are in line on the same side of the earth (new moon, or eclipse of the sun).

or disappear from one day to the next, as owing their origin only to shadows of prominences.

But here I foresee that many persons will be assailed by uncertainty and drawn into a grave difficulty, feeling constrained to doubt a conclusion already explained and confirmed by many phenomena. If that part of the lunar surface which reflects sunlight more brightly is full of chasms (that is, of countless prominences and hollows), why is it that the western edge of the waxing moon, the eastern edge of the waning moon, and the entire periphery of the full moon are not seen to be uneven, rough, and wavy? On the contrary they look as precisely round as if they were drawn with a compass; and yet the whole periphery consists of that brighter lunar substance which we have declared to be filled with heights and chasms. In fact not a single one of the great spots extends to the extreme periphery of the moon, but all are grouped together at a distance from the edge.

Now let me explain the twofold reason for this troublesome fact, and in turn give a double solution to the difficulty. In the first place, if the protuberances and cavities in the lunar body existed only along the extreme edge of the circular periphery bounding the visible hemisphere, the moon might (indeed, would necessarily) look to us almost like a toothed wheel, terminated by a warty or wavy edge. Imagine, however, that there is not a single series of prominences arranged only along the very circumference, but a great many ranges of mountains together with their valleys and canyons disposed in ranks near the edge of the moon, and not only in the hemisphere visible to us but everywhere near the boundary line of the two hemispheres. Then an eye viewing them from afar will not be able to detect the separation of prominences by cavities, because the intervals between the mountains located in a given circle or a given chain will be hidden by the interposition of other heights situated in yet other ranges. This will be especially true if the eye of the observer is placed in the same straight line with the summits of these elevations. Thus on earth the summits of several mountains close together appear to be situated in one plane if the spectator is a long way off and is placed at an equal elevation. Similarly in a rough sea the tops of the waves seem to lie in one plane, though between one high crest and another there are many gulfs and chasms of such depth as not only to hide the hulls but even the bulwarks, masts, and rigging of stately ships. Now since there are many chains of mountains and chasms on the moon in addition to those around its periphery, and since the eye, regarding these from a great distance, lies nearly in the plane of their summits, no one need wonder that they appear as arranged in a regular and unbroken line.

To the above explanation another may be added; namely, that there exists around the body of the moon, just as around the earth, a globe of some substance denser than the rest of the aether.[11] This may serve to receive and reflect the sun's radiations without being sufficiently opaque to prevent our seeing through it, especially when it is not illuminated. Such a globe, lighted by the sun's rays, makes the body of the moon appear larger than it really is, and if it were thicker it would be able to prevent our seeing the actual body of the moon. And it actually is thicker near the circumference of the moon; I do not mean in an absolute sense, but relatively to the rays of our vision, which cut it obliquely there. Thus it may obstruct our vision, especially when it is lighted, and cloak the lunar periphery that is exposed to the sun. This may be more clearly understood from the figure below, in which the body of the moon, ABC, is surrounded by the vaporous globe DEG.

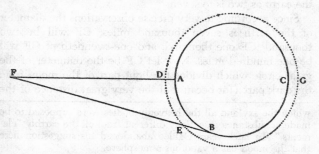

[11] The aether, or "ever-moving," was the special substance of

The eyesight from F reaches the moon in the central region, at A for example, through a lesser thickness of the vapors DA, while toward the extreme edges a deeper stratum of vapors, EB, limits and shuts out our sight. One indication of this is that the illuminated portion of the moon appears to be larger in circumference than the rest of the orb, which lies in shadow. And perhaps this same cause will appeal to some as reasonably explaining why the larger spots on the moon are nowhere seen to reach the very edge, probable though it is that some should occur there. Possibly they are invisible by being hidden under a thicker and more luminous mass of vapors.

That the lighter surface of the moon is everywhere dotted with protuberances and gaps has, I think, been made sufficiently clear from the appearances already explained. It remains for me to speak of their dimensions, and to show that the earth's irregularities are far less than those of the moon. I mean that they are absolutely less, and not merely in relation to the sizes of the respective globes. This is plainly demonstrated as follows.

I had often observed, in various situations of the moon with respect to the sun, that some summits within the shadowy portion appeared lighted, though lying some distance from the boundary of the light. By comparing this separation to the whole diameter of the moon, I found that it sometimes exceeded one-twentieth of the diameter. Accordingly, let CAF be a great circle of the lunar body, E its center, and CF a diameter, which is to the diameter of the earth as two is to seven.

Since according to very precise observations the diameter of the earth is seven thousand miles, CF will be two thousand, CE one thousand, and one-twentieth of CF will be one hundred miles. Now let CF be the diameter of the great circle which divides the light part of the moon from the dark part (for because of the very great distance of the

which the sky and all the heavenly bodies were supposed to be made, a substance essentially different from all the earthly "elements." In later years Galileo abandoned his suggestion here that the moon has a vaporous atmosphere.

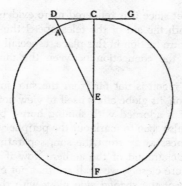

sun from the moon, this does not differ appreciably from a
great circle), and let A be distant from C by one-twentieth
of this. Draw the radius EA, which, when produced, cuts
the tangent line GCD (representing the illuminating ray)
in the point D. Then the arc CA, or rather the straight line
CD, will consist of one hundred units whereof CE contains
one thousand, and the sum of the squares of DC and CE
will be 1,010,000. This is equal to the square of DE; hence
ED will exceed 1,004, and AD will be more than four of
those units of which CE contains one thousand. Therefore
the altitude AD on the moon, which represents a summit
reaching up to the solar ray GCD and standing at the distance CD from C, exceeds four miles. But on the earth we
have no mountains which reach to a perpendicular height
of even one mile.[12] Hence it is quite clear that the prominences on the moon are loftier than those on the earth.

Here I wish to assign the cause of another lunar phenomenon well worthy of notice. I observed this not just recently, but many years ago, and pointed it out to some of
my friends and pupils, explaining it to them and giving its

[12] Galileo's estimate of four miles for the height of some lunar
mountains was a very good one. His remark about the maximum
height of mountains on the earth was, however, quite mistaken.
An English propagandist for his views, John Wilkins, took pains
to correct this error in his anonymous *Discovery of a New World
. . . in the Moon* (London, 1638), Prop. ix.

true cause. Yet since it is rendered more evident and easier to observe with the aid of the telescope, I think it not unsuitable for introduction in this place, especially as it shows more clearly the connection between the moon and the earth.

When the moon is not far from the sun, just before or after new moon, its globe offers itself to view not only on the side where it is adorned with shining horns, but a certain faint light is also seen to mark out the periphery of the dark part which faces away from the sun, separating this from the darker background of the aether. Now if we examine the matter more closely, we shall see that not only does the extreme limb of the shaded side glow with this uncertain light, but the entire face of the moon (including the side which does not receive the glare of the sun) is whitened by a not inconsiderable gleam. At first glance only a thin luminous circumference appears, contrasting with the darker sky coterminous with it; the rest of the surface appears darker from its contact with the shining horns which distract our vision. But if we place ourselves so as to interpose a roof or chimney or some other object at a considerable distance from the eye, the shining horns may be hidden while the rest of the lunar globe remains exposed to view. It is then found that this region of the moon, though deprived of sunlight, also shines not a little. The effect is heightened if the gloom of night has already deepened through departure of the sun, for in a darker field a given light appears brighter.

Moreover, it is found that this secondary light of the moon (so to speak) is greater according as the moon is closer to the sun. It diminishes more and more as the moon recedes from that body until, after the first quarter and before the last, it is seen very weakly and uncertainly even when observed in the darkest sky. But when the moon is within sixty degrees of the sun it shines remarkably, even in twilight; so brightly indeed that with the aid of a good telescope one may distinguish the large spots. This remarkable gleam has afforded no small perplexity to philosophers, and in order to assign a cause for it some have offered one idea and some another. Some would say it is an inherent and natural light of the moon's own; others, that it is imparted by Venus; others yet, by all the stars together; and still others derive it from the sun, whose rays they would have permeate the thick solidity of the moon. But statements of this sort are refuted and their falsity evinced with little difficulty. For if this kind of light were the moon's own, or were contributed by the stars, the moon would retain it and would display it particularly during eclipses, when it is left in an unusually dark sky. This is contradicted by experience, for the brightness which is seen on the moon during eclipses is much fainter and is ruddy, almost copper-colored, while this is brighter and whitish. Moreover the other light is variable and movable, for it covers the face of the moon in such a way that the place near the edge of the earth's shadow is always seen to be brighter than the rest of the moon; this undoubtedly results from contact of the tangent solar rays with some denser zone which girds the moon about.[13] By this contact a sort of twilight is diffused over the neighboring regions of the moon, just as on earth a sort of crepuscular light is spread both morning and evening; but with this I shall deal more fully in my book on the system of the world.[14]

To assert that the moon's secondary light is imparted by Venus is so childish as to deserve no reply. Who is so ignorant as not to understand that from new moon to a separation of sixty degrees between moon and sun, no part of the moon which is averted from the sun can possibly be seen from Venus? And it is likewise unthinkable that this light should depend upon the sun's rays penetrating the thick

[13] Kepler had correctly accounted for the existence of this light and its ruddy color. It is caused by refraction of sunlight in the earth's atmosphere, and does not require a lunar atmosphere as supposed by Galileo.

[14] The book thus promised was destined not to appear for more than two decades. Events which will presently be recounted prevented its publication for many years, and then it had to be modified to present the arguments for both the Ptolemaic and Copernican systems instead of just the latter as Galileo here planned. Even then it was suppressed, and the author was condemned to life imprisonment.

solid mass of the moon, for then this light would never dwindle, inasmuch as one hemisphere of the moon is always illuminated except during lunar eclipses. And the light does diminish as the moon approaches first quarter, becoming completely obscured after that is passed.

Now since the secondary light does not inherently belong to the moon, and is not received from any star or from the sun, and since in the whole universe there is no other body left but the earth, what must we conclude? What is to be proposed? Surely we must assert that the lunar body (or any other dark and sunless orb) is illuminated by the earth. Yet what is there so remarkable about this? The earth, in fair and grateful exchange, pays back to the moon an illumination similar to that which it receives from her throughout nearly all the darkest gloom of night.

Let us explain this matter more fully. At conjunction the moon occupies a position between the sun and the earth; it is then illuminated by the sun's rays on the side which is turned away from the earth. The other hemisphere, which faces the earth, is covered with darkness; hence the moon does not illuminate the surface of the earth at all. Next, departing gradually from the sun, the moon comes to be lighted partly upon the side it turns toward us, and its whitish horns, still very thin, illuminate the earth with a faint light. The sun's illumination of the moon increasing now as the moon approaches first quarter, a reflection of that light to the earth also increases. Soon the splendor on the moon extends into a semicircle, and our nights grow brighter; at length the entire visible face of the moon is irradiated by the sun's resplendent rays, and at full moon the whole surface of the earth shines in a flood of moonlight. Now the moon, waning, sends us her beams more weakly, and the earth is less strongly lighted; at length the moon returns to conjunction with the sun, and black night covers the earth.

In this monthly period, then, the moonlight gives us alternations of brighter and fainter illumination; and the benefit is repaid by the earth in equal measure. For while the

moon is between us and the sun (at new moon), there lies
before it the entire surface of that hemisphere of the earth
which is exposed to the sun and illuminated by vivid rays.
The moon receives the light which this reflects, and thus
the nearer hemisphere of the moon—that is, the one deprived of sunlight—appears by virtue of this illumination to
be not a little luminous. When the moon is ninety degrees
away from the sun it sees but half the earth illuminated
(the western half), for the other (the eastern half) is en-
veloped in night. Hence the moon itself is illuminated less
brightly from the earth, and as a result its secondary light
appears fainter to us. When the moon is in opposition to the
sun, it faces a hemisphere of the earth that is steeped in
the gloom of night, and if this position occurs in the plane
of the ecliptic the moon will receive no light at all, being
deprived of both the solar and the terrestrial rays. In its
various other positions with respect to the earth and sun,
the moon receives more or less light according as it faces a
greater or smaller portion of the illuminated hemisphere of
the earth. And between these two globes a relation is maintained such that whenever the earth is most brightly lighted
by the moon, the moon is least lighted by the earth, and
vice versa.

Let these few remarks suffice us here concerning this
matter, which will be more fully treated in our *System of
the world*. In that book, by a multitude of arguments and
experiences, the solar reflection from the earth will be shown
to be quite real—against those who argue that the earth
must be excluded from the dancing whirl of stars for the
specific reason that it is devoid of motion and of light. We
shall prove the earth to be a wandering body surpassing
the moon in splendor, and not the sink of all dull refuse of
the universe; this we shall support by an infinitude of arguments drawn from nature.

Thus far we have spoken of our observations concerning
the body of the moon. Let us now set forth briefly what
has thus far been observed regarding the fixed stars. And
first of all, the following fact deserves consideration: The

stars, whether fixed or wandering,[15] appear not to be enlarged by the telescope in the same proportion as that in which it magnifies other objects, and even the moon itself. In the stars this enlargement seems to be so much less that a telescope which is sufficiently powerful to magnify other objects a hundredfold is scarcely able to enlarge the stars four or five times. The reason for this is as follows.

When stars are viewed by means of unaided natural vision, they present themselves to us not as of their simple (and, so to speak, their physical) size, but as irradiated by a certain fulgor and as fringed with sparkling rays, especially when the night is far advanced. From this they appear larger than they would if stripped of those adventitious hairs of light, for the angle at the eye is determined not by the primary body of the star but by the brightness which extends so widely about it. This appears quite clearly from the fact that when stars first emerge from twilight at sunset they look very small, even if they are of the first magnitude; Venus itself, when visible in broad daylight, is so small as scarcely to appear equal to a star of the sixth magnitude. Things fall out differently with other objects, and even with the moon itself; these, whether seen in daylight or the deepest night, appear always of the same bulk. Therefore the stars are seen crowned among shadows, while daylight is able to remove their headgear; and not daylight alone, but any thin cloud that interposes itself between a star and the eye of the observer. The same effect is produced by black veils or colored glasses, through the interposition of which obstacles the stars are abandoned by their surrounding brilliance. A telescope similarly accomplishes the same result. It removes from the stars their adventitious and accidental rays, and then it enlarges their simple globes (if indeed the stars are naturally globular) so that they seem to be magnified in a lesser ratio than other objects. In fact a star of the fifth or sixth magnitude when seen through a telescope presents itself as one of the first magnitude.

[15] That is, planets. Among these bodies Galileo counted his newly discovered satellites of Jupiter. The term "satellites" was introduced somewhat later by Kepler.

Deserving of notice also is the difference between the appearances of the planets and of the fixed stars.[16] The planets show their globes perfectly round and definitely bounded, looking like little moons, spherical and flooded all over with light; the fixed stars are never seen to be bounded by a circular periphery, but have rather the aspect of blazes whose rays vibrate about them and scintillate a great deal. Viewed with a telescope they appear of a shape similar to that which they present to the naked eye, but sufficiently enlarged so that a star of the fifth or sixth magnitude seems to equal the Dog Star, largest of all the fixed stars. Now, in addition to stars of the sixth magnitude, a host of other stars are perceived through the telescope which escape the naked eye; these are so numerous as almost to surpass belief. One may, in fact, see more of them than all the stars included among the first six magnitudes. The largest of these, which we may call stars of the seventh magnitude, or the first magnitude of invisible stars, appear through the telescope as larger and brighter than stars of the second magnitude when the latter are viewed with the naked eye. In order to give one or two proofs of their almost inconceivable number, I have adjoined pictures of two constellations. With these as samples, you may judge of all the others.

In the first I had intended to depict the entire constellation of Orion, but I was overwhelmed by the vast quantity of stars and by limitations of time, so I have deferred this to another occasion. There are more than five hundred new stars distributed among the old ones within limits of one or two degrees of arc. Hence to the three stars in the Belt of Orion and the six in the Sword which were previously known, I have added eighty adjacent stars discovered re-

[16] Fixed stars are so distant that their light reaches the earth as from dimensionless points. Hence their images are not enlarged by even the best telescopes, which serve only to gather more of their light and in that way increase their visibility. Galileo was never entirely clear about this distinction. Nevertheless, by applying his knowledge of the effects described here, he greatly reduced the prevailing overestimation of visual dimensions of stars and planets.

cently, preserving the intervals between them as exactly as I could. To distinguish the known or ancient stars, I have depicted them larger and have outlined them doubly; the other (invisible) stars I have drawn smaller and without the extra line. I have also preserved differences of magnitude as well as possible.

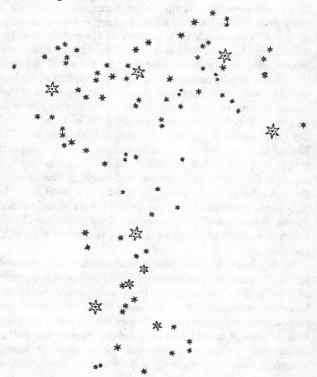

The Belt and Sword of Orion

In the second example I have depicted the six stars of Taurus known as the Pleiades (I say six, inasmuch as the seventh is hardly ever visible) which lie within very narrow limits in the sky. Near them are more than forty others, invisible, no one of which is much more than half a degree away from the original six. I have shown thirty-six of these in the diagram; as in the case of Orion I have preserved their intervals and magnitudes, as well as the distinction between old stars and new.

The Pleiades

Third, I have observed the nature and the material of the Milky Way. With the aid of the telescope this has been scrutinized so directly and with such ocular certainty that all the disputes which have vexed philosophers through so many ages have been resolved, and we are at last freed from wordy debates about it. The galaxy is, in fact, nothing but a congeries of innumerable stars grouped together in clusters. Upon whatever part of it the telescope is directed, a vast crowd of stars is immediately presented to view. Many of them are rather large and quite bright, while the number of smaller ones is quite beyond calculation.

But it is not only in the Milky Way that whitish clouds are seen; several patches of similar aspect shine with faint light here and there throughout the aether, and if the telescope is turned upon any of these it confronts us with a tight mass of stars. And what is even more remarkable, the stars which have been called "nebulous" by every astronomer up to this time turn out to be groups of very small stars arranged in a wonderful manner. Although each star separately escapes our sight on account of its smallness or the immense distance from us, the mingling of their rays gives rise to that gleam which was formerly believed to be some denser part of the aether that was capable of reflecting rays from stars or from the sun. I have observed some of these constellations and have decided to depict two of them.

In the first you have the nebula called the Head of Orion, in which I have counted twenty-one stars. The second contains the nebula called Praesepe,[17] which is not a single star but a mass of more than forty starlets. Of these I have shown thirty-six, in addition to the Aselli, arranged in the order shown.

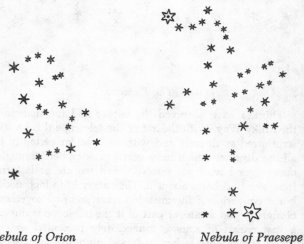

Nebula of Orion   *Nebula of Praesepe*

We have now briefly recounted the observations made thus far with regard to the moon, the fixed stars, and the Milky Way. There remains the matter which in my opinion deserves to be considered the most important of all—the disclosure of four PLANETS never seen from the creation of

[17] Praesepe, "the Manger," is a small whitish cluster of stars lying between the two Aselli (ass-colts) which are imagined as feeding from it. It lies in the constellation Cancer.

the world up to our own time, together with the occasion of my having discovered and studied them, their arrangements, and the observations made of their movements and alterations during the past two months. I invite all astronomers to apply themselves to examine them and determine their periodic times, something which has so far been quite impossible to complete, owing to the shortness of the time. Once more, however, warning is given that it will be necessary to have a very accurate telescope such as we have described at the beginning of this discourse.

On the seventh day of January in this present year 1610, at the first hour of night, when I was viewing the heavenly bodies with a telescope, Jupiter presented itself to me; and because I had prepared a very excellent instrument for myself, I perceived (as I had not before, on account of the weakness of my previous instrument) that beside the planet there were three starlets, small indeed, but very bright. Though I believed them to be among the host of fixed stars, they aroused my curiosity somewhat by appearing to lie in an exact straight line parallel to the ecliptic, and by their being more splendid than others of their size. Their arrangement with respect to Jupiter and each other was the following:

East   *   *   ○   *   *West*

that is, there were two stars on the eastern side and one to the west. The most easterly star and the western one appeared larger than the other. I paid no attention to the distances between them and Jupiter, for at the outset I thought them to be fixed stars, as I have said.[18] But re-

---

[18] The reader should remember that the telescope was nightly revealing to Galileo hundreds of fixed stars never previously observed. His unusual gifts for astronomical observation are illustrated by his having noticed and remembered these three merely by reason of their alignment, and recalling them so well that when by chance he happened to see them the following night he was certain that they had changed their positions. No such plausible and candid account of the discovery was given by the rival astronomer Simon Mayr, who four years later claimed priority. See pp. 233 ff. and note 4, pp. 233-34.

turning to the same investigation on January eighth—led by
what, I do not know—I found a very different arrangement.
The three starlets were now all to the west of Jupiter,
closer together, and at equal intervals from one another as
shown in the following sketch:

East   O * * *   *West*

At this time, though I did not yet turn my attention to
the way the stars had come together, I began to concern
myself with the question how Jupiter could be east of all
these stars when on the previous day it had been west of
two of them. I commenced to wonder whether Jupiter
was not moving eastward at that time, contrary to the computations of the astronomers, and had got in front of them
by that motion.[19] Hence it was with great interest that I
awaited the next night. But I was disappointed in my hopes,
for the sky was then covered with clouds everywhere.

On the tenth of January, however, the stars appeared in
this position with respect to Jupiter:

East   *   *   O   *West*

that is, there were but two of them, both easterly, the third
(as I supposed) being hidden behind Jupiter. As at first,
they were in the same straight line with Jupiter and were
arranged precisely in the line of the zodiac. Noticing this,
and knowing that there was no way in which such alterations could be attributed to Jupiter's motion, yet being
certain that these were still the same stars I had observed
(in fact no other was to be found along the line of the
zodiac for a long way on either side of Jupiter), my perplexity was now transformed into amazement. I was sure
that the apparent changes belonged not to Jupiter but to the
observed stars, and I resolved to pursue this investigation
with greater care and attention.

And thus, on the eleventh of January, I saw the following
disposition:

[19] See note 4, p. 12. Jupiter was at this time in "retrograde"
motion; that is, the earth's motion made the planet appear to be
moving westward among the fixed stars.

East   ✳ ✳   ◯   *West*

There were two stars, both to the east, the central one being three times as far from Jupiter as from the one farther east. The latter star was nearly double the size of the former, whereas on the night before they had appeared approximately equal.

I had now decided beyond all question that there existed in the heavens three stars wandering about Jupiter as do Venus and Mercury about the sun, and this became plainer than daylight from observations on similar occasions which followed. Nor were there just three such stars; four wanderers complete their revolutions about Jupiter, and of their alterations as observed more precisely later on we shall give a description here. Also I measured the distances between them by means of the telescope, using the method explained before. Moreover I recorded the times of the observations, especially when more than one was made during the same night—for the revolutions of these planets are so speedily completed that it is usually possible to take even their hourly variations.

Thus on the twelfth of January at the first hour of night I saw the stars arranged in this way:

East   ✳ ✳◯ ✳   *West*

The most easterly star was larger than the western one, though both were easily visible and quite bright. Each was about two minutes of arc distant from Jupiter. The third star was invisible at first, but commenced to appear after two hours; it almost touched Jupiter on the east, and was quite small. All were on the same straight line directed along the ecliptic.

On the thirteenth of January four stars were seen by me for the first time, in this situation relative to Jupiter:

East   ✳   ◯ ✳ ✳ ✳   *West*

Three were westerly and one was to the east; they formed a straight line except that the middle western star departed slightly toward the north. The eastern star was two minutes

of arc away from Jupiter, and the intervals of the rest from
one another and from Jupiter were about one minute. All
the stars appeared to be of the same magnitude, and though
small were very bright, much brighter than fixed stars of
the same size.[20]

.   .   .   .

On the twenty-sixth of February, midway in the first hour
of night, there were only two stars:

East   *   O   *   West

One was to the east, ten minutes from Jupiter; the other to
the west, six minutes away. The eastern one was somewhat
smaller than the western. But at the fifth hour three stars
were seen:

East   *   O *   *   West

In addition to the two already noticed, a third was discovered to the west near Jupiter; it had at first been hidden
behind Jupiter and was now one minute away. The eastern
one appeared farther away than before, being eleven minutes from Jupiter.

This night for the first time I wanted to observe the progress of Jupiter and its accompanying planets along the
line of the zodiac in relation to some fixed star, and such a
star was seen to the east, eleven minutes distant from the
easterly starlet and a little removed toward the south, in
the following manner:

East   *   O *   *   West

★

On the twenty-seventh of February, four minutes after
the first hour, the stars appeared in this configuration:

[20] Galileo's day-by-day journal of observations continued in
unbroken sequence until ten days before publication of the book,
which he remained in Venice to supervise. The observations
omitted here contained nothing of a novel character.

East   ✳   * ◯   * ✳   *West*

★

The most easterly was ten minutes from Jupiter; the next, thirty seconds; the next to the west was two minutes thirty seconds from Jupiter, and the most westerly was one minute from that. Those nearest Jupiter appeared very small, while the end ones were plainly visible, especially the westernmost. They marked out an exactly straight line along the course of the ecliptic. The progress of these planets toward the east is seen quite clearly by reference to the fixed star mentioned, since Jupiter and its accompanying planets were closer to it, as may be seen in the figure above. At the fifth hour, the eastern star closer to Jupiter was one minute away.

At the first hour on February twenty-eighth, two stars only were seen; one easterly, distant nine minutes from Jupiter, and one to the west, two minutes away. They were easily visible and on the same straight line. The fixed star, perpendicular to this line, now fell under the eastern planet as in this figure:

East   ✳   ◯   *   *West*

★

At the fifth hour a third star, two minutes east of Jupiter, was seen in this position:

East   ✳   * ◯ *   *West*

On the first of March, forty minutes after sunset, four stars all to the east were seen, of which the nearest to Jupiter was two minutes away, the next was one minute from this, the third two seconds from that and brighter than any of the others; from this in turn the most easterly was four minutes distant, and it was smaller than the rest. They marked out almost a straight line, but the third one counting from Jupiter was a little to the north. The fixed star formed an equilateral triangle with Jupiter and the most easterly star, as in this figure:

East   *   * * *   ◯   West

★

On March second, half an hour after sunset, there were three planets, two to the east and one to the west, in this configuration:

East   * *   ◯   *   West

★

The most easterly was seven minutes from Jupiter and thirty seconds from its neighbor; the western one was two minutes away from Jupiter. The end stars were very bright and were larger than that in the middle, which appeared very small. The most easterly star appeared a little elevated toward the north from the straight line through the other planets and Jupiter. The fixed star previously mentioned was eight minutes from the western planet along the line drawn from it perpendicularly to the straight line through all the planets, as shown above.

I have reported these relations of Jupiter and its companions with the fixed star so that anyone may comprehend that the progress of those planets, both in longitude and latitude, agrees exactly with the movements derived from planetary tables.

Such are the observations concerning the four Medicean planets recently first discovered by me, and although from these data their periods have not yet been reconstructed in numerical form, it is legitimate at least to put in evidence some facts worthy of note. Above all, since they sometimes follow and sometimes precede Jupiter by the same intervals, and they remain within very limited distances either to east or west of Jupiter, accompanying that planet in both its retrograde and direct movements in a constant manner, no one can doubt that they complete their revolutions about Jupiter and at the same time effect all together a twelve-year period about the center of the universe. That they also revolve in unequal circles is manifestly deduced from the fact that at the greatest elongation[21] from Jupiter it is never possible to see two of these planets in conjunction, whereas in the vicinity of Jupiter they are found united two, three, and sometimes all four together. It is also observed that the revolutions are swifter in those planets which describe smaller circles about Jupiter, since the stars closest to Jupiter are usually seen to the east when on the previous day they appeared to the west, and vice versa, while the planet which traces the largest orbit appears upon accurate observation of its returns to have a semimonthly period.

Here we have a fine and elegant argument for quieting the doubts of those who, while accepting with tranquil mind the revolutions of the planets about the sun in the Copernican system, are mightily disturbed to have the moon alone revolve about the earth and accompany it in an annual rotation about the sun. Some have believed that this structure of the universe should be rejected as impossible. But now we have not just one planet rotating about another while both run through a great orbit around the sun; our own eyes show us four stars which wander around Jupiter as does the moon around the earth, while all together trace out a grand revolution about the sun in the space of twelve years.

And finally we should not omit the reason for which the Medicean stars appear sometimes to be twice as large as at other times, though their orbits about Jupiter are very restricted. We certainly cannot seek the cause in terrestrial vapors, as Jupiter and its neighboring fixed stars are not seen to change size in the least while this increase and diminution are taking place. It is quite unthinkable that the cause of variation should be their change of distance from

[21] By this is meant the greatest angular separation from Jupiter attained by any of the satellites.

the earth at perigee and apogee, since a small circular rotation could by no means produce this effect, and an oval motion (which in this case would have to be nearly straight) seems unthinkable and quite inconsistent with the appearances.[22] But I shall gladly explain what occurs to me on this matter, offering it freely to the judgment and criticism of thoughtful men. It is known that the interposition of terrestrial vapors makes the sun and moon appear large, while the fixed stars and planets are made to appear smaller. Thus the two great luminaries are seen larger when close to the horizon, while the stars appear smaller and for the most part hardly visible. Hence the stars appear very feeble by day and in twilight, though the moon does not, as we have said. Now from what has been said above, and even more from what we shall say at greater length in our *System*, it follows that not only the earth but also the moon is surrounded by an envelope of vapors, and we may apply precisely the same judgment to the rest of the planets. Hence it does not appear entirely impossible to assume that around Jupiter also there exists an envelope denser than the rest of the aether, about which the Medicean planets revolve as does the moon about the elemental sphere. Through the interposition of this envelope they appear larger when they are in perigee by the removal, or at least the attenuation, of this envelope.

Time prevents my proceeding further, but the gentle reader may expect more soon.

FINIS

[22] The marked variation in brightness of the satellites which Galileo observed may be attributed mainly to markings upon their surfaces, though this was not determined until two centuries later. The mention here of a possible oval shape of the orbits is the closest Galileo ever came to accepting Kepler's great discovery of the previous year (cf. p. 17). Even here, however, he was probably not thinking of Kepler's work but of an idea proposed by earlier astronomers for the moon and the planet Venus.

INTRODUCTION: SECOND PART

X

News of Galileo's startling discoveries spread rapidly throughout Italy and far beyond its borders. Five hundred copies of his book had been printed. These were sold out at once, and within three months orders for as many more had come in from all over Europe. Kepler enthusiastically hailed his friend's achievements and a second edition of *The Starry Messenger* was printed at Frankfurt in the same year. A great demand for telescopes sprang up, especially for those made by Galileo. Few others were sufficiently powerful to show the satellites of Jupiter. So long as this prevented widespread direct observations, philosophers continued to scoff at the discoveries and even astronomers were slow to accept them. But meanwhile Galileo's name was on everybody's lips. An amusing illustration of his sudden fame is an event that occurred at Florence only two weeks after his book was published. The courier from Venice brought a package to one of his friends there, and neighbors at once surrounded him, demanding that it be opened at once. They were sure that a telescope must be inside. When instead the contents turned out to be a copy of the already famous book, they insisted that its new owner read aloud to them that very evening Galileo's account of his discovery of the Medicean stars.[1]

Galileo lost no time in utilizing his sudden celebrity to

---

[1] *Le Opere di Galileo Galilei, Edizione Nazionale,* vol. x, p. 305. The extent and rapidity of the spread of Galileo's telescopic discoveries can scarcely be exaggerated. Only five years after *The Starry Messenger* appeared, the principal facts announced by Galileo were published in Chinese by a Jesuit missionary in Peking.

further his long-standing scheme of securing a position at the Tuscan court. His former pupil Cosimo had succeeded to the throne about a year before, and since then Galileo had made renewed efforts through various friends in Florence to keep his name remembered there. The dedication of his new book and the naming of Jupiter's satellites had supplied him with a pretext for much correspondence with Cosimo's secretary of state, Belisario Vinta. During the Easter vacation of 1610 he visited Pisa and discussed his wishes quite frankly with Vinta, following this up with the ensuing letter written after his return to Padua:

"As I mentioned to you in my last letter, I have given three public lectures on the subject of the four Medicean planets and my other observations. The whole university turned out, and I so convinced and satisfied everyone that in the end those very leaders who at first were my sharpest critics and the most stubborn opponents of the things I had written, seeing their case to be desperate and in fact lost, publicly stated that they are not only persuaded but are ready to defend and support my doctrines against any philosopher who dares to attack them. Thus the threatened writings will come to nothing, as has the whole idea which these fellows have thus far tried to bring against me with some hope of succeeding, thinking that I would be quite overthrown by the force of their authority or dismayed by the abundance of their credulous followers, and would withdraw into a corner and wall myself in. Well, things have turned out just the opposite; and indeed it was necessary that truth should remain on top.

"Your Excellency, and their Highnesses through you, should know that I have received a letter—or rather an eight-page treatise—from [Johannes Kepler] the Imperial Mathematician, written in approbation of every detail contained in my book without the slightest doubt or contradiction of anything. And you may believe that this is the way leading men of letters in Italy would have spoken from the beginning if I had been in Germany or somewhere far away—just as we may believe that neighboring princes in Italy look with dimmer vision upon the eminence and power of our noble sovereign than upon the immense strength and treasures of Moscow or of the Chinese, which are at such a long distance from them. Well, the way things stand now, envy has no attack left with which to put down my book, or convict it of falsehood, or even to raise doubts concerning it. It remains for us, and particularly for our noble patrons, to sustain it in reputation and glory by showing that they render it the esteem deserved by such distinguished novelties, recognized as such by all who speak sincerely of them.

"The illustrious ambassador of the Medici at Prague writes me that the only telescopes at that court are of very mediocre power. Hence he requests one from me, and hints that this is also desired by His Majesty, writing that I should send it to the resident secretary at Venice in order that it be safely delivered. However, I do not intend the said secretary to receive or send anything without Your Excellency's orders, so if you wish me to send one in this way, please give orders to that effect at Venice. Meanwhile, since there are no very good telescopes at hand, I shall see that one or two are made—though this is a good deal of trouble for me, and I do not wish to show the proper method of making them to anyone except a subject of the Grand Duke, as I have said before. For that reason and many others, but especially for my own peace of mind, I very much desire a decision on the matter already mentioned to you recently at Pisa; for as one day goes by after another I am determined to settle my future career and devote all my attention to bringing to fruition all my labors and studies of the past, from which I hope to win some fame. And since it is up to our sovereign whether I spend the rest of my days here or at Florence, I shall tell you what I have here and what I desire there, placing myself ever at the disposal of His Serene Highness.

"Here I have a salary of one thousand florins for life, and this is perfectly secure, coming to me from a deathless and immutable ruler. I can earn more from private instruction as long as I care to go on teaching gentlemen from abroad, and if I were so inclined I could lay aside this much and more every year by taking scholars into my house. Moreover, my obligations here do not detain me more than sixty half-hours a year,[2] and even then not so strictly that I cannot get in many free days; the balance of my time is perfectly free, and I am absolutely my own master. But because giving private lessons and taking scholars as boarders constitute something of an obstacle to me and impede my studies, I should like to live completely free from the one and largely free of the other. Hence if I am to return to my native land, I desire that the primary intention of His Highness shall be to give me leave and leisure to draw my works to a conclusion without my being occupied in teaching.

"I should not like to have him believe that on this account my labors would be less profitable to my professional colleagues; rather, they would be the more so, as in my public lessons I can teach only those rudiments for which the majority of people are prepared, and such teaching is merely a hindrance and no help in completing my works, which I think will not take the last place among matters concerning my profession. Likewise, just as I deem it my greatest glory to be able to teach princes, I prefer not to teach others. I should like my books (dedicated always to my lord) to become my source of income, to say nothing of such inventions as no other prince can match, for of these I have a great many and am certain I can find more as occasion presents itself. Concerning these inventions which belong to my calling, His Highness may rest assured that he will not be wasting his money on them, as perhaps he has done at other times in great quantity, nor will he miss out on any that are useful and good which have been proposed to him by other men.

"Particular secrets, as useful as they are curious and admirable, I have in great plenty. Their very abundance

---

[2] This passage is difficult to understand. University records indicate that Galileo lectured daily at three o'clock in the afternoon during most of his years at Padua (*Opere* xix, 119–20). Perhaps the word "year" should have been "month," or the word "sixty" should be "six hundred."

has worked to my disadvantage (and still does), for had I but a single one of these I should esteem it highly, and with that incentive I could have interested some great ruler, which I have not hitherto done or attempted. Great and remarkable things are mine, but I can only serve (or rather, be put to work by) princes; for it is they who carry on wars, build and defend fortresses, and in their royal diversions make those great expenditures which neither I nor other private persons may.

"The works which I must bring to conclusion are these. Two books on the system and constitution of the universe —an immense conception full of philosophy, astronomy, and geometry. Three books on local motion—an entirely new science in which no one else, ancient or modern, has discovered any of the most remarkable laws which I demonstrate to exist in both natural and violent movement; hence I may call this a new science and one discovered by me from its very foundations. Three books on mechanics, two relating to demonstrations of its principles, and one concerning its problems; and though other men have written on this subject, what has been done is not one-quarter of what I write, either in quantity or otherwise. I have also lesser works on physical topics, such as treatises on sound and the voice, on vision and colors, on the ocean tides, on the nature of continuous quantities, on the motions of animals, and yet other works. I have also in mind the writing of some books about military matters, setting these forth not merely theoretically but showing by very elegant rules everything in that science which depends upon mathematics, such as the practice of fortification, ordnance, assaults, sieges, estimation of distances, artillery matters, the uses of various instruments, and so on.[3] I must also

---

[3] Only three of the works mentioned were published during Galileo's lifetime. That named first became the *Dialogue* of 1632; the next, the *Discourses . . . on Two New Sciences* of 1638. The *Mechanics* appeared in French in 1634. Works on fortification and on the tides have been printed in collected editions, but the others mentioned have perished or exist only in fragments.

reprint my instructions for the use of the military compass (dedicated to His Highness), as no more copies are available, and this instrument has become so popular in the world that other devices of the kind are no longer made, while I have manufactured thousands.

"I shall not describe to you my occupations in following up the observation and investigation of the four new planets, but this is a matter that becomes more difficult the more I think about it, because one can never separate them from one another except for brief intervals, their colors and sizes being very similar. Hence, Your Excellency, I must get rid of distracting thoughts that retard my studies, and especially of those which others can take care of as well as I can. Therefore I pray you to propose these considerations to His Highness (and to weigh them yourself), and let me know the decision.

"Meanwhile I must say that as to salary, I shall be content with what you suggested to me in Pisa, it being an honor to serve such a prince; and just as I add nothing to this, so I rest assured that His Highness in his beneficence will not cut me off (in my wish to leave here) from anything that is usual for others who are less needy than I am. Of this I shall say no more. But finally, as to the title of my position, I desire that in addition to the title of "mathematician" His Highness will annex that of "philosopher"; for I may claim to have studied more years in philosophy than months in pure mathematics. And as to my deserving this full title, Their Highnesses may judge for themselves as soon as they give me an opportunity to deal in their presence with the men most esteemed in this subject.

"I have written at length in order not to have to go over this material again in all its tediousness. Please excuse me if it seems frivolous and light to you, who are accustomed to managing most weighty matters; to me it is the most serious matter that exists, concerning as it does the continuation or the complete alteration of my present way of life. I shall await your reply, and meanwhile I kiss your hands with all reverence, bowing humbly to Their Highnesses; and may God send you every happiness."[4]

Cosimo, who had always liked Galileo, was not unmoved by this eloquent appeal and by the tributes already paid to him in the dedications of Galileo's books and of his most famous discovery. In July, four months after publication of *The Starry Messenger*, Galileo was appointed chief mathematician and philosopher to the Grand Duke of Tuscany, at an annual salary of one thousand florins. At the same time he was made head mathematician of the University of Pisa, without obligation to reside or teach there.

XI

The authorities of the Venetian Republic were much incensed over Galileo's departure. Less than a year had elapsed since he had ceremoniously presented his telescope to the Doge in the presence of the Senate, and in return he had been confirmed for life in his professorship at Padua with his salary doubled. It was Venice that had welcomed him eighteen years before when he had been practically driven from Tuscany, and had supported him in a distinguished and honored position ever since. His decision to leave was accordingly looked upon as an act of rank ingratitude. Yet Galileo had never seen any possibility of achieving his ultimate goals under these authorities, and a year before had set forth one of his reasons in a letter to a friend at Florence. "It is impossible," he wrote, "to obtain wages from a republic, however splendid and generous it may be, without having duties attached. For to have anything from the public one must satisfy the public and not any one individual; and so long as I am capable of lecturing and serving, no one in the republic can exempt me from duty while I receive pay. In brief, I can hope to enjoy these benefits only from an absolute ruler."[5]

Galileo's closest friend and best adviser on practical

[4] *Opere* x, 348 ff.
[5] *Opere* x, 233.

affairs at Venice was absent on a diplomatic mission when the decision was made. This was Giovan Francesco Sagredo, whom Galileo later immortalized by making him one of the three interlocutors in the *Dialogue*. When Sagredo returned to Venice a year after Galileo's departure, he expressed in the following eloquent letter not only his personal regret but the danger to Galileo which he foresaw in this removal from the free air of the proudly independent Republic:

"*Imagination creates events.* Last Saturday I made a list of all those to whom I wished to write to advise them of my return. Having put you first on the list, I then proceeded to write to some whom I merely wished to be rid of. For I did not want to occupy my mind in dealing with them and I left you to the last, desiring to dwell awhile with you. But so strongly did I imagine myself conversing with you, even when writing to the others, that by the time I had carried out my task and sent off the letters I thought I had written to you. The following Sunday while I was at the Council I began to doubt this, and after long thought I realized I had written to you in imagination rather than in fact.

"By the grace of God my voyage went smoothly by way of Marseilles, and from thence by land to this country. To my great pleasure I have seen many cities, for I like to observe the buildings and situations and customs of foreigners in comparison with those of our cities. And truly it seems to me that God has much favored me by letting me be born in this place, so beautiful and so different from all others. . . . Here the freedom and the way of life of every class of persons seem to me an admirable thing, perhaps unique in the world. Well, though I consume time thinking of these things, believe me my mind has run swiftly on to yourself, considering your departure; and my reflections all turn upon my interests and your own.

"As to mine, I find no sufficient remedy or consolation, for there is too great a gap between presence and absence; and though some things, where there is mutual understanding, may be enjoyed by the use of imagination and the act of writing during absence almost as well as in company, nevertheless it is impossible to have the pleasure of conversation and mutual dealings, with accompaniments which are almost more essential than that ultimate pleasure which most people deem the final goal. Now I can well imagine being with my Galileo; I can turn my memory upon many of his most pleasant discourses; but how is it possible for me to sense or for my imagination to represent to me those many welcome novelties that I used to extract from your noble direct conversation? Can these be compensated for by weekly correspondence, which I may read with great pleasure but which you can write perhaps only with too much inconvenience? As far as my interests are concerned, then, your departure produces an inconsolable unhappiness which cannot be made up.

"As to your interests, I bow to your judgment—or rather to your feelings. Here your salary and other commodities were not, I believe, entirely worthless; your expenses I think were quite small and much at your pleasure, and surely your need was not such as to start you thinking of a change, perhaps an uncertain and a dubious one. Where will you find freedom and self-determination as you did in Venice? Especially having the support that you enjoyed, which grew greater every day with the increase of your age and your authority. At present you are in your noble fatherland, but it is equally true that you have left the place from which you had your good. At present you serve your natural prince; a great man, virtuous, young, and of singular promise; but here you had command over those who govern and command others; you had to serve no one but yourself; you were as monarch of the universe. The power and magnanimity of your prince gives good hope that your devotion and merit will be welcomed and appreciated; but in the tempestuous seas of courts who can promise himself that he will not, in the furious winds of envy, be—I shall not say sunk, but at least tossed about and disquieted? I say nothing of the prince's age, for it seems necessarily that with the years he will mature in temperament and inclination and in his other tastes, as indeed I know that his virtue

has such good roots that one may hope from it better and
more abundant fruits. But who knows what may be caused
by the infinite and incomprehensible accidents of the world?
Impostures of evil and envious men, sowing and raising in
the mind of the prince some false and malicious idea, may
make justice and virtue themselves serve to ruin a gallant
man. Princes take pleasure for a while in this or that curiosity; but then, called by interests in greater matters, they
turn their minds elsewhere. I can well believe that your
Grand Duke may be pleased to go about with one of your
telescopes looking at the city of Florence and some nearby
place; but if through some important requirement of his he
must look at what goes on in all Italy, in France, in Spain,
in Germany, and in the Near East, he will put aside your
telescope. And even if by your skill you shall discover some
other instrument useful for these new purposes, who will
ever be able to invent a spyglass for distinguishing madmen
from the wise, good men from those of evil counsel, the ingenious architect from the obstinate and ignorant foreman?
And who does not know that in this judgment must lie the
undoing of millions of fools whose votes are esteemed according to their number and not their weight?

"I do not wish to delve deeper into your interests, for I
obliged myself at the outset to stand by your judgment and
wishes. Other friends of yours speak very differently; one,
indeed, who was among your dearest, declared to me that
he would renounce my friendship if I wished to continue
in yours—which, since one may not recover what is lost,
makes me believe that one should know how to keep what
has been acquired. But I am much disturbed by your being in a place where the authority of the friends of the
Jesuits counts heavily. . . .

"I see this to be too long and tedious; the rest will follow
next week, and I shall reply to your courteous letters as
swiftly as they are received. And most cordially I salute
you."[6]

Sagredo was quite right about the new perils which

6 *Opere* xi, 170–72.

Galileo would have to face, though he underestimated the integrity of Cosimo and overestimated the threat of interference by the Jesuits. It was only after the accession of Cosimo's successor that Galileo found himself in need of greater support from his sovereign than he was able to secure. As to the Jesuits, many years elapsed before they turned against him, and then not without some provocation; at first his most effective support came from the scientists of that society, and Galileo himself had a good opinion of these men. It was the Dominican order which produced the zealots who made trouble for Galileo within the church. But on the whole Sagredo's analysis was sound, and historians generally are agreed that Venice would never have delivered Galileo up to the Inquisition. Cesare Cremonino, head of the philosophy department at the University of Padua, Galileo's good personal friend and stubborn philosophical enemy, was for years suspected of heretical opinions by the inquisitors; yet he was never brought to trial, probably because he remained in Venetian territory. The Republic tolerated no outside interference even from the church, and not long before had defied a papal interdiction. Galileo himself had witnessed the expulsion of all Jesuits from Venetian territory for infringing upon the prerogatives of the university. He must have recognized the importance of such a policy to a teacher of his own originality and independence. In view of these facts there is some justification in seeking motives for his decision beyond those stated in his letters, and without too much violence to credibility we may see a connection between it and the inner needs of the sciences he was creating.

The decisive conscious motivation of Galileo's return to Tuscany appears to have been nostalgia. It is hard to reconcile this with the sophistication of a brilliant middle-aged professor, surrounded by friends and followers wherever he lived, and able frequently to visit his old home during vacations. Yet homesickness shows through his letters and his acts; he was a Florentine by lineage and early training, living abroad among Venetians. The differences of the two cultures were profound. Anton Francesco Doni, who styled himself "a recorder of the people's chatter," saw an expression of life's ideals and of the popular mind in the recreations favored by men in different Italian cities. His comments have been paraphrased by Professor Antonio Banfi in the following words:

"The people of Naples, when free from other occupations, delight in parades and cavalcades; one might say that they love spectacles for their own sake in which they are simultaneously spectators and participants, being in this way raised to a role of dignity in the comedy of life. Rome knows only too well these pomps and spectacles; the Romans admire them and at the same time laugh at them, for they are almost a part of everyday life. When the Romans are free, they most enjoy jolly picnics on sunny hills, with their rustic tables and the golden sparkle of wine, the high laughter of women and the sound of instruments. But at Venice the gondolas glide silently over the waters of the canals; the maritime air brings the cool of evening, and the distant songs have a tired sweetness. A quiet and dying abandon seizes the mind and body in the light glide of embarkation; each person is to all the others a sort of dreamy image of grace. Wherever people collect—whether in the plazas to which they are called by popular shows, or in the salons luminous with gold and jewels, or in the narrow streets window to window over the still water of small canals—the gossiping is light, lively, mysterious; everything is a graceful and vibrant fantasy embroidered on everyday life.

"Now at Florence, when the air is red with the summer sunset and the campaniles begin to sound vespers and the day's work is done, everyone collects in the plazas. The steps of Santa Maria del Fiore swarm with men of every rank and every class; artisans, merchants, teachers, artists, doctors, technicians, poets, scholars. A thousand minds, a thousand arguments; a lively intermingling of questions, problems, news, of disputes, of jokes; an inexhaustible play of language and of thought, a vibrant curiosity; the changeable temper of a thousand spirits by whom every object of discussion is broken into an infinity of senses and significations—all these spring into being, and then are spent. And this is the pleasure of the Florentine public."[7]

If Galileo longed to return to his native province, perhaps it was because this constant turbulent interplay of ideas was a rich source of stimulation to his mind that teaching at Padua could never afford. Galileo's new sciences needed the closest possible contact with technology and with actual problems of practical arts, something which the university could not offer and did not even look upon with favor. It may well have been this lack which found its expression in Galileo's nostalgia and led him to take a step that not only offended many of his true friends but to some degree must also have gone against his own better judgment. His critics at Venice and Padua were not in the least appeased by the argument that the demands of teaching upon his time would prevent the completion of his books. And certainly there is some inconsistency in his letter to Vinta when Galileo uses this argument hard upon the heels of the statement that all his courses were elementary and left him with much free time.

Indeed, Galileo's increasing distaste for university teaching may have been caused less by the compulsion to lecture than by restrictions on what he could say—restrictions that were not clearly defined, but were nevertheless real, imposed as they were by tradition and the conservative nature of such institutions. His early attacks upon the physics of Aristotle had greatly annoyed his colleagues at Pisa. Nothing in the regulations made Aristotle sacred, but the philosophical faculty was the most potent body in the university, and could make things very uncomfortable for anyone who deliberately offended it. To attack the astronomy of Ptolemy was a thousand times as offensive, for the central position and motionlessness of the earth were backed not only by philosophy but by Christian tradition and by common sense itself. Hence, so far as astronomy was concerned, Galileo never overstepped the conventional bounds in his teaching either at Pisa or at Padua. He knew per-

[7] Doni, *I Marmi*, as paraphrased by Professor Antonio Banfi in his *Galileo Galilei* (Milan, 1948), p. 52.

fectly well that to do so would cause serious trouble, and as early as 1597 he had given this reason to Kepler for not openly supporting Copernicus.

Until the autumn of 1609, when Galileo first turned his telescope upon the heavens, there had been no concrete evidence for the Copernican system; its appeal had been only to the love of mathematicians for elegance and simplicity. Now this was all changed. Within a few months more had been discovered about the real nature of heavenly bodies than had been known to any previous astronomer. Galileo did not yet have the clinching argument against Ptolemy, though this was soon to come, but he already had learned enough so that he felt safe in promising his readers that his next book would prove the earth to be in motion, and to shine more brightly than the moon. It must have been hard to contemplate calmly teaching at the university after publishing a book of that sort.

In our day universities are looked upon with some misgiving by conservative men, as places in which the most novel and unsettling discoveries and opinions are likely to crop out. In Galileo's time, however, they could be counted upon to combat anything that was really new or discordant with tradition. A man who found himself in the possession of new and startling truths today would consider a governmental position, especially under a dictator, far less attractive than a professorship, but at that time the patronage of some benevolent despot was likely to be the only hope of such a man.

It is true that Galileo did move from the frying pan into the fire when he exchanged Padua and the firm but gentle philosophical discipline of the university, for Florence and the violent opposition of jealous rivals and theologians at the court. But when he made this move the opposition of philosophers was already real and palpable, while that of other forces was but a cloud on the distant horizon.

XII

The arguments that were brought forward against the new discoveries were so silly that it is hard for the modern mind to take them seriously. Galileo did not bother to reply to them in print, though he answered many of them in personal correspondence with his friends, often quite amusingly. The chief argument at first was that the phenomena he had described were merely illusions created by his telescope and had no real existence in the skies. Galileo countered such assertions by offering a large reward to anyone who could devise an instrument that would show stars moving around Jupiter but not around every other heavenly body.[8] One of his opponents, who admitted that the surface of the moon looked rugged, maintained that it was actually quite smooth and spherical as Aristotle had said, reconciling the two ideas by saying that the moon was covered with a smooth transparent material through which mountains and craters inside it could be discerned. Galileo, sarcastically applauding the ingenuity of this contribution, offered to accept it gladly—provided that his opponent would do him the equal courtesy of allowing him then to assert that the moon was even more rugged than he had thought before, its surface being covered with mountains and craters of this invisible substance ten times as high as any he had seen.[9] At Pisa the leading philosopher had refused even to look through the telescope; when he died a few months afterward, Galileo expressed the hope that since he had neglected to look at the new celestial objects while on earth, he would now see them on his way to heaven.[10] This sort of good-natured raillery, characteristic of Galileo, was taken up by friends who sprang to his de-

[8] *Opere* xi, 107.

[9] *Opere* xi, 143. This feeble attempt to rescue Aristotle was sponsored by Galileo's most troublesome adversary at Florence, Lodovico delle Colombe (see pp. 79, 148–49, 223).

[10] *Opere* x, 484. The philosopher was Giulio Libri (1550–1610), who had taught both at Pisa and at Padua during Galileo's service in those universities.

fense while he was occupying himself in new researches. A particularly objectionable opponent named Horky, an assistant of Galileo's old rival Magini, argued that no new stars or planets could exist because astrologers had already taken into account everything in the sky that could have any influence upon the earth and man. Since nature does nothing in vain, and the new planets could serve no purpose, they could not exist. In reply to this it was retorted that the new planets served a very useful purpose, which was to torment Horky and throw the superstitious into confusion.[11] One after another, all attempts to cleanse the heavens of the new celestial bodies came to grief. Philosophers had come up against a set of facts which their theories were utterly unable to explain. The more persistent and determined adversaries of Galileo eventually had to give up arguing and resort to threats.

Meanwhile he had made two more important discoveries and communicated them to Kepler and other serious students, especially to the Jesuits at the Roman College whose support would be most effective of all in Italy. The first was the curious shape of Saturn, which his telescope was unable to resolve into the well-known rings, and which he interpreted as being caused by two stationary satellites adjoining the planet. The other discovery, made after his arrival at Florence to take up his new duties, was of much weightier consequence. It was that Venus passes through a regular series of changes in shape precisely like those of the moon. This discovery proved Ptolemy wrong in a vital part of his planetary theory, for when considered in terms of the relative positions of Venus and the sun it showed that this planet must move not around the earth but around the sun. Copernicus had been puzzled at the apparent absence of such changes, which were required by his theory.[12]

[11] *Opere* iii: 1, 177–78. Galileo's defender was his former Scotch pupil John Wedderburn.
[12] *De Revolutionibus* i, 10: "Neither do they grant that any darkness similar to that of the moon is found in the planets, but they assume that these are either self-luminous or are lighted by sunlight throughout their whole bodies." Copernicus refrained

Galileo was now able to show their existence, to explain why they had not been seen before, and to explain at the same time why Venus seemed to change very little in size as it moved from its nearest to its farthest position with respect to the earth.

By the end of 1610 Galileo had the great satisfaction of learning from the eminent Jesuit astronomer Father Christopher Clavius, chief mathematician at the Roman College, that the new fixed stars and the satellites of Jupiter had been observed there. Clavius had previously been reported as saying that in order to see such things one would first have to put them inside the telescope. His support, both as an old acquaintance and as an influential church astronomer, was of the greatest importance to Galileo, who would have visited Rome before this in order to exhibit the phenomena with his own telescope had it not been for illness. As it was he did not arrive there until March of the following year, by which time his two new discoveries had also been confirmed by Clavius and his colleagues. Galileo's visit to Rome in 1611 was described by a contemporary as a triumphal tour. He was welcomed by noblemen and by dignitaries of the church, and was given a friendly interview by Pope Paul V. Cardinal Robert Bellarmine, head of the Roman College, requested an official opinion on the reality of Galileo's discoveries from the mathematicians of the faculty, and received a formal confirmation of them. Clavius and his colleagues then honored Galileo with a full day of ceremonies at the college, during which Father Odo Maelcote delivered an address celebrating his achievements and his book.

But about the time Galileo left Rome to return to Florence, a letter went secretly to the chief inquisitor at Padua upon instructions from Bellarmine and six of his fellow cardinals. It contained the ominous words: "See if Gali-

---

from giving his own opinion on the problem. Galileo was much impressed by the fact that this apparent contradiction of the senses had not deterred Copernicus from adhering to the heliocentric system; cf. *Dialogue*, pp. 334–35.

leo is mentioned in the proceedings against Dr. Cesare Cremonino."[13] The leading theologian at Rome could already see the direction in which events were likely to go.

XIII

During Galileo's stay in Rome he had been elected to an organization that was to have the utmost importance in his own career and in the development of modern science—the *Accademia dei Lincei*, or Academy of the Lynx-eyed. First of the academies to specialize in the study of philosophy and science, it had been founded at Rome in 1603 by a young enthusiast named Federigo Cesi, Marquis of Montecelli and son of the powerful Duke of Aquasparta. At first the group consisted only of Cesi himself and three friends, who began to meet daily in order to exchange instruction and information in philosophy and mathematics. One of the members was a Dutch physician named Jan Hecke, who had been imprisoned for homicide (in self-defense) until released through the intervention of Cesi. The Duke did not approve of these studious activities, and particularly disliked his son's association with Hecke. Aided by intriguing courtiers the Duke soon succeeded in driving the latter from Italy and forcing the new academy into inactivity. Cesi, however, did not desist from his scientific pursuits in order to take part in political affairs as his father had hoped. Instead he went to Naples, where he studied under Giambattista Porta, the author of several books, including a renowned treatise on natural magic.[14] By 1609 Cesi was able

13 *Opere* xix, 275.
14 Porta's book contained passages which after the invention of the telescope were interpreted as demonstrating that he had known the principle of the instrument long before. Without entering into the merits of the case, one may see in it a sort of parable. If Porta knew the principle, he failed to apply it. Lipperhey knew nothing of the principle, but chanced upon an application of it. Thus for centuries trial-and-error experimentation had led craftsmen to great practical achievements, while theoretical speculation had led philosophers to many ingenious ideas. The systematic combination of experiment with theorizing

to reactivate the Academy, and Porta was elected its fifth member. Galileo became the sixth member in April 1611, an honor which he valued highly all the rest of his life; and from that time on the Academy expanded rapidly in size and influence. Cesi, however, provided most of its organizational stimulus and financial support, and his death in 1630 resulted in its dispersion.

The growth of modern science has been closely associated with academies and societies separate from the universities. These organizations have provided facilities for mutual discussion, speedy publication, and rapid communication by their members as well as providing them with means of uniting their efforts in combating opposition from various forces as occasion arose. The Lincean Academy anticipated in a remarkable way the functions of its illustrious successors in this field. In its constitution, published in 1624, principles were set forth which have been emulated in such organizations ever since. This may be illustrated by the following extracts from that document:

"The Lincean Academy desires as its members philosophers who are eager for real knowledge and will give themselves to the study of nature, especially mathematics; at the same time it will not neglect the ornaments of elegant literature and philology, which, like graceful garments, adorn the whole body of science. . . . It is not within the Lincean plan to find leisure for recitations and debates; the meetings will neither be frequent nor lengthy, and chiefly for the transaction of necessary business of the academy; but those who wish to enjoy such exercises will not be hindered in any way, so long as they perform them as incidental studies, decently and quietly, and not as vain promises and professions of how much they are about to do. For there is ample philosophical employment for everyone by himself, particularly if pains are taken in traveling and in the observation of natural phenomena and the book of nature

---

was a fundamental process introduced resolutely and successfully by Galileo and a few of his contemporaries. Prior to that time a number of great isolated thinkers had perceived its value, but they had been unable to secure its general adoption.

which is always at hand; that is, the heavens and the earth.
. . . Let members add to their names the title of Lincean,
which has been advisedly chosen as a caution and a constant stimulus, especially when they write on any literary
subject, or in their private letters to associates, and in general when any work of theirs is wisely and well performed.
. . . The Linceans will pass over in silence all political controversies and every kind of quarrels and wordy disputes,
especially gratuitous ones which give occasion to deceit, un-
friendliness and hatred, as men who desire peace and seek
to preserve their studies free from molestation and to avoid
every sort of disturbance. And if anyone by command of
his superiors or some other requirement shall be reduced to
handling such matters, let them be printed without the
name of Lincean, since they are alien to physical and mathematical science and hence to the object of the Academy."[15]

The existence of the Lincean Academy was a godsend
to Galileo at this crucial period in his career. Engineers,
military officers, and men of affairs who frequented the
court would be better able than his former professorial colleagues to supply him with material for the practical application of his science. But the university had provided
him with true intellectual companionship and in addition
served him as a center for the interchange of news in all
scholarly fields—functions which had no exact counterparts
in his new surroundings. Cesi's academy restored to Galileo
both these essential things, and simultaneously opened to
him a channel of news and an avenue for communication of
his own ideas that was even more efficient than actual publication. The combination of court and academy put him
at last in a position to bring together two once separate
worlds that from his time on were destined to remain forever closely linked—the world of scientific research and that
of technology.

[15] Quoted, with slight modifications, from a translation by
John Elliot Drinkwater(-Bethune) in his *Life of Galileo*, p. 37.
(Published anonymously at London in 1829.)

XIV

Shortly after Galileo's return to Florence in the summer of 1611 he found himself once more in collision with the followers of Aristotle. This time the subject of dispute was not astronomy but physics. It concerned a topic that had been one of Galileo's first interests, the behavior of bodies placed in water. When he was still a student at Pisa he had ingeniously reconstructed the probable method of Archimedes in solving a very famous problem. His first known scientific composition, written in 1586, deals with the invention of the hydrostatic balance to which he was led by these reflections. He had never lost interest in the subject; a letter written in 1609 shows that he was then investigating floating bodies, and it appears that he discussed this with the Jesuits at Rome two months before his return to Florence.

The precise origin of the dispute at Florence is not known. According to Lodovico delle Colombe,[16] his most determined adversary, some correspondence between them on floating bodies had culminated in an agreement to settle certain points of difference by means of experiments before

[16] Lodovico delle Colombe was born at Florence in 1565. Because of the important part he played in the opposition to Galileo, it is unfortunate that nothing is known of him save that he was a "philosopher, astronomer, mathematician, and poet, and in sum an erudite man versed in every sort of learning, but critical, satirical, and caustic to a fault. . . . He was large, humorless, and personally not very pleasant." (*Opere* xx, 422.) Colombe seems to have been an amateur. His name is not associated with the universities of Florence or Pisa, and the title pages of his books reveal no professional activity of his. It may be conjectured that he was educated by the Jesuits and that he knew Father Clavius, with whom he corresponded in an attempt to discredit Galileo's ideas among the mathematicians at the Roman College. Colombe was doubtless much in Galileo's mind when he later created the composite character of Simplicio, spokesman for all the conventional ideas in the *Dialogue*. Many of the arguments presented by Simplicio may be found in Colombe's dissertation against the motion of the earth, in much the same order as they appeared later in the *Dialogue*.

mutually acceptable judges. But before the matter was settled in this way, the same question came up in Colombe's absence at the table of the Grand Duke, and immediately thereafter Galileo became ill. The meeting therefore never took place, and Colombe charged Galileo with having deliberately avoided it, which is likely enough, though not for the reasons Colombe alleged.

At any rate it was the custom of the Grand Duke often to invite scholars to dinner in order that he might hear them discuss current topics in their fields and present new ideas before him. During the last week of September 1611, it happened that two cardinals were visiting Florence, and both were present at one of these dinners. The subject of ice in particular and floating bodies in general came under discussion, and Cardinal Maffeo Barberini[17] took sides with Galileo while the other cardinal, Ferdinand Gonzaga, joined with his opponents. The combined interest of the arguments and importance of the guests moved the Grand Duke to request Galileo to publish his views, a task which occupied much of his time toward the end of 1611 and the beginning of 1612.[18]

The *Discourse on Floating Bodies* was so damaging to Aristotle's principles of physics that it could not be ignored by his supporters, particularly as it was written in Italian and could be read and understood by anyone. Several refutations were attempted, of which more will be said presently. This time Galileo's opponents could not fall back upon the argument that Galileo's claims were based upon optical illusions. Neither could they trust to the absence of costly apparatus to keep the people in ignorance as they had done with his telescopic observations. Now they were

[17] Maffeo Barberini (1568–1644) later became Urban VIII, the pope who encouraged Galileo to publish his *Dialogue* and then compelled him to submit to trial and imprisonment by the Inquisition for doing so. The causes of this complete change of heart by Barberini are still obscure.

[18] See the English translation of Galileo's *Discourse on Bodies in Water* (Urbana, 1960) for a further account of the origin of this dispute and its consequences.

confronted with a record of experimental data that anyone could verify at will, and the only thing open to question was the matter of interpretation. But in this they were no match for Galileo, whose specialty was the study of experimental results; and even in their own field of constructing ingenious arguments they were hopelessly outclassed for once. Galileo had in fact amused himself while writing this book by anticipating all their arguments, strengthening these, adding others that had not occurred to them, and then demolishing the whole structure with his own demonstrations and proofs. It was a device which he was to employ extensively in his later works, and one which accounts for his vast influence with nonprofessional readers as well as his extreme unpopularity with the targets of his polemic compositions.

XV

While Galileo was occupied with this excursion into physics (for which he apologized to those readers who were impatiently awaiting the promised book on the system of the world), a German astronomer appeared on the scene with a new telescopic discovery—or rather one which he honestly but mistakenly thought to be new. Father Christopher Scheiner, a Jesuit professor at the University of Ingolstadt, had made a number of observations of sunspots and was eager to publish his findings. This he was forbidden to do in his own name, as his superior feared that he might be mistaken and would only bring discredit upon the Jesuit order. Accordingly Scheiner set forth his observations and theories in the form of several letters addressed to Mark Welser, a wealthy merchant of Augsburg who was a good friend of the Jesuits and an enthusiastic amateur of science. Welser promptly published Scheiner's letters and sent a copy to Galileo (with whom he had corresponded once before concerning the lunar mountains), asking his opinion. Scheiner's identity was concealed under the pseudonym *Apelles latens post tabulam*[19] and was not known to Galileo until more than a year later, though it had soon become apparent that the author was a Jesuit.

In later years great bitterness arose between Scheiner and Galileo concerning the question of priority in the discovery of sunspots, and this dispute appears to have had a great deal to do with Galileo's ultimate trouble with the church. Even apart from this it is most unfortunate that such a debate should have arisen, as neither man was first to observe sunspots—a phenomenon that was certainly mentioned in the time of Charlemagne, and possibly was referred to by Virgil—or even first to publish on the subject. That honor belongs to Johann Fabricius of Wittenberg, whose booklet printed in the summer of 1611 seems to have escaped their attention. But since the dispute was historically if not scientifically important, and since Galileo has sometimes been unjustly charged with having first learned of sunspots from Scheiner's letters, it is necessary to review the evidence very briefly.

Scheiner's initial letter states that he had first noticed some spots on the sun seven or eight months before he began to record them, but that he had ignored them as of no interest at that time. His first recorded observation was made on October 21, 1611. The first known mention of sunspots by Galileo occurs in a letter dated October 1, 1611, and addressed to the painter Lodovico Cigoli at Rome.[20] Cigoli had already written to Galileo twice in September regarding sunspots observed by his friend

[19] The meaning of this cumbersome pseudonym is "the author, awaiting comment and criticism before revealing himself." Apelles was court painter to Alexander the Great. He is reported on one occasion to have stationed himself behind one of his paintings in order to listen to the remarks of the spectators. When a passing shoemaker was heard criticizing the representation of a boot, Apelles stepped out to thank the workman and ask for correction. But the emboldened cobbler then began to extend his adverse remarks to other parts of the picture, and Apelles stopped him with the now proverbial admonition: "Let the shoemaker stick to his last."

[20] *Opere* xi, 214.

Domenico Passignani.[21] Moreover Cigoli's letters do not seem to have been intended to communicate a new discovery, but to transmit certain observations which Passignani thought would indicate a clockwise rotation of the spots during the day. Galileo's reply certainly deals with sunspots as a matter with which he had long been acquainted and from which he had already deduced a very different (and substantially correct) idea of the sun's rotation. Other evidence supports Galileo's assertion in his reply to Welser that he had shown the spots to others while at Rome, but this evidence is not conclusive; his later assertion that he had observed them before leaving Padua is still more dubious. Yet it is quite clear that he knew of them independently of Scheiner, as did Fabricius and at least one other early observer, the Englishman Thomas Harriot.

XVI

It is a curious fact that the conservative astronomers who for philosophical reasons had previously rejected Galileo's discovery of new moving stars in the heavens, now for philosophical reasons commenced to populate the sky with moving stars at a rate which made Galileo blush. Forgotten were the arguments which they had employed not long before to prove that everything in the heavens had been taken into account by the astrologers. This new threat to all good philosophy was much more serious; if blemishes could appear and disappear on the face of the sun itself, the incorruptibility and inalterability of the heavenly bodies was destroyed. To avoid such unthinkable consequences, Scheiner accounted for sunspots by assuming a number of small planets to revolve about (or beneath) the sun and to obstruct our vision. Galileo, untroubled by the philosophical scruples of his opponents, placed the spots right on the surface of the sun, or at least no farther from it than clouds are from the earth. His evidence as to their location was beyond dispute, for it was mathematical. As to the nature

[21] *Opere* xi, 208 and 212.

of the spots, he remained uncommitted, though he did not hesitate to reason about this matter by analogy with terrestrial phenomena, a very radical departure at the time. Two years earlier he had applied such reasoning to the moon; now he extended it on out to the sun, and once more his adversaries failed in all their attempts to call it back to earth.

Galileo's reply to the theories of his unknown rival was written in the same form as that in which they had been propounded—a series of letters to Mark Welser. Since ostensibly he was replying not to Apelles but to Welser, and since Welser had addressed him in Italian, he had a suitable pretext for answering in that language. But his real reasons were set forth in a letter to his friend Paolo Gualdo at Padua:

"I have received word from Sig. Welser that my letter has arrived and is very welcome, but that Apelles will not be able to read it right away because he does not understand the language. I wrote in the colloquial tongue because I must have everyone able to read it, and for the same reason I wrote my last book in this language. I am induced to do this by seeing how young men are sent through the universities at random to be made physicians, philosophers, and so on; thus many of them are committed to professions for which they are unsuited, while other men who would be fitted for these are taken up by family cares and other occupations remote from literature. The latter are, as Ruzzante would say, furnished with 'horse sense,' but because they are unable to read things that are 'Greek to them' they become convinced that in those 'big books there are great new things of logic and philosophy and still more that is way over their heads.' Now I want them to see that just as nature has given to them, as well as to philosophers, eyes with which to see her works, so she has also given them brains capable of penetrating and understanding them. All the same, I hope that Apelles also, and other foreigners, will be able to read it; and since I am very busy here I should appreciate it if you and Sig. Sandelli would translate it into Latin and send it back to me at once, as plans are afoot here and at Rome to print it, together with some other letters of mine."[22]

Scheiner succeeded before long in getting a translation of Galileo's first letter, and he then wrote a reply which he entitled *A More Accurate Discussion of Sunspots and the Stars which Move around Jupiter*. This extension of the debate enabled Galileo to bring up the matter of the Copernican system and for the first time to endorse it unequivocally in print, predicting that it would soon be universally adopted. Printed at Rome in 1613 under the auspices of the Lincean Academy, Galileo's *Letters on Sunspots* thus brought the question of the earth's motion to the attention of practically everyone in Italy who could read.

[22] *Opere* xi, 326 ff.

HISTORY AND DEMONSTRATIONS CONCERNING SUNSPOTS AND THEIR PHENOMENA

Contained in three letters, written
to the Illustrious Mark Welser,
Duumvir of Augsburg and
Counselor to His
Imperial Majesty

By

GALILEO GALILEI
Gentleman of Florence
Chief Philosopher and Mathematician
of the Most Serene Cosimo II,
Grand Duke of Tuscany

ROME
1613

FIRST LETTER FROM MARK WELSER TO GALILEO GALILEI

Most Illustrious and Excellent Sir:

Already the minds of men are assailing the heavens, and gain strength with every acquisition. You have led in scaling the walls, and have brought back the awarded crown. Now others follow your lead with the greater courage, knowing that once you have broken the ice for them it would indeed be base not to press so happy and honorable an undertaking. See, then, what has arrived from a friend of mine; and if it does not come to you as anything really new, as I suppose, nevertheless I hope you will be pleased to see that on this side of the mountains also men are not lacking who travel in your footsteps. With respect to these solar spots, please do me the favor of telling me frankly your opinion—whether you judge them to be made of starry matter or not; where you believe them to be situated, and what their motion is. My deepest respects, and a happy New Year; and I beg you not to withhold from me the results of your latest observations.

From Your Excellency's most affectionate servant,

MARK WELSER

AUGSBURG, January 6, 1612

FIRST LETTER FROM GALILEO GALILEI TO MARK WELSER
Concerning the Solar Spots,
In Reply to the Foregoing Letter

Most Worthy Sir:

Tardy in replying to the courteous letter Your Excellency wrote me three months ago, I have been forced to silence by various circumstances. In particular a long indisposition —or I should say a series of long indispositions preventing all exercises and occupations on my part—has made it impossible for me to write. And so it does to a large extent yet, though not so completely that I cannot reply to at least some letters from my friends and patrons, of which I find not a few awaiting answers.

I have remained silent also until I might hope to give some satisfaction to your inquiry about the solar spots, concerning which you have sent me some brief essays by the mysterious "Apelles." The difficulty of this matter, combined with my inability to make many continued observations, has kept (and still keeps) my judgment in suspense. And I, indeed, must be more cautious and circumspect than most other people in pronouncing upon anything new. As Your Excellency well knows, certain recent discoveries that depart from common and popular opinions have been noisily denied and impugned, obliging me to hide in silence every new idea of mine until I have more than proved it. Even the most trivial error is charged to me as a capital fault by the enemies of innovation, making it seem better to remain with the herd in error than to stand alone in reasoning correctly. I might add that I am quite content to be last and to come forth with a correct idea, rather than to get ahead of other people and later be compelled to retract what might be said sooner, indeed, but with less consideration.

These considerations have made me slow to respond to Your Excellency's requests and still make me hesitate to do more than advance a rather negative case by appearing to know rather what sunspots are not than what they really are, it being much harder for me to discover the truth than to refute what is false. But in order to satisfy Your Excellency's wishes in part at least, I shall consider those things which seem to me worthy of notice in the three letters of this man Apelles, as you require, and in particular what he has to say with regard to determining the essence, the location, and the motion of these spots.

First of all, I have no doubt whatever that they are real

objects and not mere appearances or illusions of the eye or of the lenses of the telescope, as Your Excellency's friend well establishes in his first letter. I have observed them for about eighteen months, having shown them to various friends of mine, and at this time last year I had many prelates and other gentlemen at Rome observe them there. It is also true that the spots do not remain stationary upon the body of the sun, but appear to move in relation to it with regular motions, as your author has noted in that same letter. Yet to me it appears that this motion is in the opposite direction from what Apelles says—that is, they move from west to east, slanting from south to north, and not from east to west and north to south. This may be clearly perceived in the observations he himself describes, which compare in this regard with my own observations and with what I have seen of those made by other people. The spots seen at sunset are observed to change place from one evening to the next, descending from the part of the sun then uppermost, and the morning spots ascend from the part then below; and they appear first in the more southerly parts of the sun's body and disappear or separate from it in the more northerly regions. Thus the spots describe lines on the face of the sun similar to those along which Venus and Mercury proceed when those planets come between the sun and our eyes. Hence they move with respect to the sun as do Venus and Mercury and the other planets, which motion is from west to east and obliquely to the horizon from south to north. If Apelles assumes that the spots do not revolve about the sun, but merely pass beneath it, then their motion may be properly called "from east to west." But assuming that the spots circle about the sun, being now beyond it and now this side of it, their rotation should be said to be from west to east, since that is the direction in which they move when they are in the more distant portions of their orbits.

Having established the fact that the spots observed are not telescopic illusions or optical defects, the author next seeks to determine something about their location, attempting to show that they are neither in the atmosphere of the earth nor in the body of the sun. On the first point, their

lack of any perceptible parallax shows that we must conclude them to be not in the atmosphere; that is, not near
the earth within the space commonly assigned to the element of air. But that they cannot be on the surface of the
sun appears to me to be not quite conclusively demonstrated. For it proves nothing to say, as this author does in
his first argument, that it is unbelievable for dark spots to
exist in the sun simply because the sun is a most lucid body.
So long as men were in fact obliged to call the sun "most
pure and most lucid," no shadows or impurities whatever
had been perceived in it; but now that it shows itself to us
as partly impure and spotty, why should we not call it
"spotted and not pure"? For names and attributes must be
accommodated to the essence of things, and not the essence
to the names, since things come first and names afterwards.

Next Apelles says that the spots seen in the sun are much
blacker than any of those ever observed in the moon. This
I believe to be absolutely false; I hold, on the contrary, that
the sunspots are at least as bright as the brightest part of
the moon, and my reasoning is as follows. When Venus
appears as evening star it is very splendid; yet it is not seen
until many degrees distant from the sun, particularly if
both are well above the horizon. This is because the regions
of the sky around the sun are no less bright than Venus
itself. From this we may deduce that if we could place the
full moon directly beside the sun, it would remain quite
invisible, being situated in a field no less bright than itself.
Now consider the fact that when we look at the brilliant
solar disk through the telescope, it appears much brighter
than the field which surrounds it; and then let us compare
the blackness of the sunspots both with the sun's own light
and with the darkness of the adjacent surroundings. From
the two comparisons we shall find that the sunspots are no
darker than the field surrounding the sun. Now if this is so,
and if the moon itself would remain imperceptible in the
brightness of those same surroundings, then we are forced
to the conclusion that the sunspots are not a bit less bright
than the shining parts of the moon—even though, situated
as they are in the very brilliant field of the sun's disk, they

look cloudy and black to us. And if they yield nothing in brightness to the lightest parts of the moon, what will they be in comparison with the moon's darkest spots? Remember that the latter spots are caused by projected shadows of the lunar mountains, and in comparison with the lighted portions they are as dark as is the ink with respect to this paper. I say this not to contradict Apelles, but to show that we need not assume the material of the sunspots to be very dense and opaque, as we may reasonably suppose with regard to the material of the moon and the planets. A density and opacity similar to that of a cloud is enough, if interposed between us and the sun, to produce the required obscurity and blackness.

Next Apelles suggests that sunspot observations afford a method by which he can determine whether Venus and Mercury revolve about the sun or between the earth and the sun. I am astonished that nothing has reached his ears—or if anything has, that he has not capitalized upon it—of a very elegant, palpable, and convenient method of determining this, discovered by me about two years ago and communicated to so many people that by now it has become notorious. This is the fact that Venus changes shape precisely as does the moon; and if Apelles will now look through his telescope he will see Venus to be perfectly circular in shape and very small (though indeed it was smaller yet when it [recently] emerged as evening star). He may then go on observing it, and he will see that as it reaches its maximum departure from the sun it will be semicircular. Thence it will pass into a horned shape, gradually becoming thinner as it once more approaches the sun. Around conjunction it will appear as does the moon when two or three days old, but the size of its visible circle will have much increased. Indeed, when Venus emerges [from behind the sun] to appear as evening star, its apparent diameter is only one-sixth as great as at its evening disappearance [in front of the sun] or its emergence as morning star [several days thereafter], and hence its disk appears forty times as large on the latter occasions.

These things leave no room for doubt about the orbit of

Venus. With absolute necessity we shall conclude, in agreement with the theories of the Pythagoreans and of Copernicus, that Venus revolves about the sun just as do all the other planets. Hence it is not necessary to wait for transits and occultations[1] of Venus to make certain of so obvious a conclusion. No longer need we employ arguments that allow any answer, however feeble, from persons whose philosophy is badly upset by this new arrangement of the universe. For these opponents, unless constrained by some stronger argument, would say that Venus either shines with its own light or is of a substance that may be penetrated by the sun's rays, so that it may be lighted not only on its surface but also throughout its depth. They take heart to shield themselves with this argument because there have not been wanting philosophers and mathematicians who have actually believed this—meaning no offense to Apelles, who says otherwise. Indeed, Copernicus himself was forced to admit the possibility and even the necessity of one of these two ideas, as otherwise he could give no reason for Venus failing to appear horned when beneath the sun.[2] As a matter of fact nothing else could be said before the telescope came along to show us that Venus is naturally and actually dark like the moon, and like the moon has phases.

Besides, I seriously question the method by which Apelles would try to detect Venus against the sun's disk at conjunction. He supposes it ought to be seen there in the guise of a spot much larger than any we observe, saying that its visible diameter is three minutes of arc, and therefore its surface is one one-hundred-thirtieth that of the sun. With all due respect to him, this is not true. The visible diameter of Venus is not even the sixth part of one minute, and its surface is less than one forty-thousandth that of the sun, as in due course I shall make evident to anyone by direct

[1] Transits of Venus occur when the planet passes directly across the face of the sun; occultations, when it passes directly behind the sun. Galileo calls both events "bodily conjunctions."

[2] See note 12, p. 74.

experiment. So Your Excellency may see that there is still a large field left for those who, with Ptolemy, wish to keep Venus always beneath the sun. They would say that one would seek in vain for such a tiny speck in its immense and gleaming face. And finally anyone who would deny the revolution of Venus about the sun could say that its orbit lay beyond the sun, supporting themselves upon the authority of Aristotle, who thought that it did.[3] Therefore the argument of Apelles is insufficient for his purpose. . . .

I come now to his third letter, in which he speaks more positively about the position, motion, and substance of the sunspots, concluding that they are stars not far removed from the body of the sun, and that they revolve about it in the manner of Mercury and Venus.

In order to determine their place, he begins with a proof that they are not located on the very body of the sun and moved by its rotation. Passing across the visible hemisphere of the sun in fifteen days, he says, the same spots ought to return every month, which does not happen. This argument would be conclusive if we could first be sure that these spots were permanent; that is, that they do not spring up anew, and likewise become erased or vanish. But anyone who will say that some are produced and others decay will likewise be able to maintain that the sun, revolving upon its axis, carries them around without ever showing us spots which are identical with previous ones, or which are arranged the same, or shaped the same. Now I think it is a very difficult thing—even impossible—to prove that they are permanent. Our senses themselves oppose this. Apelles himself must have seen some of them appear for the first time well within the circumference of the sun, and others vanish before they have finished crossing the sun, for I have observed many such. I am not affirming or denying that the spots are located on the sun; I merely say that it is insufficiently proved that they are not.

[3] Aristotle himself seems not to have been specific about this, but his teacher, Plato, gave this order: moon, sun, Venus, Mercury, Mars, Jupiter, Saturn, the fixed stars. The scheme is that of Eudoxus; cf. note 3, p. 11.

In all the rest which this author adds, to prove that the spots are not situated in the atmosphere or in any of the orbs beneath the sun, I seem to perceive some confusion and inconsistency. He once more takes up as true the ancient and common system of Ptolemy. A short time before he showed his awareness that this system is false; that is, when he concluded that Venus does not have an orbit beneath the sun but revolves around it. He also affirmed the same of Mercury, whose [maximum] elongation is much smaller than that of Venus, requiring it to be placed much closer to the sun. Yet at this point he refutes that true arrangement in which a moment ago he believed. He now introduces the false one, placing Mercury after the moon, followed by Venus. I wish I could excuse this slight error of his by saying that he was not paying attention when he named Mercury and Venus in that order after the moon. To get the cart before the horse in this way would not matter much so far as the words are concerned, if only he had kept the things arranged correctly. But next I see that he proves by means of parallax[4] that the sunspots are not in Mercury's orb, and adds that this method would not apply to Venus because of its small parallax. This vitiates my excuses for him, as Venus will [sometimes] have a parallax much greater than those of Mercury and the sun.

Yet I seem to see in Apelles a free and not a servile mind. He is quite capable of understanding true doctrines; for, led by the force of so many novelties, he has begun to lend his ear and his assent to good and true philosophy, especially that part which concerns the arrangement of the universe. Still, he cannot detach himself entirely from those previously impressed fancies to which his intellect turns back and lends assent from long use and habit. This may be seen once again when he tries to prove that the spots are not in the lunar orb or in those of Venus or Mercury. In doing so he continues to adhere to eccentrics, deferents, equants, epicycles, and the like as if they were real, actual,

---

[4] By parallax is meant the apparent difference of location with respect to the fixed stars of an object viewed from different positions on the earth.

and distinct things. These, however, are merely assumed by mathematical astronomers in order to facilitate their calculations. They are not retained by philosophical astronomers who, going beyond the demand that they somehow save the appearances, seek to investigate the true constitution of the universe—the most important and most admirable problem that there is. For such a constitution exists; it is unique, true, real, and could not possibly be otherwise; and the greatness and nobility of this problem entitle it to be placed foremost among all questions capable of theoretical solution.

Now I do not deny the existence of circular movements about the earth or other centers, or even circular motions completely separated from the earth and outside its orbit. The approaches and retreats of Mars, Jupiter, and Saturn assure me of the former, while Venus, Mercury, and the four Medicean planets make me certain of the latter. Hence I am quite sure that there exist circular motions which describe eccentric and epicyclic circles.[5] But that Nature, in order to provide these, really makes use of that farrago of spheres and orbs composed by the astronomers is, I think, not so much something we are expected to believe as it is a convenience in astronomical computations. My opinion lies midway between that of astronomers who assume eccentric movements on the part of stars as well as eccentric orbs and spheres to conduct them, and that of philosophers who deny equally the existence of such orbs and all movements not concentric with the earth. In any case, when it comes to investigating the location of the solar spots, I wish Apelles would not drive them away from a real place that exists in the immense spaces wherein the tiny bodies of the moon,

[5] Galileo means that eccentric motions exist physically in the sense that the earth cannot be at the center of the orbits of the outer planets. And his opponent admits that Venus and Mercury move around the sun; hence epicyclic motions with respect to the earth must exist. The satellites of Jupiter serve as an additional example. Here Galileo is not concerned with the system adopted, but with showing that the old mechanism of solid crystalline spheres in the heavens is entirely untenable and must be abandoned. Cf. note 7, p. 112.

Venus, and Mercury revolve, merely because of an imaginary supposition that these spaces are completely occupied by eccentric, epicyclic and deferent orbs disposed (or even obliged) to carry along with them every other body that happens to be situated there, so that nothing can wander by itself through that space in any other direction than that in which it is dragged by the surrounding sky.

.   .   .   .

It now remains for us to consider the judgment of Apelles concerning the essence and substance of these spots, which in sum is that they are neither clouds nor comets, but stars that go circling about the sun. I confess to Your Excellency that I am not yet sufficiently certain to affirm any positive conclusion about their nature. The substance of the spots might even be any of a thousand things unknown and unimaginable to us, while the phenomena commonly observed in them—their shapes, their opacity, and their movement—may lie partly or wholly outside the realm of our general knowledge. Therefore I see nothing discreditable to any philosopher in confessing that he does not know, and cannot know, what the material of the solar spots may be. But if, proceeding on a basis of analogy with materials known and familiar to us, one may suggest something that they may be from their appearance, my view would be exactly opposite to that of Apelles. To me it seems that none of the essentials belonging to stars are in any way adapted to the spots, while on the other hand I find in them nothing at all which does not resemble our own clouds. This may be seen by arguing as follows.

Sunspots are generated and decay in longer and shorter periods; some condense and others greatly expand from day to day; they change their shapes, and some of these are most irregular; here their obscurity is greater and there less. They must be simply enormous in bulk, being either on the sun or very close to it. By their uneven opacity they are capable of impeding the sunlight in differing degrees; and sometimes many spots are produced, sometimes few, sometimes none at all.

Now of all the things found with us, only clouds are vast and immense, are produced and dissolved in brief times, endure for long or short periods, expand and contract, easily change shape, and are more dense and opaque in some places and less so in others. Indeed, all other materials not only lack these properties but are far from having them. Moreover there is no doubt that if the earth shone with its own light and not by that of the sun, then to anyone who looked at it from afar it would exhibit congruent appearances. For as now this country and now that was covered by clouds, it would appear to be strewn with dark spots that would impede the terrestrial splendor more or less according to the greater or less density of their parts. These spots would be seen darker here and less dark there, now more numerous and again less so, now spread out and now restricted; and if the earth revolved upon an axis, they would follow its motion. And since clouds are of no great depth with respect to the breadth in which they are normally extended, those seen at the center of the visible hemisphere would appear quite broad, while those toward the edges would look narrower. In a word, no phenomena would be perceived that are not likewise seen in sunspots.

.   .   .   .

From observations already made and from others which may be made at any time, it clearly follows that no material of ours better imitates the properties of these spots than terrestrial clouds, and the arguments which Apelles adduces to the contrary seem to me to be ineffective. To his query, "Who would ever place clouds around the sun?" I shall reply, "Anyone who sees these spots and wants to say something probable about their nature, for nothing known to us more resembles them." To his question about how large they are I shall say, "As large as we see them to be with respect to the sun; as large as those clouds that sometimes cover a large province on earth," and if that is not large enough I shall say two, three, four, or ten times that. And finally, to the third "impossibility" he adduces—how sunspots could possibly be so dark—I shall respond that their blackness is less than that revealed to us by our densest clouds when those are interposed between the sun and our eyes. This can be clearly observed sometimes when a very dark cloud covers a part of the sun and simultaneously some sunspots are seen in the part that remains visible, for no small difference will be discerned between their blackness and that of the cloud, despite the fact that the edge of the cloud cannot be of any great thickness. Thus a very thick cloud may create much greater blackness than the darkest of the spots. But even if this were not so, who would forbid us to say that some solar clouds are thicker and denser than clouds above the earth?

I do not assert on this account that the spots are clouds of the same material as ours, or aqueous vapors raised from the earth and attracted by the sun. I merely say that we have no knowledge of anything that more closely resembles them. Let them be vapors or exhalations then, or clouds, or fumes sent out from the sun's globe or attracted there from other places; I do not decide on this—and they may be any of a thousand other things not perceived by us.

It may readily be deduced from what has been said that the name "stars" is ill-suited to these spots. Stars, whether fixed or wandering, are seen always to keep the same shape, which is spherical. They are not seen to be destroyed in one place and produced in another, but remain always constant. They have their periodic movements and return after some determinate period, whereas I think one would wait in vain for the return of those "stars" which Apelles would have revolve in tight circles about the sun. Hence sunspots lack the chief properties that belong to those bodies in nature to which we assign the name "stars." Nor should the spots be called "stars" because they are opaque bodies denser than the material of the sky, which consequently stand out against the sun, being brightly lighted by its rays on one side and producing deep shade on the other, and so on. Why, these are properties that belong to any rock, to wood, to the thickest clouds and, in a word, to all opaque bodies. A ball of marble reflects the light of the sun where it is illuminated and produces shade on the opposite side, just as does the moon or Venus; so in those respects it too might be called a "star." But since these things lack other and more essential properties which sunspots also lack, it seems inappropriate to assign to them the name "stars."

It grieves me to see Apelles enumerate the companions of Jupiter in this company, referring (I think) to the four Medicean planets. These show themselves constant, like any other star, and they are always light except when they run into the shadow of Jupiter, at which times they are eclipsed just as is the moon in the earth's shadow. They have their orderly periods, which differ among the four, and which have been already exactly determined by me. Nor do they move in a single orbit, as Apelles either believes or thinks that others have believed; they have distinct orbits about Jupiter as their center, the various sizes of which I have likewise discovered. I have also detected the reasons for which one or another of them occasionally tilts northward or southward in relation to Jupiter, and the times when this happens. And perhaps I shall have replies to the objections that Apelles hints at concerning these things, whenever he gets round to specifying them. That there may be more of these planets than the four hitherto observed, as Apelles says he holds for certain, may possibly be true; such positiveness on the part of a person who is (so far as I know) very well-informed makes me believe that he must have very good grounds for his assertion which I lack. Hence I should not like to say anything definite about this, lest I might have to take it back later.

For the same reason I have resolved not to put anything around Saturn except what I have already observed and revealed—that is, two small stars which touch it, one to the east and one to the west, in which no alteration has ever yet been seen to take place and in which none is to be expected in the future, barring some very strange event remote from every other motion known to or even imagined by us. But as to the supposition of Apelles that Saturn is sometimes oblong and sometimes accompanied by two stars on its flanks, Your Excellency may rest assured that this results either from the imperfection of the telescope or the eye of the observer, for the shape of Saturn is thus: o()o , as shown by perfect vision and perfect instruments, but appears thus: where perfection is lacking, the shape and distinction of the three stars being imperfectly seen. I, who have observed it a thousand times at different periods with an excellent instrument, can assure you that no change whatever is to be seen in it. And reason, based upon our experiences of all other stellar motions, renders us certain that none ever will be seen, for if these stars had any motion similar to those of other stars, they would long since have been separated from or conjoined with the body of Saturn, even if that movement were a thousand times slower than that of any other star which goes wandering through the heavens.

Apelles comes finally to the conclusion that the spots are planets rather than fixed stars, and that they lie precisely between the sun and Mercury or Venus, which are the only planets that ever appear between us and the sun. To this I say that I do not believe the spots to be planets, or fixed stars, or stars of any kind, nor that they move about the sun in circles separated and distant from it. If I may give my own opinion to a friend and patron, I shall say that the solar spots are produced and dissolve upon the surface of the sun and are contiguous to it, while the sun, rotating upon its axis in about one lunar month, carries them along, perhaps bringing back some of those that are of longer duration than a month, but so changed in shape and pattern that it is not easy for us to recognize them. This is as far as I am willing to hazard a guess at present, and I hope that Your Excellency will consider the matter closed by what I have suggested. There may indeed be some other planet between the sun and Mercury which moves about the sun but remains invisible to us because it never gets far from the sun; such a one might become visible to us only when it passes in direct line with the solar disk. This presents no improbability to me; I think it equally likely that there may be one such and that there may not. But I certainly do not believe there is a great multitude of them, for if they existed in great number it would be reasonable for us to see some of them when they were beneath the sun. This has never happened for me so far; I have not seen anything other than the spots themselves, and it is not very likely that any such star should have passed among the spots in the form of a black spot, because the movement of such a star should appear uniform and very swift in comparison with the motion of the spots—most swift, since it ought to move faster than Mercury, and Mercury passes across the sun in about six hours.

. . . .

I know that I have wearied Your Excellency with too many words and too few conclusions. Please see in my loquacity the pleasure I take in conversing with you and the desire I feel to obey and to serve you; excuse my verbosity, and be gladdened by my affection. And forgive me my indecision, because of the novelty and difficulty of the subject, in which various thoughts have passed through my mind and met now with assent and again with rejection, leaving me abashed and perplexed, for I do not like to open my mouth without declaring anything whatever. Nevertheless, I shall not abandon the task in despair. Indeed, I hope that this new thing will turn out to be of admirable service in tuning for me some reed in this great discordant organ of our philosophy—an instrument on which I think I see many organists wearing themselves out trying vainly to get the whole thing into perfect harmony. Vainly, because they leave (or rather preserve) three or four of the principal reeds in discord, making it quite impossible for the others to respond in perfect tune.

As Your Excellency's servant I desire to share in your friendship with Apelles, deeming him a person of high intelligence and a lover of truth. Therefore I beg you to salute him amicably for me, and tell him that in a few days I shall send him some observations and diagrams of sunspots which are absolutely exact both as to their shape and their variation of position from day to day, drawn without a hairsbreadth of error in a very elegant manner discovered by a pupil of mine; these may serve him in further theorizing about their nature. And now it is time to cease troubling you. Kissing your hands with all reverence, and commending myself to your grace, I pray Almighty God for your happiness.

From the Villa delle Selve, May 4, 1612.

From Your Excellency's most devoted servitor,

GALILEO GALILEI

SECOND LETTER OF MARK WELSER TO GALILEO GALILEI

Illustrious and Most Excellent Sir:

You have paid a high rate of interest for the favor of a little time, sending me so copious and diffuse a treatise in reply to a few lines. I have read it, or rather devoured it, with a pleasure equal to the appetite and longing I had for it. Let me assure you that it has served to alleviate for me a long and painful illness that has been causing me extreme discomfort in the left thigh. For this the physicians have not yet found any effective remedy; indeed, the doctor in charge has told me in very plain words that the first men of his profession have written of this disease that "some cases are cured, but others are incurable."[6] One must therefore submit to the fatherly disposition of God's providence; "Thou art the Lord, do what is good in Thy sight."

But I stray too far in melancholy matters. I say that your discourse was most welcome to me. From the little which I can master of the subject it seems to me so well written and contains such good and well-founded arguments, set forth most modestly, that despite your having in the main contradicted the views of Apelles, he should consider himself much honored by it. It will take time to make him master of its contents, since he does not understand Italian

---

[6] Welser's affliction was gout, and the seizures had begun in 1606. His case was incurable, and he died within two years after writing this.

and translators who comprehend the sciences are not always at hand, but an attempt will be made to conquer this difficulty as well. I have written to the learned Sig. Sagredo (and I repeat to you) that if I were in a city where Italian printers were to be found, I should entreat your kind permission to publish the work at once. I believe that might safely be done since you proceed in so judicious and circumspect a manner that, even if something is discovered in these matters which we do not suspect at present, you could never be charged with precipitousness nor with having spoken positively about things that are doubtful. It would be a public benefit for these little treatises concerning new discoveries to come out one by one, keeping things fresh in everyone's mind and inspiring others to apply their talents more to such things; for it is impossible that so great a framework should be sustained upon the shoulders of one man, however strong.

As Your Excellency requests, I shall promise Apelles your absolutely exact observations and diagrams of sunspots, which I know he will treasure. At present I cannot go on, so I close by kissing your hands and wishing you every good.

Augsburg, June 1, 1612.

From Your Excellency's most affectionate servitor,

MARK WELSER

SECOND LETTER FROM GALILEO GALILEI TO MARK WELSER ON SUNSPOTS

Most Illustrious Sir, and Worshipful Patron:
Some time ago I sent Your Worship a very long letter concerning the things discussed in the three letters of the masked Apelles, setting forth the difficulties which prevented my lending assent to his opinions, and suggesting in part the direction of my own thought at that time. Since

then I have not strayed from that inclination, but am completely confirmed in it by continued daily observations. Despite [seeking] all possible occasions for reversing my ideas, a complete lack of contradictory evidence shows that my opinion squares with the truth. It seems to me that I should render an account of this to Your Excellency, now that I am sending you precisely drawn diagrams of the spots. I include also a description of the way in which these are drawn, as well as a copy of a little treatise of mine concerning things that float on water or sink in it, which has just come from the printer.

I therefore repeat and more positively confirm to Your Excellency that the dark spots seen in the solar disk by means of the telescope are not at all distant from its surface, but are either contiguous to it or separated by an interval so small as to be quite imperceptible. Nor are they stars or other permanent bodies, but some are always being produced and others dissolved. They vary in duration from one or two days to thirty or forty. For the most part they are of most irregular shape, and their shapes continually change, some quickly and violently, others more slowly and moderately. They also vary in darkness, appearing sometimes to condense and sometimes to spread out and rarefy. In addition to changing shape, some of them divide into three or four, and often several unite into one; this happens less near the edge of the sun's disk than in its central parts. Besides all these disordered movements they have in common a general uniform motion across the face of the sun in parallel lines. From special characteristics of this motion one may learn that the sun is absolutely spherical, that it rotates from west to east around its own center, carries the spots along with it in parallel circles, and completes an entire revolution in about one lunar month. Also worth noting is the fact that the spots always fall in one zone of the solar body, lying between the two circles which bound the declinations of the planets—that is, they fall within 28° or 29° of the sun's equator.

The different densities and degrees of darkness of the spots, their changes of shape, and their collecting and separating are evident directly to our sight, without any need of reasoning, as a glance at the diagrams which I am enclosing will show. But that the spots are contiguous to the sun and are carried around by its rotation can only be deduced and concluded by reasoning from certain particular events which our observations yield.

First, to see twenty or thirty spots at a time move with one common movement is a strong reason for believing that each does not go wandering about by itself, in the manner of the planets going around the sun. In order to explain this, let us define the poles in the solar globe and its circles of longitude and latitude as we do in the celestial sphere. If the sun is spherical and rotates, there will be two points at rest called the poles, and all other points on its surface will describe parallel circles which are larger or smaller according to their distance from the poles. The largest of all will be the central circle, equally distant from the two poles. The dimension of the spots along these circles will be called their breadth, and by their length we shall mean their dimension extending toward the poles and determined by a line perpendicular to that which determines their breadth.

These terms defined, let us consider the specific events observed in the sunspots from which one may arrive at a knowledge of their positions and movements. To begin with, the spots at their first appearance and final disappearance near the edges of the sun generally seem to have very little breadth, but to have the same length that they show in the central parts of the sun's disk. Those who understand what is meant by foreshortening on a spherical surface will see this to be a manifest argument that the sun is a globe, that the spots are close to its surface, and that as they are carried on that surface toward the center they will always grow in breadth while preserving the same length. All of them do not thin out equally to a hairsbreadth when close to the circumference, but this is because they are not all simple spots on the surface, but also have a certain height. Some have more thickness and some have less, just as our clouds, which may spread out for tens or hundreds of miles in length and breadth and may have greater or less thickness; yet these are not more than a few hundred or perhaps a thousand yards thick. And the thickness of the sunspots, though small in comparison with their other two dimensions, may be much greater in one spot than another, so that the thinnest spots when close to the edge of the sun look extremely slender—especially as the inner part of this edge is brightly lighted—while the thicker spots appear broader. But many of them are reduced to a threadlike thinness, and this could not happen at all if their motion across the face of the sun took place at even a short distance from the solar globe. For this maximum thinning takes place at the point of greatest foreshortening, and it would occur outside the face of the sun if the spots were any perceptible distance away from its surface.

In the second place, one must observe the apparent travel of the spots day by day. The spaces passed by the same spot in equal times become always less as the spot is situated nearer the edge of the sun. Careful observation shows also that these increases and decreases of travel are quite in proportion to the versed sines of equal arcs, as would happen only in circular motion contiguous to the sun itself. In circles even slightly distant from it, the spaces passed in equal times would appear to differ very little against the sun's surface.

A third thing which strongly confirms this conclusion may be deduced from the spaces between one spot and another. Some of these separations remain constant, others greatly increase toward the center of the solar disk, being quite narrow elsewhere, and insensible near the edge; still others show extreme variability. The events are such that they could be met with only in circular motion made by different points on a rotating globe. Spots located close together along the same parallel of solar latitude seem almost to touch each other at their first emergence; if farther apart, they will at any rate be much closer near the edge than near the center of the sun. As they move away from the edge, they are seen to separate more and more; at the center, they have their maximum separation; and as they move on from there they approach each other again. Accurate observation of the ratios of these separations and approaches shows that they can occur only upon the very surface of the solar globe.

.   .   .   .

That the spots are very thin in comparison with their length and breadth may be deduced from the gaps between them, for they are often distinct all the way out to the very limb of the sun. This would not happen if they were very high and thick, especially when quite close together. Likewise separations among groups of very small spots have been seen all the way to the edge, though much foreshortened by the curvature of the surface. Some may say from this that such spots must be surfaces of little or no thickness, since when close to the edge of the disk the bright spaces between them are not foreshortened more than their own breadths are diminished, which it seems could not happen if their height were appreciable. But I say this is not a necessary consequence, because one must consider also the brilliance of the sunlight which illuminates the spots edgewise. . . . I could give many examples, but in order to avoid prolixity I shall save this to write of in another place.

It should be mentioned that the spots are not completely fixed and motionless on the face of the sun, but continually change in shape, collect together, and disperse. But this variation is small in relation to the general rotation of the sun, and should not trouble anyone who will judiciously weigh the general movement against the small accidental variation. And just as all the phenomena in these observations agree exactly with the spots' being contiguous to the surface of the sun, and with this surface being spherical rather than any other shape, and with their being carried around by the rotation of the sun itself, so the same phenomena are opposed to every other theory that may be proposed to explain them.

Suppose someone wished to locate them in the air, where indeed other things are continually produced and dissolved with extraordinary variations of shape, or condensed and rarefied. Then first, since the spots take up very little space on the solar disk, proximity to the earth would require them to be no larger than the tiniest clouds—for small indeed would be a cloud that did not cover the face of the sun. And in this case, how could there be sufficient density of material in so small a bulk as to prevent the sun's rays from penetrating it, or for that matter evaporating it during a period of many days by means of their great strength? Why should all the spots happen to fall between us and the sun, and nowhere else in the sky? For none are perceived against the lighted face of the moon, or are picked out by the sunlight at a distance from the sun, as happens with clouds. Besides, considering the variable nature of these spots, what power can keep them arranged in such perfect order that in all their collecting and separating they never fail to accompany the sun? Other aerial phenomena move in a few moments not only across the face of the sun, but through much larger distances.

These and other arguments are so plausible that no one can reply to them without introducing great improbabilities. But there are additional absolute proofs which admit of no reply whatever. One of these is that spots observed simultaneously from widely separated positions on earth are nevertheless arranged in the same order and in the same places on the sun, as may be seen from diagrams made on several occasions at various cities. For instance, all spots are seen to fall within that narrow zone of the solar globe corresponding to the space in the celestial sphere that lies within the tropics. I do not think that seeing them this way is a special privilege of the city of Florence, where I live; I suppose they are seen within the same limits from any place, as far north or south as you please. Hence they must be much farther away than the moon; otherwise, as Apelles well notes, in the time between the rising and setting of the sun they would all appear outside the solar disk because of parallax. And if anyone were to assign them a motion of their own to compensate such an aspect, the same spots could not return the next day; whereas in fact they are seen not only the next day, but the third, and fourth, and the fourteenth. Hence they are proved to be beyond the moon. And being in the celestial regions, no other location than the surface of the sun and no other movement than its own rotation can be assigned to them without contradiction. Among all imaginable hypotheses, the most suitable alternative to fit the appearances would be to place them on a little sphere somewhere between us and the sun, so that our eyes were in line with its center and the center of the sun, this sphere being equal in diameter to the sun. This would satisfy the appearances, provided the sphere was placed far enough away to overcome the objection of [negligible] parallax. But with all this there would be the insuperable difficulty that we should unavoidably see the spots moving both ways under the solar disk, which does not happen. Hence the introduction of such a globe between the sun and ourselves is a fiction; and it would be a waste of time to attack every other conceivable theory.

As to the maximum duration of the largest and densest spots, it cannot be said with certainty that any spots return after a complete rotation, because continuous changes in shape prevent our recognizing them surely. Yet I am of the opinion that some spots do return and show themselves to us more than once. I have been led to believe this by sometimes seeing a very large spot appear and continue to grow until the visible hemisphere has turned it away; and just as this spot was likely to have been generated long before it emerged to view, so we may reasonably believe that it might endure long after parting, in which case its duration would be much longer than the period of one semirevolution of the sun. Hence some spots may—even must—be seen by us twice; they would be those which are produced on the visible hemisphere shortly before disappearance, and are not dissolved until they have returned to view. For this, a duration of two or three days more than the period of a single semirotation would suffice. Indeed, I think there are some which traverse the visible hemisphere more than once, these being spots which go on growing to an extraordinary size, for they may continue to grow while hidden from us. I have often observed the departure of a large spot and have later seen one which in my opinion was the same, and which passed along the same parallel.

From what has been said thus far, if I am not mistaken, one must conclude that sunspots are situated upon or very close to the body of the sun; that they are of material which is not permanent and fixed, but variable in shape and size; that they are movable to some extent by little irregular motions; and that they are all generated and dissolved, some in longer and some in shorter times. It is also manifest that their rotation is about the sun, though it remains questionable whether this happens because the sun itself rotates and carries them along with it, or whether the sun remains motionless and the spots are conducted by a rotation of some surrounding medium. It could happen either way. Yet to me it seems much more probable that the movement is of the solar globe than of its surroundings. I am led to believe this first because I think this circumambient substance to be very fluid and yielding—a proposition that appears quite novel in the ordinary philosophy,[7] but of which I am assured by seeing how easily the spots contained in it change their shapes, aggregate together, and divide up, which could not happen in a solid and consistent material. Now an orderly movement such as the universal motion of all the spots seems incapable of having its root and basis in a fluid substance, whose parts do not cohere, and which is therefore subject to commotions, disturbances, and other accidental movements. But orderly motion would occur in a solid and consistent body, where the motion of the whole and of the parts is necessarily one, as may be believed of the solar body itself in contrast with its ambient. Such motion, then, communicated to the ambient by

[7] The heavens were generally regarded literally as a "firmament," or rather as a series of firmaments. Each heavenly body (except the fixed stars, which were treated as a single unit in this regard) was supposed to be embedded in a solid transparent orb that bore it along its circular course. Tycho had definitely repudiated this idea, but many astronomers of Galileo's time still clung to it.

contact, and to the spots by the ambient, or else conferred by contact directly to the spots, could carry them around.

And if anyone should wish to have the rotation of the spots around the sun proceed from motion that resides in the ambient and not in the sun, I think it would be necessary in any case for the ambient to communicate this movement to the solar globe as well. For I seem to have observed that physical bodies have physical inclination to some motion (as heavy bodies downward), which motion is exercised by them through an intrinsic property and without need of a particular external mover, whenever they are not impeded by some obstacle. And to some other motion they have a repugnance (as the same heavy bodies to motion upward), and therefore they never move in that manner unless thrown violently by an external mover. Finally, to some movements they are indifferent, as are these same heavy bodies to horizontal motion, to which they have neither inclination (since it is not toward the center of the earth) nor repugnance (since it does not carry them away from that center). And therefore, all external impediments removed, a heavy body on a spherical surface concentric with the earth will be indifferent to rest and to movements toward any part of the horizon. And it will maintain itself in that state in which it has once been placed; that is, if placed in a state of rest, it will conserve that; and if placed in movement toward the west (for example), it will maintain itself in that movement.[8] Thus a ship, for instance,

---

[8] The importance of this paragraph to the history of modern physics cannot be exaggerated. What it contains is the first announcement of the principle of inertia, according to which a body will preserve a state of uniform motion or of rest unless acted upon by some force. Galileo's explicit statement of this principle is confined to the cases of (1) rotating bodies and (2) heavy bodies moving freely upon smooth spheres concentric with the earth. In applying the principle to physical problems, however, he included the more important case of bodies moving uniformly along straight lines, neglecting the force of gravitation. But even in such cases Galileo restricted his inertial principle to terrestrial objects. He did not, as is sometimes stated, attribute the orbital motions of the planets

having once received some impetus through the tranquil sea, would move continually around our globe without ever stopping; and placed at rest it would perpetually remain at rest, if in the first case all extrinsic impediments could be removed, and in the second case no external cause of motion were added.

Now if this is true (as indeed it is), what would a body of ambiguous nature do if continually surrounded by an ambient that moved with a motion to which it was indifferent? I do not see how one can doubt that it would move with the motion of the ambient. And the sun, a body of spherical shape suspended and balanced upon its own center, cannot fail to follow the motion of its ambient, having no intrinsic repugnance or extrinsic impediment to rotation. It cannot have an internal repugnance, because by such a rotation it is neither removed from its place, nor are its parts permuted among themselves. Their natural arrangement is not changed in any way, so that as far as the constitution of its parts is concerned, such movement is as if it did not exist. As to external impediments, it does not seem that any obstacle can impede without contact, except perhaps by magnetic power; and in this case all that is in contact with the sun is its ambient, which not only does not impede the movement which we seek to attribute to it, but itself has this movement. This may be further confirmed, as it does not appear that any movable body can have a repugnance to a movement without having a natural propensity to the opposite motion, for in indifference no repugnance exists; hence anyone who wants to give the sun a resistance to the circular motion of its ambient would be putting in it a natural propensity for circular motion opposite to that. But this cannot appeal to any balanced mind.

And since the apparent rotation of the spots must necessarily be placed in the sun, it seems better to put it there

---

to an inertial principle acting circularly. In fact he did not attempt any explanation of the cause of planetary motions, except to imply that if the nature of gravity were known this too might be discovered (*Dialogue*, p. 235). The achievement of this prodigious step remained to Newton.

by nature than by participation, for the reasons earlier
adopted.

Many other considerations might be set forth in confirmation of my opinion, but they would take me beyond the
proper limits of a letter. Hence, in order to fulfill my
promise to Apelles, I shall now describe the method of drawing the spots with complete accuracy. This was discovered,
as I hinted in my other letter, by a pupil of mine, a monk
of Cassino named Benedetto Castelli,[9] of a noble family of
Brescia—a man of excellent mind, and free (as one must
be) in philosophizing.

The method is this: Direct the telescope upon the sun as
if you were going to observe that body. Having focused and
steadied it, expose a flat white sheet of paper about a foot
from the concave lens; upon this will fall a circular image
of the sun's disk, with all the spots that are on it arranged
and disposed with exactly the same symmetry as in the sun.
The more the paper is moved away from the tube, the
larger this image will become, and the better the spots will
be depicted. Thus they will all be seen without damage to
the eye, even the smallest of them—which, when observed
through the telescope, can scarcely be perceived, and only
with fatigue and injury to the eyes. In order to picture them
accurately, I first describe on the paper a circle of the size
that best suits me, and then by moving the paper towards
or away from the tube I find the exact place where the
image of the sun is enlarged to the measure of the circle
I have drawn. This also serves me as a norm and rule for
getting the plane of the paper right, so that it will not be

[9] Benedetto Castelli (1578–1643) was probably the greatest
of Galileo's scientific pupils. A Benedictine monk, Castelli
wrote several works on the measurement and control of running waters, and may be considered the father of hydro-
dynamics. Among Castelli's pupils were the three greatest
leaders in Italian physical science after Galileo: Bonaventura
Cavalieri (1598–1647), who paved the way for the invention
of the calculus; Evangelista Torricelli (1608–47), best known
for his invention of the barometer; and Giovanni Borelli
(1608–79), the first man to indicate the nature of the forces
present in planetary motions.

tilted to the luminous cone of sunlight that emerges from the telescope. For if the paper is oblique, the section will be oval and not circular, and therefore will not perfectly fit the circumference drawn on the paper. By tilting the paper the proper position is easily found, and then with a pen one may mark out the spots in their right sizes, shapes, and positions. But one must work dextrously, following the movement of the sun and frequently moving the telescope, which must be kept directly on the sun. The correct position may be recognized by looking in the convex lens, where one may see a little luminous circle that is concentric with this lens when the tube is properly pointed toward the sun. Also, in order for the spots to be seen distinctly and with sharp boundaries, it is good to darken the room by shutting all the windows so that no light enters except through the tube, or at least to darken it as much as one can by fitting a rather large paper upon the tube to shade the other paper upon which one intends to draw, thus preventing any other light from falling upon that paper.

Next one must note that the spots come from the telescope inverted, and reversed from their positions on the sun; that is, from left to right and from top to bottom; for the rays intersect one another inside the tube before coming through the concave lens. But since we draw them on the side of the paper facing the sun, we have the picture opposite to our sight, so that the right-to-left reversal is already effected. Only the upper and lower parts remain inverted, so if we merely turn the paper upside down and bring the top ones to the bottom, we have then only to look through the transparency of the paper against the light, and the spots will be seen precisely as if we were looking directly at the sun. And in that aspect they are to be traced upon another paper, in order to have them properly drawn.

I have since been much impressed by the courtesy of nature, which thousands of years ago arranged a means by which we might come to notice these spots, and through them to discover things of greater consequence. For without any instruments, from any little hole through which sunlight passes, there emerges an image of the sun with its spots, and at a distance this becomes stamped upon any surface opposite the hole. It is true that these spots are not nearly as sharp as those seen through the telescope, but the majority of them may nevertheless be seen. If in church some day Your Excellency sees the light of the sun falling upon the pavement at a distance from some broken windowpane, you may catch this light upon a flat white sheet of paper, and there you will perceive the spots. I might add that nature has been so kind that for our instruction she has sometimes marked the sun with a spot so large and dark as to be seen merely by the naked eye, though the false and inveterate idea that the heavenly bodies are devoid of all mutation or alteration has made people believe that such a spot was the planet Mercury coming between us and the sun, to the disgrace of past astronomers. Such a spot, no doubt, was that which is mentioned in the *Annals of French History* by Pithoeus, printed at Paris in 1588, on page 62, where (in the *Life of Charlemagne*) one reads that for eight days together the people of France saw a black spot in the solar disk, whose ingress and exit from the sun's face could not be observed because of clouds. This was believed to be Mercury, then in conjunction with the sun; but this is too gross an error, seeing that Mercury's movement is so fast that it cannot remain conjoined with the sun for even seven hours when it passes between us and the sun. Therefore this phenomenon was definitely one of those very large and very dark spots, of which another may be encountered in the future; and perhaps by applying ourselves to diligent observation we may see one very soon. Had this discovery been made several years ago, it would have saved Kepler the trouble of interpreting the above passage by altering the text and emending the reported times.[10] But I

[10] Drinkwater, in his *Life of Galileo*, pp. 39–40, tells the story as follows: "Kepler, whose astronomical knowledge would not suffer him to overlook that it was impossible that Mercury could remain so long in conjunction with the sun, preferred to solve the difficulty by supposing that in Aimon's original account the expression was not *octo dies* (eight days), but *octoties*—a barbarous word which he supposed to have been written for *octies* (eight times); and that the other ac-

shall not bother about this at present, being certain that Kepler, as a true philosopher and not recalcitrant about manifest events, will no sooner hear of these observations and discourses of mine than he will lend his assent to them.

Now, in order that we may harvest some fruit from the unexpected marvels that have remained hidden until this age of ours, it will be well if in the future we once again lend ear to those wise philosophers whose opinion of the celestial substance differed from Aristotle's. He himself would not have departed so far from their view if his knowledge had included our present sensory evidence, since he not only admitted manifest experience among the ways of forming conclusions about physical problems, but even gave it first place. So when he argued the immutability of the heavens from the fact that no alteration had been seen in them during all the ages, it may be believed that had his eyes shown him what is now evident to us, he would have adopted the very opinion to which we are led by these remarkable discoveries. I should even think that in making the celestial material alterable, I contradict the doctrine of Aristotle much less than do those people who still want to keep the sky inalterable; for I am sure that he never took its inalterability to be as certain as the fact that all human reasoning must be placed second to direct experience. Hence they will philosophize better who give assent to propositions that depend upon manifest observations, than they who persist in opinions repugnant to the senses and supported only by probable reasons. And as if to remove all doubt from our minds, a host of observations come to

counts, in which the number of days mentioned is different, copied loosely from the first and mistook the word. . . . In 1609 Kepler himself observed upon the sun a black spot which he similarly mistook for Mercury; and unluckily, the day being cloudy, he could not observe it long enough to discover his error. . . . No sooner was Galileo's discovery announced than he, with that candor which as much as his flighty disposition characterized him at all times, retracted his former opinion and owned . . . that he had been mistaken."

teach us that comets are generated in the celestial regions.[11] If their evidence is quickly come and gone, still greater things stubbornly remain for our instruction: behold how new flames of longer duration are sent in the form of bright novae, produced and then dissolved in the most remote parts of the sky—though of course even this is not enough to persuade people who cannot be reached by the force of geometric demonstrations. But finally, in that part of the sky which deserves to be considered the most pure and serene of all—I mean in the very face of the sun—these innumerable multitudes of dense, obscure, and foggy materials are discovered to be produced and dissolved continually in brief periods. Here is a parade of productions and destructions that does not end in a moment, but will endure through all future ages, allowing the human mind time to observe at pleasure and to learn those doctrines which will finally prove the true location of the spots.

Yet in this respect also we must recognize divine Providence, in that the means to such knowledge are very easy and may be speedily apprehended. Anyone is capable of procuring drawings made in distant places, and comparing them with those he has made himself on the same days. I have already received some made in Brussels by Sig. Daniello Antonini which fit to a hair those made by me, and others sent to me from Rome by Sig. Lodovico Cigoli, the famous painter and architect. This argument alone should be enough to persuade anybody that such spots are a long way beyond the moon.

And here I shall stop troubling Your Excellency further. Do me the favor of sending the drawings to Apelles at your convenience, accompanied by my highest regard to him. I kiss Your Excellency's hand reverently, and pray God for your happiness.

From Florence, August 14, 1612.

Your Illustrious Excellency's very devoted servitor,

GALILEO GALILEI L.

[11] This seems to be Galileo's only recorded tribute to Tycho, who had collected many observations of the 1577 comet in

Third Letter of Mark Welser to Galileo Galilei

Most Illustrious and Excellent Sir:

My grave illness continues, and still troubles me so that I cannot visit my friends with frequent and lengthy letters as would be my duty and desire—particularly in regard to Your Excellency, with whom I take great pleasure in discussing things. But I am prevented, and I consider it a treasure when God's grace allows me to salute you briefly with a few lines as I do now.

I send to Your Excellency some new speculations by my friend which I have agreed to publish, chiefly for the observations, which I believe will be welcome to all lovers and investigators of truth. For the rest, I hazard no decision one way or the other, as I have no zest to apply my mind to it properly. I hear that you have written me a second long letter on this subject, but it has not yet arrived here. I await it with particular interest. Meanwhile I close very cordially by kissing Your Excellency's hand and wishing you every good thing.

Augsburg, September 28, 1612.

From Your Excellency's most affectionate servitor,

Mark Welser L.[12]

---

order to determine whether its apparent position varied for different observers with respect to the fixed stars. Since it did not (that is, since the comet displayed no parallax), he correctly concluded that it was located far beyond the moon. But Galileo subsequently withdrew his approval of Tycho even on this point.

[12] Early in this month Welser had been elected to the Lincean Academy, and thereafter he signed his letters to Galileo with this designation. Correspondence with this "German Academician" was one of the points later utilized by his main religious antagonist to damage him with the Inquisition (*Opere* xix, 310).

FOURTH LETTER OF MARK WELSER TO GALILEO GALILEI

Most Revered, Illustrious, and Excellent Sir:

Your second letter, dated August 14, has finally arrived, having been forwarded to me by Sig. Sagredo. Believe me, it was received like manna from heaven, such was my desire to see it. Thus far I have not had time to read it carefully, but from running quickly through it I can tell you sincerely that it gives me the greatest pleasure. And though I know myself incompetent to form judgments in such weighty matters, especially at present when my illness prevents applying my mind to much speculation, I shall venture the remark that Your Excellency's arguments proceed with great plausibility and probability. That they arrive precisely at the truth, human frailty prevents our affirming until beneficent God shall give us the grace to look down from on high upon that which we now contemplate from this vale of misery.

I render infinite thanks to Your Excellency for the favor you have shown me on this occasion, and our leader Sig. Federico Cesi would perform an act worthy of his rank and profession as a patron of learning and literature by printing both your letters, as I hear he has decided to do. The diagrams and observations may cause a little trouble, but if they were reduced to smaller size they would not occupy too much space. I wish that Apelles might have seen this composition of yours before publishing his last discourse, though I suppose that in some respects it is better this way. I shall not fail to communicate it to him as soon as I have satiated myself with it. But he will suffer much inconvenience from not understanding the Italian language, as translations proceed slowly and often not only lose the energy of the originals but also distort the sense, unless the translator is very expert.

Sig. Sagredo is keeping for a while the treatise on things which float on water, much desired by a friend of his (a senator) who insists upon being able to read it; this may have been Protogenes.[13] I can dispense with it, as I have managed to see another copy, the perusal of which has so won me over (and I do not blush to confess this) that though at the outset your position appeared to me to be most paradoxical, I now find it to be unquestionable. It is so well provided and fortified with reasons and experiments that I certainly fail to see how and where your adversaries are going to assail it, though I suppose they cannot be very happy about it.

Your Excellency continues to honor himself and our age by drawing one truth after another out of the dark well of ignorance. Do not be discouraged by the envious and by imitators, and keep me always in your grace. God bless you.

From Augsburg, October 5, 1612.

From Your Excellency's most affectionate servitor,

MARK WELSER LINCEAN

THIRD LETTER ON SUNSPOTS, FROM GALILEO GALILEI
TO MARK WELSER
In which Venus, the Moon, and the Medicean Planets
are also dealt with, and new appearances of Saturn
are revealed.

Most Illustrious Sir, and Worshipful Patron:

I must reply to Your Excellency's two most welcome letters, dated September 28, and October 5, with the first of which I received the second treatise of the masked Apelles. In the other you have acknowledged my second letter regarding sunspots, which I sent to you on August 23. I shall reply briefly to this and then turn back to the other

[13] Protogenes was the pseudonym of an otherwise unidentified friend of Scheiner's at Venice who intended to publish an answer to Galileo's sunspot letters.

matter in order to weigh at some length the specific things
contained in this answer from Apelles. Inasmuch as he has
seen my considerations concerning his original letters, I am
under some obligation to offer a few remarks concerning
my original letter and this second essay of his.

It is indeed with pleasure that I learn from Your Excellency's last letter how, in a hasty reading, you have considered plausible and even probable the arguments that I
have adopted in confirmation of the conclusions I undertook
to prove. The question remains what view you will take of
them after a second perusal, since even the most clear-
minded of men may at first glance accept as a work of some
perfection that which later turns out to be less meritorious
when studied more closely. This happens particularly when
some special affection for the author exists, and a precon-
ceived good opinion preoccupies an impartial mind. Therefore I suspend judgment and await your further decision.
That, when it comes, will serve me until the knowledge for
which we now search almost like blind men in the impure
and material sun shall come to us from the true, pure, and
immaculate Sun, together with all other truths in Him, as
Your Excellency very prudently says.

But in my opinion we need not entirely give up con-
templating things just because they are very remote from
us, unless we have indeed determined that it is best to defer
every act of reflection in favor of other occupations. For in
our speculating we either seek to penetrate the true and
internal essence of natural substances, or content ourselves
with a knowledge of some of their properties. The former
I hold to be as impossible an undertaking with regard to
the closest elemental substances as with more remote celestial things. The substances composing the earth and the
moon seem to me to be equally unknown, as do those of
our elemental clouds and of sunspots. I do not see that in
comprehending substances near at hand we have any advantage except copious detail; all the things among which
men wander remain equally unknown, and we pass by
things both near and far with very little or no real acquisition of knowledge. When I ask what the substance of

clouds may be and am told that it is a moist vapor, I shall wish to know in turn what vapor is. Peradventure I shall be told that it is water, which when attenuated by heat is resolved into vapor. Equally curious about what water is, I shall then seek to find that out, ultimately learning that it is this fluid body which runs in our rivers and which we constantly handle. But this final information about water is no more intimate than what I knew about clouds in the first place; it is merely closer at hand and dependent upon more of the senses. In the same way I know no more about the true essences of earth or fire than about those of the moon or sun, for that knowledge is withheld from us, and is not to be understood until we reach the state of blessedness.

But if what we wish to fix in our minds is the apprehension of some properties of things, then it seems to me that we need not despair of our ability to acquire this respecting distant bodies just as well as those close at hand—and perhaps in some cases even more precisely in the former than in the latter. Who does not understand the periods and movements of the planets better than those of the waters of our various oceans? Was not the spherical shape of the moon discovered long before that of the earth, and much more easily? Is it not still argued whether the earth rests motionless or goes wandering, whereas we know positively the movements of many stars? Hence I should infer that although it may be vain to seek to determine the true substance of the sunspots, still it does not follow that we cannot know some properties of them, such as their location, motion, shape, size, opacity, mutability, generation, and dissolution. These in turn may become the means by which we shall be able to philosophize better about other and more controversial qualities of natural substances. And finally by elevating us to the ultimate end of our labors, which is the love of the divine Artificer, this will keep us steadfast in the hope that we shall learn every other truth in Him, the source of all light and verity.

I owe to Your Excellency still another debt of thanks, for if I have arrived at any truth in this matter it is the fruit of your commands. Let this likewise be my excuse if I fail to get to the heart of so novel and difficult an enterprise.

Regarding your hint about the intentions of our most excellent leader Sig. Federico Cesi, it is indeed true that I sent to him copies of my two solar letters. Yet I did not intend that he should print and publish them, as in that case I should have applied greater care and study to the matter. For although I desire nothing further than Your Excellency's assent and applause, which I esteem as highly as that of the whole world, yet from your good will and your courteous feelings toward me I have promised myself an indulgence that cannot be expected from the scrupulous inquiry and severe criticism of other men. Moreover, there are still many things that I have not well digested nor determined after my own fashion. One of these is the occurrence of sunspots in particular regions of the sun and not elsewhere. Representing the progress of all the spots as along straight lines (a necessary argument that the axis of the sun's rotation is perpendicular to the plane of the ecliptic[14]), it remains worthy of careful consideration why it is that sunspots fall only within a zone whose width does not extend more than 29° or 30° on either side of the sun's equator. In this respect they imitate the planets, which are limited to a similar zone in their departure from the celestial equator. This and one other consideration have made me postpone the publication of a longer treatise on the subject. Yet Sig. Cesi may dispose of my things as he sees

[14] As a matter of fact the sun's axis is not perpendicular to the ecliptic. At some time between 1613 and 1631 Galileo became aware of this, and utilized its consequences in the *Dialogue* as an argument to support the motion of the earth. Meanwhile Scheiner had noted the tilt of the sun's axis and published it triumphantly in his *Rosa Ursina* in 1630. Many students have suspected Galileo of having first learned of the tilt from reports of Scheiner's book though he spoke in the *Dialogue* of mentioning it under circumstances which could not have existed after 1613. Very likely his account is correct. He had received his first clue to this phenomenon in July 1613, but it came from an old enemy whom he wished to avoid crediting. Cf. note 19, p. 189, and *Opere* xi, 491 ff.

fit; knowing the quality of his judgment and the interest he has in my good name, I am sure that if he lets them appear, he will have deemed them worthy of publication.

As for Apelles, I too regret that he did not see my second letter before the publication of his "More Accurate Inquiry . . . ," and that by my procrastination and poor style I have failed to retard his readiness to make up his mind. This delay was caused by the holding back of my letters at Venice for over a month, through too high a regard for them on the part of the illustrious Sig. Giovanni Francesco Sagredo. He wished a copy of them to remain in that city (where it would seem to me they had been sufficiently honored by his mere reading of them), and this required a good deal of time because of the multitude of diagrams. I also am sorry about the trouble I have given Apelles by writing in our Florentine dialect. I did this for a number of reasons, one of which is my desire not to let the richness and perfection of that language go to waste, for it is capable of dealing with and explaining the concepts of every field of study. For that reason our Academicians (and everyone else in the city) are better pleased by essays in this idiom than in any other. But in addition to this I have a selfish interest not to deprive myself of getting Your Excellency's replies in this same language. My friends and I look upon these with more delight than if they were written in the purer Latin style, and when we read letters of such commendable expression as yours, it seems to us that Florence has extended her boundaries and her very city walls to Augsburg.

Your Excellency remarks that at your first reading of my tract on floating bodies it appeared paradoxical to you, but that in the end the conclusions were seen to be true and clearly demonstrated. You will be pleased to learn that the same has happened here with many persons who have the reputation of good judgment and sound reasoning. There remain in opposition to my work some stern defenders of every minute point of the Peripatetics. So far as I can see, their education consisted in being nourished from infancy on the opinion that philosophizing is and can be nothing but to make a comprehensive survey of the texts of Aristotle, that from divers passages they may quickly collect and throw together a great number of solutions to any proposed problem. They wish never to raise their eyes from those pages—as if this great book of the universe had been written to be read by nobody but Aristotle, and his eyes had been destined to see for all posterity. These fellows who subject themselves to such strict laws put me in mind of certain capricious painters who occasionally constrain themselves, for sport, to represent a human face or something else by throwing together now some agricultural implements, again some fruits, or perhaps the flowers of this or that season.[15] Such bizarre actions, so long as they are proposed in jest, are both pretty and pleasant, and reveal greater resourcefulness in some artists than in others according as they have been able the more cleverly to select and apply this or that material to the form depicted. But if anyone were to pursue all his studies in such a school of painting, and should then conclude in general that every other manner of representation was blameworthy and imperfect, it is certain that Cigoli and other illustrious painters would laugh him to scorn.

Some of the men whose opinions are against me have already written essays, and others are working at it, but thus far only two such compositions have been published. One is by an "Unknown Academician," and the other by a professor of Greek[16] in the University of Pisa. I send copies

[15] This reference is almost certainly to "the queer pictures especially produced by a North Italian painter named Arcimboldo, active at the end of the sixteenth century, and therefore a most characteristic manifestation of Mannerism." (Communication from Professor Erwin Panofsky.) See also *Isis*, v. 147, pt. 1 (March 1956), p. 7. In Plate III accompanying Professor Panofsky's paper there is a reproduction of such a painting by Arcimboldo.

[16] The professor of Greek was Giorgio Coresio, whose book was left unanswered in print because of its author's subsequent insanity (*Opere* xii, 126). The "Unknown Academician" has been identified by Favaro as Arturo d'Elci, overseer of the University of Pisa, who signed the letter of dedication in

of both to Your Excellency with this letter. My friends are of the opinion, and I do not disagree, that unless some opposition more solid than this comes forth there is no need to reply further. They think that any labor would be vain to silence those who still remain inquiet, while for those who are already convinced it would be superfluous. I must consider my own conclusions true and the reasons for them valid; for without having lost the adherence of anyone who listened to me from the beginning, I have won over many others who held the contrary view. Hence we are waiting to hear from the rest, and then we shall do whatever seems most appropriate.

Coming now to Your Excellency's letter, I sympathize with you in the persistence of your troublesome malady, in the affliction which you feel, and in the silence of so many of your friends and servants—myself above all. Troubled likewise by the usual indispositions which impede me almost constantly in every exercise, I am reminded by the passage of years that a man would have to be continually active if he wished to leave any trace of his having passed through this world. But whatever the course of our lives we should receive them as the highest gift from the hand of God, in which equally reposed the power to do nothing whatever for us. Indeed, we should accept misfortune not only in thanks, but in infinite gratitude to Providence, which by such means detaches us from an excessive love for earthly things and elevates our minds to the celestial and divine.

It is superfluous to apologize for your brevity in writing to me, for I am always pleased merely to know that I continue in your good graces. Rather it is I who should excuse my prolixity—or, to speak more properly, should beg you to excuse it. And so I should, were I not certain of the pardon that I promise myself from your courtesy.

And now to the new essay of the masked Apelles which I received with Your Excellency's second letter. I set myself to read this with great curiosity, moved both by the author's

---

this book as its translator only. This was also left unanswered (although Galileo had prepared a reply to it), by reason of its author's death soon after it was published.

name and by the nature of his title, which promised a "more accurate inquiry" into not only the sunspots but also the Medicean planets. Since I thought the title *More Accurate Inquiry* must refer to other inquiries made concerning the same material, I could not doubt that he had in mind my *Starry Messenger*, which dealt with the nature of such things and hence ought not to be neglected by Apelles. Thus I commenced to read, hoping to find all those problems solved which I could not touch upon in that work beyond the first rough sketches. Well, apart from what was promised in the title, I have found the observations of Venus explained more at length than in the first letters, in addition to which there are some particulars about the moon; but I find Apelles' opinion in these things contrary to mine, as it is in various arguments and replies relating to things I wrote in the first letter addressed to Your Excellency. Because of my esteem for their author, I must not pass these by or pretend not to have noticed them; having no picture to conceal me from spectators, the least I can do is to salute him in passing.

Since he has dealt with the whole progress of our differences in a new arrangement for Your Excellency, I must briefly set forth what has occurred to me on this matter. Following the order employed by Apelles, I shall consider first the objective of his opening section, which is to demonstrate in this way and no other that Venus rotates about the sun. He bases his entire demonstration (as he did in his first essay) upon the morning conjunction of Venus with the sun which occurred on December 11, 1611; and he gives us an investigation of its motion under the solar disk, deduced with calculations and geometrical demonstrations. Two doubts at once arise in me; one concerns the manner of his handling these demonstrations, which would not entirely satisfy a scrupulous mathematician, while the other concerns the utility of such apparatus and arguments for the primary intention of their author.

As to the manner of demonstration, I skip over something that a more fastidious astronomer might object to—namely, the treatment of arcs of circles as if they were straight lines.

I leave this out of account, since in our particular case we do not encounter arcs so large that this source of error in computation would produce a notable excess. But in the lemma which Apelles proposes, I might have wished him to be a rather more decisive geometer. I fail to see why he creates a lemma in the form of a special proposition explained at enormous length, when this is a general proposition demonstrable in a few words. For in every triangle it happens that if we prolong the sides and produce through their intersections a line parallel to the opposite side, the three angles created on one side of this parallel (or on one of the extended sides) will be equal to the interior angles of the triangle. I shall not add, as he does, that the said angles taken together are equal to the three combined, as I should say this is rather obvious and superfluous.

But even if Apelles' whole demonstration were admitted to be exquisite, I still cannot fathom what he thinks to achieve by it against anyone who persists in denying the rotation of Venus about the sun. An understanding of what Copernicus wrote in his *Revolutions* suffices for the most expert astronomers to ascertain that Venus revolves about the sun, as well as to verify the rest of his system. And for people of mediocre understanding it would be necessary to remove the refuges I have mentioned before. But I do not see that Apelles has even touched on these, with the exception of two, and even those seem to be not completely refuted.

I said in my first letter that his adversaries could escape by saying that Venus is not seen beneath the sun because of its smallness, or because it is inherently light, or because it is always beyond the sun. What Apelles says is insufficient to take away the first of these escapes from his opponents, because they would deny that the shadow of Venus on the sun would appear as large as does its lighted body when that is near the sun, since the extra irradiation makes the star look larger than it is. This is evident from Venus itself, for when thinly horned and but a few degrees away from the sun, it still looks to the naked eye as round as the other stars, hiding its shape under its luminous irradiation;

and no one can doubt that it seems much larger to us than it would if deprived of light. On the other hand, if placed under the very bright disk of the sun, unquestionably the appearance of its little dark body would be much diminished by the great brilliance of the sun, and hence it is quite fallacious to conclude that it would appear equal to a spot of average size. Who knows that such spots, in order to be visible to us in the bright field of the sun, are not indeed much larger than they appear to be? The best witness for this is Apelles himself, if we call to mind what he wrote in his third letter: "The spots are quite large, as otherwise they would be hidden by the great irradiation of the sun." Thus it is a double error to equate the size of luminous Venus with that of a dark spot, as the splendor of the sun diminishes the latter and enlarges the former.

No more effective is what Apelles adds next in order to represent Venus as larger than I suggested in my first letter. Against what we are shown by sense and experience, he vainly adduces the authority of men who were great enough in other respects, but who were quite mistaken about assigning Venus a diameter one tenth that of the sun. Partly they deserve to be excused, but not entirely. Their partial excuse is in the lack of the telescope, which has brought no small contribution to astronomy; but two things leave them open to criticism. One is that they ought to have observed the size of Venus by day and not by night, for its nocturnal headgear of rays makes it look ten times as large as in daytime when deprived of this. Thus they might easily have learned that the diameter of its tiny globe sometimes is not the hundredth part of the diameter of the sun. In the second place they should have distinguished one of its positions from the other, instead of indiscriminately pronouncing its diameter to be one tenth that of the sun. For when the planet is nearest the earth, its diameter is more than six times as great as when it is most distant, and although this difference can be precisely observed only with the telescope, it is nevertheless quite perceptible to the naked eye. In these regards, then, the astronomers cited by Apelles cease to afford him any support by their authority. And even admitting that some spots visible on the face of the sun are not one hundredth nor one thousandth of its surface, Apelles may not claim that this strengthens his proof of Venus being seen there, for I say again that its diameter in morning conjunction is not one two-hundredth that of the sun, nor its surface one forty-thousandth of the visible solar disk.

Then his adversaries have a second escape, saying that Venus would not necessarily obscure any part of the sun because Venus is itself a luminous body. In my opinion this is not refuted by anything Apelles says. As to the mere authority of ancient and modern philosophers and mathematicians, I say that that has no power at all to establish a knowledge of any physical proposition; the most it may do is to incline one to believe one way or the other. Nor do I know whether it is true that Plato was induced to locate Venus beyond the sun because it could not be seen in shadowy form under the sun's face at conjunctions. I do know that Ptolemy speaks of the matter very differently from what Apelles alleges; indeed, the prince of astronomers would never have made so grave an error as to deny direct conjunctions of Venus and the sun. The weakness of the argument is shown by what Ptolemy says at the beginning of Book 9 of his *Almagest*, when seeking the probable order of the planets and refuting those who put Venus and Mercury beyond the sun by reason of having never seen it obscured by them. He says that every star beneath the sun need not eclipse it, since these need not fall upon any of the circles passing through the center of the sun and our eyes. But he does not thereby say the same of Venus; rather, by using the moon as an example, since it does not eclipse the sun in most of its conjunctions, he clearly shows that this is all he meant to say about Venus. Father Clavius certainly speaks of the shadow of Venus as remaining invisible by reason of its small size. And though the authors cited believe Venus to be not luminous but dark, still that opinion does not suffice to refute all opponents, for they are quite able to produce contrary opinions by others.

Another argument is derived by Apelles from the darkening of the moon in passing beneath the sun. But this cannot help him unless he first shows that any similar event in the sun would be perfectly visible even if it occupied but one forty-thousandth of its surface. Surely it is evident that this would be hard to prove.

As to Mercury, it is not merely dubious but even incredible that that planet has been seen beneath the sun by various people, as I have remarked before. Kepler, who is cited by Apelles here, is a man of free and brilliant mind and more a friend to truth than to his own opinions. He would undoubtedly be persuaded that the blackness he saw in the sun was a sunspot, and that the conjunction of Mercury at that hour merely afforded the occasion for having applied himself to look at it closely.[17] With equal attention, such spots would also be seen at other times; they have often been visible in the past, and I have shown them to others. In reality the opaqueness of Venus is indubitably proved by the single experience I reported in my first letter (and which Apelles now puts in third place); namely, our seeing Venus vary in shape as does the moon. This is the only strong argument for proving Venus to revolve about the sun; let it suffice for us, as it leaves no room for doubt. Indeed, Apelles ought to have deemed it worthy of a principal place in his diagrams, and should not have drawn it out in one corner in the guise of a pilaster to support and sustain some other figures which without it would seem to the reader to be threatened with ruin.

In general it appears to me that Apelles is now rather less positive in his judgments than before, though on the whole he seems to want to modify rather than change them; in the end he even affirms that everything he said in his first letters stands unaltered. Still, despite all this, I have some hopes of seeing from him a third essay stating opinions essentially in agreement with mine. Not yet, I mean, nor in virtue of my letters, since those cannot be read by him because of this difficulty of the language; but in thinking things over, there will yet come into his mind the very ar-

[17] See note 10, pp. 117–118.

guments and solutions which have persuaded me to write what I have written. Already one may see how many details which he had not previously observed he puts into this second composition. Previously he thought that the sunspots were all spherical in shape and that if they could be seen separated from the sun they would look like so many tiny moons, some horned, some semicircular, some gibbous, and some quite full. Now he writes, more accurately, that they are rarely spherical and often quite irregular in shape. Likewise he has observed that they seldom or never keep the same shape during the whole time they remain visible, but change extravagantly by growing and shrinking. What is more, he has now seen how some of them unexpectedly originate and others disappear right in the center of the sun, and how some divide into several, while others unite into one. In his first letter he thought they were wandering stars situated at various distances from the sun, so that some wandered between the sun and Mercury, and others between Mercury and Venus. I no longer hear these varying distances reaffirmed, and he is content to show that they are not inside the body of the sun nor contiguous to its surface. He merely places them outside the sun, at a distance yet to be considered—as if he could escape from the very arguments he has used in establishing his opinion.

I readily agree with Apelles in believing that the spots are not immersed within the sun's substance, but not on the strength of his arguments. First he assumes something which would undoubtedly be denied by anyone who wished to take the contrary side, as no one would be so simple as to maintain that the spots are within the solar substance, admit their changes of shape, and still assert the sun to be solid and inalterable. Any adversary would resolutely reject this last assumption as well as the proof Apelles adduces for it, which is that such is the prevailing opinion (according to him) among philosophers and mathematicians. And there would be good reason to reject this, for in the sciences the authority of thousands of opinions is not worth as much as one tiny spark of reason in an individual man. Besides, the modern observations deprive all former writers of any authority, since if they had seen what we see, they would have judged as we judge. As a matter of fact those authorities who did not believe the sun could be yielding and changeable were still farther from believing that it is sprinkled with dark spots. And now that its supposed immaculacy must yield to observation, it is vain to run to such men asking for support of the opinion that the sun is hard and unchangeable. As to the mathematicians, I do not know that any of them have ever discussed the hardness and immutability of the sun, or even that mathematical science is adequate for proving such properties.

His second argument is based on the fact that some of the spots are seen darker when they are near the edge of the sun than later when they are near its center. But this does not force anyone to put them outside the sun. Rarefaction and condensation render a sufficient explanation of this effect, though in my view it would perhaps be better to say that the same spot appears less dark near the center of the sun than at the border because in the latter place it is seen edgewise. Thus a plate of glass looks quite dark when seen edgewise but is transparent when seen flat.

Everyone will concede his next point, which is that the sunspots are not lakes or caverns in the body of the sun. Neither I, nor, so far as I know, anyone else has pretended this.[18] I have written that they are contiguous to the sun or at most separated from it by an imperceptible distance. Hence it will be best to examine the reasons he adduces as proof that they are a long way from the sun. He bases his argument on the unequal duration of visibility among the spots. Those which travel along the equator, he says, remain longer than those which travel along lines distant from the center. He produces two examples, saying that one spot remained sixteen days on the equator, while the other passed at a distance from the center and completed its course in fourteen days. I really wish I knew some way of denying

[18] As a matter of fact that is precisely what sunspots are, and it appears from Cigoli's letters that Passignani had ventured a suggestion along this line.

this without offending Apelles, whom I wish always to respect. But having made a great number of careful observations concerning this matter, I find no occasion whatever for concluding anything except that all spots, without distinction, remain on the solar disk for the same period, which in my judgment is a little over fourteen days. I say this quite positively, and in the knowledge that anyone may easily make countless observations for himself. Nature, deaf to our entreaties, will not alter or change the course of her effects; and those things that we are here trying to investigate have not just occurred once and then vanished, but have always proceeded and will always proceed in the same style. This should be a great restraint upon us, and ought to render us very circumspect about pronouncing on such things. We must take care that no passion—either toward others or ourselves—bends us away from our aim of pure truth.

I hope that Apelles will be satisfied by what I have said, and especially when he has read what I wrote in my second letter. Then I believe he will put no more difficulties in the way of the proximity of the spots to the sun or the revolution of that body. In confirmation of the latter, I might add to my previous reasons the fact that on the face of the sun one sees occasionally some little places that are brighter than the rest of its surface, and by diligent observation one may discern in these the same movements as in the spots. And I think no one can doubt that these are on the surface of the sun, it being scarcely credible that substances brighter than the sun are to be found outside it. Thus it seems to me there is no longer any room for doubt that the sun revolves. And such is the mutual connection of truths that the contiguity of the spots to the sun's surface necessarily follows, as well as the fact that they are set in rotation by the sun, since there is no reason at all for them to follow its rotation if they are separated from it by any distance.

Next it remains for me to examine some consequences that Apelles draws from the matters in question. He holds that the spots are nothing but stars wandering around the sun, for he not only reverts to calling them "solar stars," but he takes the trouble to fit perquisites of stars to them to such an extent as to remove all reasons for distinguishing them from true stars. And in order to endorse my mountain ranges in the moon—for which kind thought I humbly give him thanks—he says that the same sort of thing is perceived in most of the sunspots. Well, this is truly a reason that should satisfy everyone, especially when added to the proofs that I have produced.

I agree with Apelles in regarding as false and damnable the view of those who would put inhabitants on Jupiter, Venus, Saturn and the moon, meaning by "inhabitants" animals like ours, and men in particular. Moreover, I think I can prove this. If we could believe with any probability that there were living beings and vegetables on the moon or any planet, different not only from terrestrial ones but remote from our wildest imaginings, I should for my part neither affirm it nor deny it, but should leave the decision to wiser men than I. I should follow their determination, certain that they were better grounded in the argument which Apelles adopts here; namely, that it would be absurd to put inhabitants on the moon and not on the sunspots. I do not very well comprehend this deduction.

Returning to Apelles and his "stars," I rather suspect that he, carried away by a desire to maintain what he first said, and being unable to accommodate the spots exactly to those events which previously seemed to suit the other stars, accommodates instead the stars to events which we see must be suited to the spots. This seems to be indicated by two of his main arguments. The first is that he thinks it probable that even the other stars are of various shapes and that they appear round only because of their light and their distance, as happens with a candle flame—and, he might well have added, with horned Venus. Such an assertion could not be proven false if it were not that the telescope shows us the shapes of all the stars, fixed as well as planets, to be quite round. The other thing is that, being unable to deny that the sunspots are generated and dissolved and in order not to have this distinguish them from stars, he does not hesitate to say that other stars, too, are disintegrated and refabricated. In particular he cites those which I have observed to move about Jupiter. He repeats what he said in his first letter, that these suddenly appear and vanish just like sunspots, and that one follows another without the same ones ever returning. He thinks that the difficulty or impossibility of determining their periodic times from the observations is a pretty good argument in favor of this. Well, I should not like to have Apelles think that I am so vain and light a man as to have offered to the world some spots and shadows as stars, nor that I would have dedicated to so great a prince as the Most Serene Grand Duke and to his regal house things that are merely transitory and momentary in existence.

The four Medicean planets are true and real stars, as permanent and enduring as the others. They do not become lost or hidden except when in conjunction with one another or with Jupiter, or when eclipsed for a few hours in its shadow, as the moon in that of the earth. They have their regular motions and their definite periods, and if he has been unable to calculate them, perhaps it is because he has not worked so hard at it as I have. After many vigils I have determined these, and I have already revealed and published them in the preface to my treatise on things that float in water or sink therein, as Your Excellency has seen.

I want Apelles also to turn again to observing their number. He will find that they are no more than four,[19] and that the fifth one named by him was unquestionably a fixed star. The conjectures that led him to believe it was a planet were founded on various fallacies, and his observations were often wrong to begin with, as I perceive from his diagrams, because he omits a star which was then very conspicuous. In the second place their distances from Jupiter as he gives them are almost all wrong, I suppose from lack of a suitable method and instrument for measuring

[19] Galileo was quite right about Scheiner's imagined discovery of a fifth satellite of Jupiter; only the four he had found could be seen with the telescopes of that time, and no more were discovered until late in the nineteenth century.

hese. Thirdly, he makes gross errors in their arrangements, or the satellites changed places from one evening to the next without his recognizing them. Besides, is there not some inconsistency in Apelles? Here he wants to assume, to prove some fancy of his own, that the stars he has noted in his observations and indicated in his diagrams remained the same, but elsewhere he says he firmly believes that they are continually being produced and dissolved without the same ones ever returning. Well, if the latter is the case, what can he or will he deduce from these reasonings?

Neither the satellites of Jupiter nor any other stars are spots or shadows, nor are the sunspots stars. It is indeed true that I am quibbling over names, while I know that anyone may impose them to suit himself. So long as a man does not think that by names he can confer inherent and essential properties on things, it would make little difference whether he calls these "stars." Thus the novae of 1572 and 1604 were called "stars," and meteorologists call comets and meteors "stars," and for that matter lovers and poets so refer to the eyes of their ladyloves:

> When Astolfo's successor is seen
> By the glance of those two smiling stars.[20]

For reasons of this kind the sunspots may also be called stars; but essentially they have properties that differ not a little from the true stars, which are always of one shape and quite regular, while the spots are of various shapes and most irregular; the former are consistent in size and shape, the latter always instable and changing; the former are ever the same, and permanent in a manner that transcends the memories of all past ages, while the latter are capable of being produced and dissolved from one day to the next. Stars are never seen except luminous; spots are always dark; the first are either motionless or most regular in mo-

[20] Ariosto, *Orlando Furioso* vii, 27, 1–2. Astolfo, Orlando's English cousin, was turned into a myrtle tree by Alcina when she tired of him. He was supplanted in her love by Ruggero, who had set out to undo the wrong but in turn fell under her spell.

tion; the others have but a single common motion though they are affected by myriads of irregularities; the stars are arranged at varying distances from the sun; sunspots are all contiguous to it or imperceptibly removed from its surface; we see the former only if far to one side of the sun, the latter only in line with the sun; the former are most probably made of dense and very opaque matter, the latter being rarefied in the manner of clouds and smoke.

Now I fail to see any reason for placing the spots with things differing from them in a hundred ways and having but a single property in common, instead of with things that agree with them in every way. I liken the sunspots to clouds or smokes. Surely if anyone wished to imitate them by means of earthly materials, no better model could be found than to put some drops of incombustible bitumen on a red-hot iron plate. From the black spot thus impressed on the iron, there will arise a black smoke that will disperse in strange and changing shapes. And if anyone were to insist that continual food and nourishment would have to be supplied for the refueling of the immense light that our great lamp, the sun, continually diffuses through the universe, then we have countless experiences harmoniously agreeing in showing us the conversion of burning materials first into something black or dark in color. Thus we see wood, straw, paper, candlewicks, and every burning thing to have its flame planted in and rising from neighboring parts of the material that have first become black. It might even be that if we more accurately observed the bright spots on the sun that I have mentioned, we should find them occurring in the very places where large dark spots had been a short time before. But as to this I do not mean to assert anything positively, nor to oblige myself to defend the conjecture, for I do not wish to mix dubious things with those which are definite and certain.

I believe that there are not a few Peripatetics on this side of the Alps who go about philosophizing without any desire to learn the truth and the causes of things, for they deny these new discoveries or jest about them, saying that they are illusions. It is about time for us to jest right back at these men and say that they likewise have become invisible and inaudible. They go about defending the inalterability of the sky, a view which perhaps Aristotle himself would abandon in our age. Their view of sunspots resembles that of Apelles, save that where he puts a single star for each spot, these fellows make the spots a congeries of many minute stars which gather together in greater or smaller numbers to form spots of irregular and varying shapes.[21] Now though it is true in general that when many objects unite, each in itself being too small or too distant to be visible, they may form an aggregate which becomes perceptible to our sight. Still, one may not conclude as these men do from such a generalization; one must come down to the particular things observed in stars and in spots. A captain who has but a small number of soldiers to defend a fortress must not dash with his whole force to some point under attack, leaving all other positions open and undefended. When trying to defend the inalterability of the heavens, we must not forget the perils to which other positions just as essential to the Peripatetic philosophy may be exposed. To maintain the integrity and solidity of that philosophy, its other propositions must be supported by saying that some stars are fixed and others wandering; those are called "fixed" which are all in one single sphere and which move with its motion while remaining fixed with respect to each other, and "wandering" stars are those of which each has its own special motion. These propositions being true, the "solar stars" cannot be said to be fixed, for if they did not change with respect to one another it would be impossible to see the continual mutations that are observed in the spots, and the same patterns would always return. Hence anyone who wished to maintain that the spots were a congeries of minute stars would have to introduce into the sky

[21] In September 1612, Cesi informed Galileo that a Dominican father had supported his views on sunspots in a debate at the Roman College while the Jesuits sided with Scheiner in calling them small stars. When the Dominican pointed out that stars were round and not irregular in shape, the Jesuits retorted that clusters of stars need not be (*Opere* xi, 395).

innumerable movements, tumultuous, uneven, and without any regularity. But this does not harmonize with any plausible philosophy. And to what purpose would it be done? To keep the heavens free from even the tiniest alteration of material. Well, if alteration were annihilation, the Peripatetics would have some reason for concern; but since it is nothing but mutation, there is no reason for such bitter hostility to it. It seems to me unreasonable to call "corruption" in an egg that which produces a chicken. Besides, if "corruption" and "generation" are discovered in the moon, why deny them to the sky? If the earth's small mutations do not threaten its existence (if, indeed, they are ornaments rather than imperfections in it), why deprive the other planets of them? Why fear so much for the dissolution of the sky as a result of alterations no more inimical than these?

These men are forced into their strange fancies by attempting to measure the whole universe by means of their tiny scale. Our special hatred of death need not render fragility odious. Why should we want to become less mutable? We should thereby suffer the fate caused by the Medusa's head, being converted to marble and losing our senses and qualities which could not exist in us without corporeal alterations. But I shall not go on; I reserve to another time the examination of the Peripatetic arguments, merely remarking that it appears to me not entirely philosophical to cling to conclusions once they have been discovered to be manifestly false. These men are persuaded that if Aristotle were back on earth in our age, he would do the same—as if it were a sign of more perfect judgment and a more noble consequence of deep learning to defend what is false than to learn the truth! People like this, it seems to me, give us reason to suspect that they have not so much plumbed the profundity of the Peripatetic arguments as they have conserved the imperious authority of Aristotle. It would be enough for them, and would save them a great deal of trouble, if they were to avoid these really dangerous arguments; for it is easier to consult indexes and look up texts than to investigate conclusions and form new and conclusive proofs. Besides, it seems to me that we abase our own status too much and do this not without some offense to Nature (and I might add to divine Providence), when we attempt to learn from Aristotle that which he neither knew nor could find out, rather than consult our own senses and reason. For she, in order to aid our understanding of her great works, has given us two thousand more years of observations, and sight twenty times as acute as that which she gave Aristotle.

I have demonstrated that the sunspots are neither stars nor permanent materials, and that they are not located at a distance from the sun but are produced and dissolved upon it in a manner not unlike that of clouds and vapors on the earth. That is all I have to say to Your Excellency on this subject for the present; let it seal all the new discoveries I have made in the heavens, and let me now return freely and without interruption to the studies which I shall shortly publish together with the consideration of other celestial novelties. Among these is an unexpected wonder regarding Saturn which has recently come to disturb me, of which I must render an account to Your Excellency.

About three years ago I wrote that to my great surprise I had discovered Saturn to be three-bodied; that is, it was an aggregate of three stars arranged in a straight line parallel to the ecliptic, the central star being much larger than the others. I believed them to be mutually motionless, for when I first saw them they seemed almost to touch, and they remained so for almost two years without the least change. It was reasonable to believe them to be fixed with respect to each other, since a single second of arc (a movement incomparably smaller than any other in even the largest orbs) would have become sensible in that time, either by separating or by completely uniting these stars. Hence I stopped observing Saturn for more than two years. But in the past few days I returned to it and found it to be solitary, without its customary supporting stars, and as perfectly round and sharply bounded as Jupiter. Now what can be said of this strange metamorphosis? That the two lesser stars have been consumed, in the manner of the sunspots? Has Saturn devoured his children? Or was it indeed an illusion and a fraud with which the lenses of my telescope deceived me for so long—and not only me, but many others who have observed it with me? Perhaps the day has arrived when languishing hope may be revived in those who, led by the most profound reflections, once plumbed the fallacies of all my new observations and found them to be incapable of existing!

I need not say anything definite upon so strange and unexpected an event; it is too recent, too unparalleled, and I am restrained by my own inadequacy and the fear of error. But for once I shall risk a little temerity; may this be pardoned by Your Excellency since I confess it to be rash, and protest that I mean not to register anything here as a prediction, but only as a probable conclusion. I say, then, that I believe that after the winter solstice of 1614 they may once more be observed. And perhaps this planet also, no less than horned Venus, harmonizes admirably with the great Copernican system, to the universal revelation of which doctrine propitious breezes are now seen to be directed toward us, leaving little fear of clouds or crosswinds.

I shall now cease troubling Your Excellency, praying you once more to offer my friendship and services to Apelles. Should you decide to show him this letter, add to it my excuses if he feels that I have dissented too violently from his views. Desiring nothing but to win a knowledge of the truth, I have frankly explained my opinions, which I am quite willing to change whenever my errors are revealed, and I shall hold myself especially obliged to anyone who favors me by showing them and castigating me. I kiss Your Excellency's hands, and cordially salute you on behalf of Sig. Filippo Salviati,[22] at whose most agreeable villa I continue my celestial observations in his good company. May God grant you the satisfaction of every desire.

From the Villa delle Selve, December 1, 1612.

Your Excellency's most devoted servitor,

GALILEO GALILEI LINCEAN

[22] Filippo Salviati (1582–1614) was later immortalized by Galileo as his own spokesman in the last two books he published, both being written in dialogue form.

INTRODUCTION: THIRD PART

XVII

With the publication of the *Letters on Sunspots* the period of Galileo's most famed discoveries drew to a close, to be succeeded by one in which his even more famous opinions became the subject of violent and widespread controversy. Ostensibly this battle was waged over the Copernican system; in reality it was fought over the right of a scientist to teach and defend his scientific beliefs. The real issue was perfectly clear to Galileo at all times, as it was to some of the theologians who were soon to decide the contest against him. But by his avowed enemies in the church it seems never to have been understood at all. To their minds Galileo was attacking the church; to his own mind he was protecting it from the commission of a fatal error. In place of the contempt Galileo felt toward his adversaries in science, he showed rage and indignation against his religious opponents. Ignorant men were powerless to injure science, but they could seriously damage the church. In order to prevent such a calamity Galileo undertook a struggle which involved him in grave personal danger, while his enemies acted not only in complete safety but even with a prospect of gaining glory.

The *Letter to the Grand Duchess Christina* is Galileo's most carefully considered expression of his opinions on the proper relation of science to religion. It was not written until 1615, but the train of events which led up to it may be considered as having started four years earlier. On December 16, 1611, when Galileo was still at work on his *Discourse on Floating Bodies* and had not yet turned his attention seriously to the sunspots, his friend Cigoli wrote to him from Rome:

"I have been told by a friend of mine, a priest who is very fond of you, that a certain crowd of ill-disposed men envious of your virtue and merits met at the house of the archbishop there and put their heads together in a mad quest for any means by which they could damage you, either with regard to the motion of the earth or otherwise. One of them wished to have a preacher state from the pulpit that you were asserting outlandish things. The priest, having perceived the animosity against you, replied as a good Christian and a religious man ought to do. Now I write this to you so that your eyes will be open to such envy and malice on the part of that sort of evildoers."

Galileo's health was very poor at this time, and because he had always suffered from the air of Florence he was then preparing to move to the villa of his friend Filippo Salviati[1] a few miles to the west. There he remained while writing the sunspot letters, and perhaps his absence from Florence during most of 1612 accounts for his having been temporarily left in peace by the group described in Cigoli's letter, at least with regard to religious attacks. But toward the end of the year he received word that his views had been assailed in Florence by a Dominican priest named Niccolò Lorini. He seems to have demanded an explanation at once, for three days after the alleged attack Lorini wrote in reply:

"Please know, Your Excellency, that the suspicion of my having entered into a discussion of philosophical matters against anyone on All Souls' Day is completely false and without foundation. It is not only untrue, but not even probable, as I have never strayed from my line and duty. I have never dreamed of getting involved in such matters, nor have I so much as mentioned them to Sig. Pandolfini or anybody else, so I am at a loss to know what grounds there can be for such a suspicion, this thing having never occurred to me. It is indeed true that I, not in order to argue but merely to avoid appearing a blockhead when the discussion was started by others, did say a few words just

[1] See note 22, p. 144.

o show I was alive. I said, as I still say, that this opinion of Ipernicus—or whatever his name is—would appear to be hostile to the divine Scripture. But it is of little consequence to me, for I have other things to do; for me it is enough that no occasion shall be given to anyone for believing us what we are not. For I am confident that all our nobility is steadfastly Catholic. . . ."[2]

Lorini was a Florentine patrician, then seventy years of age, who had acquired some distinction in his order and was well liked by the Grand Duke. Filippo Pandolfini was a young public official, also close to the ruling family; as a pupil and good friend of Galileo's, he appears to have informed him of some discussion that may have taken place at court.[3] It would be natural for Galileo, ever alert to possible danger in that quarter, to inquire promptly about the matter. Lorini's ignorance of and indifference to the very name of Copernicus certainly make it unlikely that he was fanatic on the subject. At any rate Galileo took his word for what had happened; a few weeks later he joked about the incident when writing to Cesi to thank him and Cigoli

[2] Opere xi, 427. The mistaken spelling of "Copernicus" is fairly good evidence that Lorini had never heard the name spoken, or at least not often. He may have seen it written in conventional Latin style by some other ignoramus who believed it to be "Compernicus," for the initial sound "com" was written much as our figure "9," and is easily mistaken for an "I."

[3] Lorini certainly had not preached publicly against Galileo, as some writers preposterously state. Apart from the fact that Galileo himself later referred to the incident as having occurred in "private discussions" (Opere v, 291), Lorini could not have hoped successfully to cover up or deny such an act. The particular discussion in question may have taken place at the University of Florence or at the court; less probably, at Lorini's Convent of San Marco. Inasmuch as Pandolfini had heard of it at once, and Galileo treated it as a serious incident, it seems most likely to have happened at court. With respect to this incident, overzealous partisans of Galileo overlook the danger of implying that he would try to stamp out opposition even in private conversations held in places with which he had no legitimate concern.

for their care in editing the *Letters on Sunspots* in such a way as to protect him from the malicious:

"Here also they do not rest from scheming, and the more because their enemy is close at hand. But since they are numerically few and belong to that league (for thus they refer to themselves in private) which may be recognized by Your Excellency in their writings, I laugh at them. And here in Florence there is a clumsy speaker who has decided to detest the mobility of the earth, but this good fellow is so unfamiliar with the author of that doctrine that he calls him 'Ipernicus.' Behold whence and by whom poor philosophy is subjected to extortion!"[4]

XVIII

The "league" which amused Galileo by printing attacks against him seems at this time to have consisted principally of certain Peripatetic philosophers who had sought, but not yet gained, support from elements in the church.[5] If the league was to be recognized from writings Cesi had seen, it must have consisted of the men who attacked Galileo's work on floating bodies, which had no direct connection with the Copernican dispute. Unquestionably the leader of this opposition was Lodovico delle Colombe, whose

---

[4] *Opere* xi, 461.

[5] Galileo's information about this self-styled league appears to have come from a letter of Tolomeo Nozzolini addressed to Alessandro Marzimedici, Archbishop of Florence, a copy of which was read to him while he lay ill about this time (*Opere* iv, 289). The role of the archbishop in all these matters is not easy to deduce. Vincenzio Viviani, Galileo's beloved pupil and biographer, mentions Marzimedici as a disciple of Galileo's (*Opere* xix, 628). The archbishop certainly permitted Nozzolini's letter to pass into the hands of Galileo's friends, and this letter was very favorable to Galileo as against the league. On the other hand, Cigoli had asserted flatly that Galileo's opponents had met at the archbishop's house to secure clerical support (p. 146). Cigoli's letter is slightly ambiguous, and it may be (though it seems unlikely) that the "priest" who rebuked them for their animosity toward Galileo was the archbishop himself.

manuscript dissertation against the motion of the earth Galileo had never dignified with a formal reply. In attacking the *Discourse on Floating Bodies,* Colombe now inserted some pointed remarks about Galileo's failure to answer his anti-Copernican arguments. A passage at the beginning of Colombe's book is particularly interesting, saying that since Galileo wrongheadedly insisted upon being an anti-Peripatetic, Colombe asserted that: "I should like to become in this regard an anti-Galileo out of respect to [Aristotle] that great leader of academies, head of so many schools, subject of so many poets, labor of so many historians, [a man] who had read more books than there were days in his life, and had written more of them than he counted years."[6] Colombe and his expression "anti-Galileo" seem to have afforded a new inspiration to his adversaries, as they took to calling themselves "Galileists" openly, and referring to their opponents as *colombi,* or pigeons

Four books in all were published against Galileo's *Discourse* during a period of six months. All the writers were men of some influence, and two of them were university professors. Hence Galileo thought they should be answered, especially as their books had been dedicated to members of the Medici family. Cesi, however, discouraged him from refuting these attacks personally, considering this a waste of valuable time and energy. He suggested instead that if they were to be answered at all, this should be done by some pupil of Galileo's, which would belittle his adversaries the more. In the end this was done; Galileo turned over the material he had written to Benedetto Castelli, who edited it for the press and published it in 1615. The villa of the Benedictines near Florence, where much of this work was done, was situated in the *Campora di Colombaia,* so Castelli customarily referred to the book as "the Columbiad" and thus added one more play on the name of Galileo's chief adversary.

Scarcely had the rash of attacks against the *Discourse* come off the press when Galileo's *Letters on Sunspots* ap-

[6] *Opere* iv, 317–18.

peared, late in March 1613. Inasmuch as Galileo had now not only openly adopted the Copernican system but had linked the proof of it with his own discoveries, from this time on he abandoned his former prudence and defended it on all occasions. It was natural that his name should thus become so firmly associated in the popular mind with the idea of a moving earth that Galileo was widely regarded as having originated the doctrine, an error which caused him no little amusement.

As late as 1612 Father Lorini still remained unfamiliar with Copernicus's name, and during that year even Cesi had shown in a letter to Galileo an unfamiliarity with the details of the Copernican system.[7] During the next two years this situation rapidly changed. The Galileists saw to it that the topic was widely discussed and debated. Inevitably a number of theologians now joined the ranks of Galileo's older opponents—the philosophers who had objected to the roughness of the moon's surface, the astronomers who could not accept new planets and stars in the heavens, and the physicists who had been bested in their attempts to defend Aristotle against him.

XIX

Early in November 1613, Benedetto Castelli went to the University of Pisa to assume the chair of mathematics, a post which Galileo had secured for him. The overseer of the university, Arturo d'Elci,[8] made a special point of telling Castelli immediately that he must under no circumstances discuss the motion of the earth and related topics. Castelli assured him that he would avoid the subject, adroitly adding that he knew his own teacher Galileo had done likewise throughout twenty-four years of teaching, both at Pisa and at Padua. D'Elci went on to make it clear that apart from Castelli's public lectures the subject was forbidden even by way of digression. Castelli replied that he would be guided by the overseer's slightest wish. But

[7] *Opere* xi, 332–33.
[8] See note 16, pp. 127–28.

less than a month went by before he was drawn into a discussion of the forbidden topic under circumstances to which
not even the strictest university martinet could have taken
exception. It was an event that turned out to be of crucial
importance in Galileo's entire career. Here is Castelli's own
account of it, written to Galileo on December 14, 1613:

"Wednesday morning I was dining at the court when I
was asked about the university by the Grand Duke. I gave
him a detailed account of things, with which he showed
himself well satisfied. Then he asked me if I had a telescope,
to which I replied yes, and fell to talking of my observations of the Medicean planets made the previous night.
Madame Christina[9] wanted to know their position, and
thereupon the talk turned to the necessity of their being
real objects and not illusions of the telescope. Their Highnesses asked Professor Boscaglia[10] about this, and he replied that their existence could not be denied. I then contributed all that I knew and could tell them about Your
Excellency's wonderful discovery and establishment of the
orbits of these planets. Don Antonio de' Medici,[11] who
was present at the table, beamed at me and showed himself
well pleased by what I said. After much talk, which went
off quite solemnly, dinner was finally over and I left. But
I had hardly come out of the palace when Madame
Christina's porter overtook me and told me that she wished
me to return. Now before I tell you what ensued, you must
first know that while we were at table Dr. Boscaglia had
had the ear of Madame for a while; and, conceding as true
all the new things you have discovered in the sky, he said
that only the motion of the earth had something incredible
in it and could not take place, in particular because the
Holy Scripture was obviously contrary to this view.

[9] Christina of Lorraine, mother of the Grand Duke Cosimo
II.

[10] Cosimo Boscaglia, a special professor of philosophy at the
University of Pisa, expounder of Plato, and a favorite of the
Grand Duke among men of letters there.

[11] Not truly one of the Medici, but accepted as a sort of
honorary cousin by Cosimo II. The story is rather too complicated for a footnote.

"Now, getting back to my story, I entered into the chambers of Her Highness, and there I found the Grand Duke, Madame Christina and the Archduchess,[12] Don Antonio, Don Paolo Giordano [Orsini],[13] and Dr. Boscaglia. Madame began, after some questions about myself, to argue the Holy Scripture against me. Thereupon, after having made suitable disclaimers, I commenced to play the theologian with such assurance and dignity that it would have done you good to hear me. Don Antonio assisted me, giving me such heart that instead of being dismayed by the majesty of Their Highnesses I carried things off like a paladin. I quite won over the Grand Duke and his Archduchess, while Don Paolo came to my assistance with a very apt quotation from the Scripture. Only Madame Christina remained against me, but from her manner I judged that she did this only to hear my replies. Professor Boscaglia said never a word."[14]

Perhaps Galileo's thoughts had been distracted from the religious implications of his position as a result of his poor health, the press of other affairs, and the apparent inactivity on this front for a whole year following the note from Lorini. If so, this experience of Castelli's at court made him once again sharply aware of the danger of neglecting this matter any longer. He promptly composed a defense against any further attack along these lines, and on December 21, 1613, he sent to Castelli a very long letter containing his opinions on the proper relations of science and religion and

---

[12] Maria Madeleine of Austria, wife of Cosimo. She is referred to by her Austrian title of Archduchess, the honorary title of Grand Duchess remaining to Christina, her mother-in-law.

[13] It was to this member of the powerful Orsini family that Scheiner later dedicated his *Rosa Ursina*, which included the bitterest personal attack ever made against Galileo, and Orsini was much distressed when he learned what was in the book. His brother, Alessandro Orsini, became a cardinal in 1615, and shortly thereafter urged the pope strongly to rule in favor of Galileo's views—an interview which resulted instead in their prohibition.

[14] *Opere* xi, 605–6.

concluding with a proposed Copernican interpretation of the miracle of Joshua. This letter seemed to quiet the new outbreak, and once again for a whole year nothing of importance is mentioned in the correspondence with regard to activities of churchmen against Galileo. Twice Castelli wrote of events related to the previous incident. From his letters it appears that the doubts of the Grand Duchess had been removed, even though a visiting Greek priest had temporarily stirred her up again; that Professor Boscaglia had been bested in debate once more; and that one of the Medici had made known his wish that the whole subject be dropped.

XX

But quiet as things may have seemed on the surface during most of 1614, opposing camps were now taking form within the church. The better-informed and more influential elements gravitated to Galileo. Father Clavius was now dead, but in his last published work he had inserted a description of Galileo's discoveries and had gone so far as to say that the arrangement of the heavens would have to be reinvestigated to accommodate them. At the Jesuit college in Rome his successor, Father Christopher Grienberger, had accepted Galileo's conclusions concerning sunspots after having at first supported the views of his fellow Jesuit Scheiner. From Naples the renowned theologian Thomas Campanella wrote to praise Galileo and to tell him that he was at work on a volume of theology in which the Copernican system would be shown to be not inconsistent with the views of many ancients or with the Bible. There also, unknown to Galileo and his friends, a Carmelite priest was composing a book in support of their views which was soon to play an important part in Galileo's affairs.

The opposition was also active, and nowhere so strongly as in Florence. From the pulpit of his church there on December 21, 1614, Father Thomas Caccini[15] denounced

[15] Thomas Caccini (1574–1648) is truly the villain of the piece. Not long before, he had made trouble at Bologna, but

Galileo, the Copernican system, mathematics, and all mathematicians as contrary to the Christian religion and inimical to the state. It is usually said that Caccini took as his text that day a passage[16] which, in its Latin version, offers the possibility of the facetious translation: "Ye men of Galileo, why stand ye gazing up into heaven?" If this tradition is correct, the selection of that text is the only really clever thing Caccini was ever reported to have done. But Caccini was certainly not being facetious that day, and Galileo was quick to protest his remarks, communicating them to friends at Rome and elsewhere. One of his letters went to Father Luigi Maraffi, a friend of Cigoli's who had perhaps been his informant three years earlier concerning activities at Florence against Galileo. Maraffi, now Preacher-general in the Dominican Order, was a great admirer of Galileo, and he sent a humane expression of regret that such stupidities should have been uttered by a member of his religion.

Cesi wrote sympathetically from Acquasparta, but he cautioned Galileo to tread lightly in seeking redress. Cardinal Bellarmine, he said, had once told him that he held the Copernican view to be heretical and the motion of the earth contrary to the Bible. Cesi felt that Copernicus himself would not have been permitted to write if he had had to consult the Congregation of the Index in his day. He advised Galileo to leave Copernicus out of it and to emphasize Caccini's excesses in attacking mathematicians generally. The Lincean leader hoped that through university pro-

at this time he was stationed at the Dominican Convent of Santa Maria Novella in Florence. His denunciation of Galileo's views had been planned for some time and had been discussed with others; he had been assigned to expound the book of Joshua in a series of sermons, and hit upon the idea of utilizing the miracle in the tenth chapter as a pretext for attacking the Galileists. Personal ambition, wrongheadedness, bigotry, lack of understanding, and a willingness on Caccini's part to make charges under oath which could not be supported, are all apparent in the documents. This contrasts sharply with the behavior of nearly every other churchman concerned in the proceedings during this period.

[16] Acts 1:11.

fessors it might be possible to induce other preachers to extol the mathematical sciences and Galileo's new discoveries as glorifications of God through the contemplation of His works. In this way Copernicus might be introduced along with Ptolemy, avoiding open mention of the earth's motion. Cesi knew the ways of the authorities in Rome and the perils of stirring anything up when that could be avoided. But Galileo had little reason to hope for any help from the professors, and did not heed Cesi's advice.

From Pisa, Castelli wrote on the last day of 1614: "As to those pickpockets and highwaymen who waylay mathematicians, I don't know what to tell you. From what I hear, Father Lorini (who is here) felt very sad that your fine priest had let himself get so far out of hand. . . . I am most unhappy over the manner in which ignorance has reached such a peak in some men that they condemn sciences of which they know nothing and attribute to them qualities which they are incapable of possessing. Even the most mediocre student knows that nothing is farther from self-interest and impious expressions than mathematics. But patience; these impertinences are not the first, and they will not be the last."[17]

Alas, Castelli himself was at least indirectly responsible that the final phrase of his letter became only too true. For while Lorini was in Pisa someone let him copy the letter which Galileo had written to Castelli a year before concerning religion and science.[18] Immediately upon his return to Florence he discussed this letter with his colleagues. All agreed that it contained damnable views. Lorini's conciliatory attitude toward Galileo three years earlier and the distress he had recently expressed over Caccini's excesses were now forgotten. Father Lorini was filled with holy zeal, and

[17] *Opere* xii, 123.

[18] It seems most unlikely that this was done by Castelli himself, but it is generally believed (though concrete evidence is not cited) that long prior to this he had permitted many copies of Galileo's letter to circulate among his friends. Copies certainly circulated widely after this incident, and many of those are extant.

he now no longer saw Galileo as a mistaken scientist who
had some foolish ideas that ought to be put right, but as a
meddling layman who held and propagated heretical views
on the interpretation of Scripture. Once aroused, the aged
and influential Dominican did not hesitate to report these
things to the Holy Office. After showing the letter to
Caccini he forwarded it to Rome. In his accompanying
letter he avoided specifically denouncing Galileo, but he
called for an investigation of the dangerous and heretical
views expressed by the Galileists. Lorini clearly thought
that Galileo's letter was occasioned by Caccini's sermon.
Modern scholars have asserted that, on the contrary,
Caccini's sermon was inspired by his having seen a privately
circulated copy of the letter. To judge from the documents,
however, the sermon and the letter must have been entirely
independent of one another.

Galileo heard almost at once that Lorini had returned
from Pisa with a copy of his letter to Castelli and was
raising a great fuss over it. He suspected that it would be
promptly forwarded to Rome, and he knew that even a few
slight alterations in it could make things look very bad indeed for him. Accordingly he recovered the original from
Castelli and sent a correct copy to his good friend Piero
Dini at Rome, asking that it be shown to Father Grienberger and if possible to Cardinal Bellarmine in its authen-
tic form. In his letter of transmittal, dated February 16,
1615, he explained that it had originally been written in
haste and that he would now apply his mind to amplifying
and improving it. In its amended and expanded form it became the *Letter to the Grand Duchess Christina*, which
was probably completed about June of the same year.

The Holy Office had received Lorini's communication
about the middle of February, and toward the end of the
month wrote to the Archbishop of Pisa, instructing him dextrously to obtain the original of Galileo's letter from Castelli.
The subtlety with which the archbishop approached this
task may be judged from Castelli's account of the interview,
written to Galileo on March 12:

"On my return to Pisa I went to do reverence to Monsignor the Archbishop, by whom I was very benignly received. Then he took me to his chambers, seated me, and began to ask after your health. I had scarcely finished answering when he began to exhort me to give up certain extravagant opinions, and particularly that of the earth's motion, adding that this would be for my own good and not my injury because these opinions, in addition to being silly, were dangerous, scandalous, and rash, being directly contrary to Scripture. Overcome by such benevolence, I could do no other than reply that my will was ever quick to respond to his suggestions, and that it only remained for me to accommodate my mind to the reasons which I might hope from his profound wisdom and sound learning. So he took for me but a single reason from his stock, omitting all others, and the substance of it was that since all created things are made for the service of man, it clearly follows as a necessary consequence that the earth could not move like the stars. And if here I had felt capable of understanding the necessary connection, perhaps my opinion would be changed; whence it was necessary for Monsignor to repeat that these opinions were folly and madness, and that this had been your ruin, and that he had been given wholesome notice of it, and that you had been refuted. He even went on to say (getting really hot under the collar) that it was soon to be made known to you and to His Serene Highness and to everyone that these ideas are all silly and that they deserve condemnation. Then he asked me if I would kindly show him that letter which you had written to me. When I said I had no copy of it, he asked me to apply to you for one, which I hereby do—asking you also to put the finishing touches on that composition, which we shall copy here immediately if you ask us to; and perhaps this very illustrious gentleman may be quieted. *I say perhaps, and not that I guarantee this to you.*"[19]

Castelli underlined the last sentence, after which he added this postscript: "Subsequently I have heard to my great satisfaction that the gossip at Rome is not such a

[19] *Opere* xii, 153–54.

great matter as it was said to be. And to me it appears that the rumor made at Rome is not Roman, but alien; I mean that it has been fabricated by these same gentlemen who have likewise produced it at Florence."

Castelli's information on this point was soon confirmed by others at Rome, but Galileo's apprehensions were never fully allayed. With regard to the transmittal of the original of his letter to Castelli, which he had presumably recovered in order to copy it for Dini, he delayed as long as he could.

XXI

During the last week of February and the first week of March, Piero Dini and Giovanni Ciampoli (another loyal friend of Galileo's then at Rome) set to work there to undo any damage that might have been caused if Lorini had sent a misleading version of the letter to the Inquisition. At the end of February Ciampoli wrote as follows:

"Cardinal Barberini, who, as you know from experience, has always admired your worth, told me only yesterday evening that with respect to these opinions he would like greater caution in not going beyond the arguments used by Ptolemy and Copernicus, and finally in not exceeding the limitations of physics and mathematics. For to explain the Scriptures is claimed by theologians as their field, and if new things are brought in, even by an admirable mind, not everyone has the dispassionate faculty of taking them just as they are said. One man amplifies, the next one alters, and what came from the author's own mouth becomes so transformed in spreading that he will no longer recognize it as his own. And I know what he means. Your opinion regarding the phenomena of light and shadow in the bright and dark spots of the moon creates some analogy between the lunar globe and the earth; somebody expands on this, and says that you place human inhabitants on the moon; the next fellow starts to dispute how these can be descended from Adam, or how they can have come off Noah's ark, and many other extravagances you never dreamed of. Hence to declare frequently that one places oneself under the authority of those who have jurisdiction over the minds of men in the interpretation of Scripture is to remove this pretext for other people's malice. Perhaps you think I go too far in playing the sage with you; please forgive me, and thank the infinite esteem which makes me speak thus."[20]

A week later, Dini, who had made several copies of Galileo's letter to Castelli and distributed them even more widely than requested, wrote to say that he had done this and had also read Galileo's letter of transmittal aloud to Grienberger and Bellarmine. He went on to say:

"With Bellarmine I spoke at length of the things you had written, which he assured me he had never heard mentioned in any connection since you had talked directly of them to him. And he said that as to Copernicus, there is no question of his book being prohibited; the worst that might happen, according to him, would be the addition of some material in the margins of that book to the effect that Copernicus had introduced his theory in order to save the appearances, or some such thing—just as others had introduced epicycles without thereafter believing in their existence. And with a similar precaution you may at any time deal with these matters. If things are fixed according to the Copernican system, [he said,] it does not appear presently that they would have any greater obstacle in the Bible than the passage [*the sun*] *exults as a strong man to run his course*,[21] etc., which all expositors up to now have understood by attributing motion to the sun. And although I replied that this also could be explained as a concession to our ordinary forms of expression, I was told in answer that this was not a thing to be done in haste, just as the condemnation of any of these opinions was not to be passionately hurried. And if you should have put together in your essay any interpretations to the purpose, he will gladly look them over. Now since I know that you will remember to submit yourself to the decisions of the holy Church as you have to me and to others, I can only rejoice for you. And the Cardi-

---

[20] *Opere* xii, 145–47.
[21] Psalms 18:6 (Douay); 19:5 (King James).

nal having told me that he had called Father Grienberger to discuss these matters, I returned this morning to see if that priest had anything new for us, and found nothing substantial. . . ."[22] Dini spoke to Cardinal Barberini a few days later, and heard a repetition of his previous advice "to speak with caution and as a professor of mathematics; and he assured me that he had never heard anything said of these interests of yours."[23] But Dini did not believe this last statement, for he knew that these things were at that moment the main topic of discussion in both Barberini's and Bellarmine's departments of the church.

For a similar reason Galileo was unable to accept Castelli's assurances that the gossip at Rome was no great matter. From still another source he had heard of this gossip; namely, the bishop of Fiesole, who had spoken of it to Galileo's friends and had intimated that Galileo was doing the Grand Duke no service by pressing his extravagant opinions. Nor could he forget that the Archbishop of Pisa had said flatly that a ban was about to be placed on Copernicus, had displayed unusual solicitude about his health, and was showing a remarkable interest in his personal correspondence.

Precisely at this juncture Cesi arrived back in Rome and found something truly exciting, which he dispatched to Galileo the same day that Dini sent the foregoing letter. This was the book recently printed at Naples, written by the Carmelite priest Paolo Antonio Foscarini; a work devoted exclusively to pointing out the implications of Galileo's discoveries and defending the Copernican system from charges that it was inconsistent with the Bible. In forwarding it, Cesi wrote: ". . . it certainly could not have appeared at a better time, unless to increase the fury of our adversaries is damaging, which I do not believe. The writer considers all Linceans to be Copernicans, though this is not so, as they unanimously claim only freedom in philosophizing about things in nature. He is now preaching in Rome."[24] Fosca-

[22] *Opere* xii, 151.
[23] *Opere* xii, 155.
[24] *Opere* xii, 149–50.

rini was not only preaching there, but had offered to meet all comers in debate on this matter, and had sent a copy of his book to Cardinal Bellarmine for his opinion.

Foscarini's book reached Galileo just about the time he heard from Castelli concerning the archbishop's inquiries. It may have been the crucial factor in his decision whether to withdraw from battle, receiving at best an unacceptable compromise with the theologians and at worst the complete prohibition of Copernicus, or whether he should run the risk of fighting things out to the end. His friends had advised him not to fight, and the outlook had indeed been dark; but now there was unequivocal support from a qualified theologian.

Galileo decided to fight. To Castelli he sent Foscarini's book and the long-delayed text of the original letter. To Dini he wrote a long reply in which he stated that it would be wrong to compromise on the Copernican system; that its author had never meant it as a mere hypothesis, and that it would have to be accepted or rejected as a whole. To Ciampoli he renewed his appeal for information about all rumors, and the patient friend replied:

"I confirm what I wrote a few days ago. I believe that those 'great rumors' have made a loud noise in the ears of four or five people and no more. Through all the diligence Monsignor Dini and I have applied in order to discover whether there is any great move afoot, absolutely nothing has been found, nor is anything known to have been said of one. Hence I fancy that the original authors of this talk have been believed to make up a good part of Rome by publicizing as a notorious matter something that no one can be found to have discussed. Hence you may begin to calm yourself as to this particular, for you do not lack affectionate friends who are more than ever admirers of the eminence of your merits. . . . I have spoken to no one yet who did not judge it a great irrelevance for preachers to want to enter their pulpits and discuss such lofty and professional subjects among women and ordinary folk, where there exist such a small number of well-informed people."[25]

XXII

Castelli received Galileo's letter and Foscarini's book, and on April 9 he reported to Galileo:

"As to the letter, it has been seen (but without leaving my hands) by various members of my order, whom it pleased very much. I read it to Monsignor the Archbishop in the presence of several canonical gentlemen. By the archbishop it was praised with majesty and decorum; I mean with a few dry words. But the other gentlemen approved its manner of expression, the elegant treatment, the subtlety of interpretation, and above all the modesty and reverence with which Your Excellency deals with the Bible. I believe that Monsignor the Archbishop, having finally seen what his fellow theologian has printed in defense of this opinion with great solemnity of crucifixes and saints, was more impressed by the latter than by the arguments, as something he would not have believed possible. But enough; Monsignor no longer says that these things are foolish; now he begins to say that Copernicus was truly a great and very brilliant man."[26]

Three days later Cardinal Bellarmine was writing his opinion of this work for its author; he was unmoved by the crucifixes and saints displayed on the title page. In writing his opinion he included his comments upon Galileo's views as expressed in the letter to Castelli. If he had also read Galileo's arguments against compromise, which Dini may have shown him by this time, he remained unchanged in the views he had previously expressed. To Foscarini he wrote:

"I have gladly read the letter in Italian and the essay in Latin that Your Reverence has sent me, and I thank you for both, confessing that they are filled with ingenuity and learning. But since you ask for my opinion, I shall give it to you briefly, as you have little time for reading and I for writing.

"First. I say that it appears to me that Your Reverence

[26] *Opere* xii, 165.

and Sig. Galileo did prudently to content yourselves with speaking hypothetically and not positively, as I have always believed Copernicus did. For to say that assuming the earth moves and the sun stands still saves all the appearances better than eccentrics and epicycles is to speak well. This has no danger in it, and it suffices for mathematicians. But to wish to affirm that the sun is really fixed in the center of the heavens and merely turns upon itself without traveling from east to west, and that the earth is situated in the third sphere and revolves very swiftly around the sun, is a very dangerous thing, not only by irritating all the theologians and scholastic philosophers, but also by injuring our holy faith and making the sacred Scripture false. For Your Reverence has indeed demonstrated many ways of expounding the Bible, but you have not applied them specifically, and doubtless you would have had a great deal of difficulty if you had tried to explain all the passages that you yourself have cited.

"Second. I say that, as you know, the Council [of Trent] would prohibit expounding the Bible contrary to the common agreement of the holy Fathers. And if Your Reverence would read not only all their works but the commentaries of modern writers on Genesis, Psalms, Ecclesiastes, and Joshua, you would find that all agree in expounding literally that the sun is in the heavens and travels swiftly around the earth, while the earth is far from the heavens and remains motionless in the center of the world. Now consider whether, in all prudence, the Church could support the giving to Scripture of a sense contrary to the holy Fathers and all the Greek and Latin expositors. Nor may it be replied that this is not a matter of faith, since if it is not so with regard to the subject matter, it is with regard to those who have spoken. Thus that man would be just as much a heretic who denied that Abraham had two sons and Jacob twelve, as one who denied the virgin birth of Christ, for both are declared by the Holy Ghost through the mouths of the prophets and apostles.

"Third. I say that if there were a true demonstration that the sun was in the center of the universe and the earth in the third sphere, and that the sun did not go around the earth but the earth went around the sun, then it would be necessary to use careful consideration in explaining the Scriptures that seemed contrary, and we should rather have to say that we do not understand them than to say that something is false which had been proven. But I do not think there is any such demonstration, since none has been shown to me. To demonstrate that the appearances are saved by assuming the sun at the center and the earth in the heavens is not the same thing as to demonstrate that in fact the sun is in the center and the earth in the heavens. I believe that the first demonstration may exist, but I have very grave doubts about the second; and in case of doubt one may not abandon the Holy Scriptures as expounded by the holy Fathers. I add that the words *The sun also riseth, and the sun goeth down, and hasteth to the place where he ariseth*[27] were written by Solomon, who not only spoke by divine inspiration, but was a man wise above all others, and learned in the human sciences and in the knowledge of all created things, which wisdom he had from God; so it is not very likely that he would affirm something that was contrary to demonstrated truth, or truth that might be demonstrated. And if you tell me that Solomon spoke according to the appearances, and that it seems to us that the sun goes round when the earth turns, as it seems to one aboard ship that the beach moves away, I shall answer thus. Anyone who departs from the beach, though to him it appears that the beach moves away, yet knows that this is an error and corrects it, seeing clearly that the ship moves and not the beach; but as to the sun and earth, no sage has needed to correct the error, since he clearly experiences that the earth stands still and that his eye is not deceived when it judges the sun to move, just as he is likewise not deceived when it judges that the moon and the stars move. And that is enough for the present."[28]

[27] Ecclesiastes 1:5.
[28] *Opere* xii, 171–72. For Galileo's point-by-point reply to these arguments see pp. 168–70.

XXIII

A few days later Foscarini left Rome, confidently expecting to reprint his book, and Galileo's informants and advisers at Rome and elsewhere were sure that the worst was over. Castelli wrote that in the opinion of the professor of law at Pisa, the church could not reach any other conclusion than Foscarini's, and he rejoiced that "those miserable wretches have fallen into the pit that they digged. To what refuge they will take, I do not know; but I should say that if they had the courage they would take to arms to vent their rage."[29] Dini wrote from Rome in the middle of May to say that he did not know what might be bothering Galileo, as nothing new had developed there; so far as Copernicus was concerned, nobody had doubts any longer. He advised Galileo to put the finishing touches on his revised letter, to fortify it with the best-founded arguments from both mathematics and the Bible, and then when the proper time came to publish them. As for Foscarini's work, Cesi had assured him that it would soon reappear with additional authorities. Many Jesuits were understood to be on Galileo's side, and Dini was sure that with them the day would be carried.

Galileo's final letter relating to the religious controversy, written some time in May, confirmed the uncompromising stand he had already decided upon:

"Eight days ago I wrote to Your Reverence in reply to yours of the second of May. My answer was very brief, because I then found myself (as now) among doctors and medicines, and much disturbed in body and mind over many things, particularly by seeing no end to these rumors set in motion against me through no fault of mine, and seemingly accepted by those higher up as if I were the originator of these things. Yet for all of me any discussion of the sacred Scripture might have lain dormant forever; no astronomer or scientist who remained within proper bounds has ever got into such things. Yet while I follow the teach-

[29] *Opere* xii, 178.

ings of a book accepted by the church, there come out against me philosophers quite ignorant of such teachings who tell me that they contain propositions contrary to the faith. So far as possible, I should like to show them that they are mistaken, but my mouth is stopped and I am ordered not to go into the Scriptures. This amounts to saying that Copernicus's book, accepted by the church, contains heresies and may be preached against by anyone who pleases, while it is forbidden for anyone to get into the controversy and show that it is not contrary to Scripture.

"To me, the surest and swiftest way to prove that the position of Copernicus is not contrary to Scripture would be to give a host of proofs that it is true and that the contrary cannot be maintained at all; thus, since no two truths can contradict one another, this and the Bible must be perfectly harmonious. But how can I do this, and not be merely wasting my time, when those Peripatetics who must be convinced show themselves incapable of following even the simplest and easiest of arguments, while on the other hand they are seen to set great store in worthless propositions?

"Yet I should not despair of overcoming even this difficulty if I were in a place where I could use my tongue instead of my pen; and if I ever get well again so that I can come to Rome, I shall do so, in the hope of at least showing my affection for the holy Church. My urgent desire on this point is that no decision be made which is not entirely good. Such it would be to declare, under the prodding of an army of malign men who understand nothing of the subject, that Copernicus did not hold the motion of the earth to be a fact of nature, but as an astronomer merely took it to be a convenient hypothesis for explaining the appearances. Thus to admit it to use but prohibit it from being considered true would be to declare that Copernicus's book had not even been read. . . . I should not like to have great men think that I endorse the position of Copernicus only as an astronomical hypothesis which is not really true. Taking me as one of those most addicted to his doctrine, they would believe all its other followers must agree, and that it is more likely erroneous than physically true. That, if I am not mistaken, would be an error."[30]

When Galileo wrote this he had almost certainly seen the letter which Bellarmine had written to Foscarini. Hence he knew that in refusing any compromise he had a mighty battle on his hands. Unquestionably in his mind this was the only honorable course. He knew very well that Bellarmine was mistaken in supposing that Copernicus had considered his own theory to be a mere fiction; hence to defend it as such would be a paltry evasion. Among the notes Galileo wrote for his impending battle we find these words:

"One reads on the verso of the title page of Copernicus's book a certain preface to the reader which is not by the author, as it speaks of him in the third person and is unsigned.[31] There it is blandly stated that Copernicus did not believe his system to be true at all, but only claimed to advance it for the calculation of heavenly motions, and finished his reasoning by concluding that it would be foolish to take his theory as real and true. This conclusion is so positively stated that anyone who did not read further, and thought this to have been put there with the author's consent, might well be excused for his mistake. But what value can we place on the opinion of a person who would judge a book by reading no more than a brief preface of the printer and bookseller? I leave this to everyone to judge for himself; and I say that this preface can be nothing but a word from the bookseller to assist the vending of the work, which would have been considered a monstrous chimera by people in general if it had not been qualified in some such way—and generally the buyer reads no more than such a preface before purchasing a book. And that this preface was not only not written by the author, but that it was

[30] *Opere* xii, 183–85.

[31] Kepler had revealed at the beginning of his *Astronomia Nova* that in his own copy of Copernicus's book there was a note, written by Jerome Schreiber of Nuremberg, stating that this preface had been inserted by Andreas Osiander (a Protestant theologian who had supervised the printing) for reasons similar to those set forth here by Galileo.

placed there without his knowledge, to say nothing of his consent, is made manifest by the misuse of certain terms in it which the author would never have permitted."

Elsewhere in these notes there is a point-by-point reply to Bellarmine's written opinion. It has the appearance of something intended to be sent to Foscarini for use in the revision and amplification of his book, though its precise date or purpose is not known. In substance it reads as follows:

"1. Copernicus assumes eccentrics and epicycles; not these, but other absurdities, were his reason for rejecting the Ptolemaic system.

"2. As to philosophers, if they are true philosophers (that is, lovers of truth), they should not be irritated; but, finding out that they have been mistaken, they must thank whoever shows them the truth. And if their opinion is able to stand up, they will have cause to be proud and not angry. Nor should theologians be irritated; for finding such an opinion false, they might freely prohibit it, or discovering it to be true they should be glad that others have opened the road to the discovery of the true sense of the Bible, and have kept them from rushing into a grave predicament by condemning a true proposition.

"As to rendering the Bible false, that is not and never will be the intention of Catholic astronomers such as I am; rather, our opinion is that the Scriptures accord perfectly with demonstrated physical truth. But let those theologians who are not astronomers guard against rendering the Scriptures false by trying to interpret against it propositions which may be true and might be proved so.

"3. It may be that we will have difficulties in expounding the Scriptures, and so on; but this is through our ignorance, and not because there really are, or can be, insuperable difficulties in bringing them into accordance with demonstrated truth.

"4. . . . It is much more a matter of faith to believe that Abraham had sons than that the earth moves. . . . For since there have always been men who have had two sons, or four, or six, or none . . . there would be no reason for the Bible to affirm in such matters anything contrary to truth.

. . . But this is not so with the mobility of the earth, that being a proposition far beyond the comprehension of the common people. . . .

"5. As to placing the sun in the sky and the earth outside it, as the Scriptures seem to affirm, etc., this truly seems to me to be simply . . . speaking according to common sense; for really everything surrounded by the sky is in the sky. . . .

"6. Not to believe that a proof of the earth's motion exists until one has been shown is very prudent, nor do we demand that anyone believe such a thing without proof. Indeed, we seek, for the good of the holy Church, that everything the followers of this doctrine can set forth be examined with the greatest rigor, and that nothing be admitted unless it far outweighs the rival arguments. If these men are only ninety per cent right, then they are defeated; but when nearly everything the philosophers and astronomers say on the other side is proved to be quite false, and all of it inconsequential, then this side should not be deprecated or called paradoxical simply because it cannot be completely proved. . . .

"7. It is true that to prove that the appearances may be saved with the motion of the earth . . . is not the same as to prove this theory true in nature; but it is equally true, or even more so, that the commonly accepted system cannot give reasons for those appearances. That system is undoubtedly false, just as . . . this one may be true. And no greater truth may or should be sought in a theory than that it corresponds with all the particular appearances.

"8. No one asks that in case of doubt the teachings of the Fathers be abandoned, but only that the attempt be made to gain certainty in the matter questioned. . . .

"9. We believe that Solomon and Moses and all the other holy writers knew the constitution of the universe perfectly well, as they also knew that God did not have hands or feet or wrath or prevarication or regret. We cast no doubt on this, but we say that . . . the Holy Ghost spoke thus for the reasons set forth.

"10. The mistake about the apparent motion of the beach and stability of the ship is known to us after we have frequently stood on the beach and observed the motion of the boat, as well as in the boat to observe the beach. And if we could stand thus now on the earth and again on the sun or some other star, we might gain positive and sensory knowledge as to which moved. Yet looking only from these two bodies, it would always appear that the one we were on stood still, just as to a man who saw only the boat and the water, the water would always seem to run and the boat to stand still. . . . It would be better to compare two ships, of which the one we are on will absolutely seem to stand still whenever we can make no other comparison than between the two ships. . . .

"Besides, neither Copernicus nor his followers make use of this appearance of the beach and the ship to prove that the earth moves and the sun stands still. They use it only as an example that serves to show . . . the lack of contradiction between the simple sense-appearance of a stable earth and a moving sun if the reverse were really true. For if nothing better than this were Copernicus's proof, I believe no one would endorse him."[32]

To accept the compromise would not have been an honest course for Galileo. Apart from the Copernican system itself, a precedent was to be established in the relation of religion to the new sciences of observation and experiment. Galileo knew better what this implied than did either his opponents or the authorities responsible for making the decision. Hence as soon as his health permitted, he requested permission to go again to Rome in order to justify himself against attacks upon certain of his works. The Grand Duke's ambassador at Rome warned that this was no time for Galileo to appear there, and that Bellarmine himself advised against it. But Galileo had made his decision, and the Grand Duke supported him. On December 11,

[32] *Opere* v, 367–70.

1615, the ambassador announced his arrival in the Eternal City. The battle was on. Galileo's side of it is eloquently stated in the *Letter to the Grand Duchess Christina*.[33]

[33] The *Letter to Christina* was not printed until many years later, for reasons which will soon become apparent. After the condemnation of Galileo in 1633 a translation of his *Dialogue* into Latin was undertaken by Matthias Bernegger in Germany, and Bernegger planned to include the *Letter* done into Latin. This translation, however, was left to Elia Diodati in France, and it did not arrive in time to be printed and bound with the Latin version of the *Dialogue*, which appeared at Strasbourg in 1635. Hence the *Letter* was published separately there the following year, with the Italian and Latin texts on facing pages. The edition was small and the book was rigorously suppressed in Catholic countries.

LETTER

TO

MADAME CHRISTINA OF LORRAINE
GRAND DUCHESS OF TUSCANY

Concerning the Use of Biblical Quotations
in Matters of Science

[1615]

GALILEO GALILEI
TO
THE MOST SERENE
GRAND DUCHESS MOTHER:

Some years ago, as Your Serene Highness well knows, I discovered in the heavens many things that had not been seen before our own age. The novelty of these things, as well as some consequences which followed from them in contradiction to the physical notions commonly held among academic philosophers, stirred up against me no small number of professors—as if I had placed these things in the sky with my own hands in order to upset nature and overturn the sciences. They seemed to forget that the increase of known truths stimulates the investigation, establishment, and growth of the arts; not their diminution or destruction.

Showing a greater fondness for their own opinions than for truth, they sought to deny and disprove the new things which, if they had cared to look for themselves, their own senses would have demonstrated to them. To this end they hurled various charges and published numerous writings filled with vain arguments, and they made the grave mistake of sprinkling these with passages taken from places in the Bible which they had failed to understand properly, and which were ill suited to their purposes.

These men would perhaps not have fallen into such error had they but paid attention to a most useful doctrine of St. Augustine's, relative to our making positive statements about things which are obscure and hard to understand by means of reason alone. Speaking of a certain physical conclusion about the heavenly bodies, he wrote: "Now keeping always our respect for moderation in grave piety, we ought not to believe anything inadvisedly on a dubious point, lest in favor to our error we conceive a prejudice against something that truth hereafter may reveal to be not contrary in any way to the sacred books of either the Old or the New Testament."[1]

Well, the passage of time has revealed to everyone the truths that I previously set forth; and, together with the truth of the facts, there has come to light the great difference in attitude between those who simply and dispassionately refused to admit the discoveries to be true, and those who combined with their incredulity some reckless passion of their own. Men who were well grounded in astronomical and physical science were persuaded as soon as they received my first message. There were others who denied them or remained in doubt only because of their novel and unexpected character, and because they had not yet had the opportunity to see for themselves. These men have by degrees come to be satisfied. But some, besides allegiance to their original error, possess I know not what fanciful interest in remaining hostile not so much toward the things in question as toward their discoverer. No longer being able to deny them, these men now take refuge in obstinate silence, but being more than ever exasperated by that which has pacified and quieted other men, they divert their thoughts to other fancies and seek new ways to damage me.

I should pay no more attention to them than to those who previously contradicted me—at whom I always laugh, being assured of the eventual outcome—were it not that in their new calumnies and persecutions I perceive that they do not stop at proving themselves more learned than I am (a claim which I scarcely contest), but go so far as to cast against me imputations of crimes which must be, and are, more abhorrent to me than death itself. I cannot remain satisfied merely to know that the injustice of this is recognized by those who are acquainted with these men and with me, as perhaps it is not known to others.

[1] *De Genesi ad literam,* end of bk. ii. (Citations of theological works are taken from Galileo's marginal notes, without verification.)

Persisting in their original resolve to destroy me and everything mine by any means they can think of, these men are aware of my views in astronomy and philosophy. They know that as to the arrangement of the parts of the universe, I hold the sun to be situated motionless in the center of the revolution of the celestial orbs while the earth rotates on its axis and revolves about the sun. They know also that I support this position not only by refuting the arguments of Ptolemy and Aristotle, but by producing many counterarguments; in particular, some which relate to physical effects whose causes can perhaps be assigned in no other way. In addition there are astronomical arguments derived from many things in my new celestial discoveries that plainly confute the Ptolemaic system while admirably agreeing with and confirming the contrary hypothesis. Possibly because they are disturbed by the known truth of other propositions of mine which differ from those commonly held, and therefore mistrusting their defense so long as they confine themselves to the field of philosophy, these men have resolved to fabricate a shield for their fallacies out of the mantle of pretended religion and the authority of the Bible. These they apply, with little judgment, to the refutation of arguments that they do not understand and have not even listened to.

First they have endeavored to spread the opinion that such propositions in general are contrary to the Bible and are consequently damnable and heretical. They know that it is human nature to take up causes whereby a man may oppress his neighbor, no matter how unjustly, rather than those from which a man may receive some just encouragement. Hence they have had no trouble in finding men who would preach the damnability and heresy of the new doctrine from their very pulpits with unwonted confidence, thus doing impious and inconsiderate injury not only to that doctrine and its followers but to all mathematics and mathematicians in general. Next, becoming bolder, and hoping (though vainly) that this seed which first took root in their hypocritical minds would send out branches and ascend to heaven, they began scattering rumors among the people that before long this doctrine would be condemned by the supreme authority. They know, too, that official condemnation would not only suppress the two propositions which I have mentioned, but would render damnable all other astronomical and physical statements and observations that have any necessary relation or connection with these.

In order to facilitate their designs, they seek so far as possible (at least among the common people) to make this opinion seem new and to belong to me alone. They pretend not to know that its author, or rather its restorer and confirmer, was Nicholas Copernicus; and that he was not only a Catholic, but a priest and a canon. He was in fact so esteemed by the church that when the Lateran Council under Leo X took up the correction of the church calendar, Copernicus was called to Rome from the most remote parts of Germany to undertake its reform. At that time the calendar was defective because the true measures of the year and the lunar month were not exactly known. The Bishop of Culm,[2] then superintendent of this matter, assigned Copernicus to seek more light and greater certainty concerning the celestial motions by means of constant study and labor. With Herculean toil he set his admirable mind to this task, and he made such great progress in this science and brought our knowledge of the heavenly motions to such precision that he became celebrated as an astronomer. Since that time not only has the calendar been regulated by his teachings, but tables of all the motions of the planets have been calculated as well.

Having reduced his system into six books, he published these at the instance of the Cardinal of Capua[3] and the Bishop of Culm. And since he had assumed his laborious enterprise by order of the supreme pontiff, he dedicated this book *On the celestial revolutions* to Pope Paul III. When printed, the book was accepted by the holy Church, and it has been read and studied by everyone without the

[2] Tiedmann Giese, to whom Copernicus referred in his preface as "that scholar, my good friend."

[3] Nicholas Schoenberg, spoken of by Copernicus as "celebrated in all fields of scholarship."

faintest hint of any objection ever being conceived against its doctrines. Yet now that manifest experiences and necessary proofs have shown them to be well grounded, persons exist who would strip the author of his reward without so much as looking at his book, and add the shame of having him pronounced a heretic. All this they would do merely to satisfy their personal displeasure conceived without any cause against another man, who has no interest in Copernicus beyond approving his teachings.

Now as to the false aspersions which they so unjustly seek to cast upon me, I have thought it necessary to justify myself in the eyes of all men, whose judgment in matters of religion and of reputation I must hold in great esteem. I shall therefore discourse of the particulars which these men produce to make this opinion detested and to have it condemned not merely as false but as heretical. To this end they make a shield of their hypocritical zeal for religion. They go about invoking the Bible, which they would have minister to their deceitful purposes. Contrary to the sense of the Bible and the intention of the holy Fathers, if I am not mistaken, they would extend such authorities until even in purely physical matters—where faith is not involved—they would have us altogether abandon reason and the evidence of our senses in favor of some biblical passage, though under the surface meaning of its words this passage may contain a different sense.

I hope to show that I proceed with much greater piety than they do, when I argue not against condemning this book, but against condemning it in the way they suggest—that is, without understanding it, weighing it, or so much as reading it. For Copernicus never discusses matters of religion or faith, nor does he use arguments that depend in any way upon the authority of sacred writings which he might have interpreted erroneously. He stands always upon physical conclusions pertaining to the celestial motions, and deals with them by astronomical and geometrical demonstrations, founded primarily upon sense experiences and very exact observations. He did not ignore the Bible, but he knew very well that if his doctrine were proved, then it could not contradict the Scriptures when they were rightly understood. And thus at the end of his letter of dedication, addressing the pope, he said:

"If there should chance to be any exegetes ignorant of mathematics who pretend to skill in that discipline, and dare to condemn and censure this hypothesis of mine upon the authority of some scriptural passage twisted to their purpose, I value them not, but disdain their unconsidered judgment. For it is known that Lactantius—a poor mathematician though in other respects a worthy author—writes very childishly about the shape of the earth when he scoffs at those who affirm it to be a globe. Hence it should not seem strange to the ingenious if people of that sort should in turn deride me. But mathematics is written for mathematicians, by whom, if I am not deceived, these labors of mine will be recognized as contributing something to their domain, as also to that of the Church over which Your Holiness now reigns."[4]

Such are the people who labor to persuade us that an author like Copernicus may be condemned without being read, and who produce various authorities from the Bible, from theologians, and from Church Councils to make us believe that this is not only lawful but commendable. Since I hold these to be of supreme authority, I consider it rank temerity for anyone to contradict them—when employed according to the usage of the holy Church. Yet I do not believe it is wrong to speak out when there is reason to suspect that other men wish, for some personal motive, to produce and employ such authorities for purposes quite different from the sacred intention of the holy Church.

Therefore I declare (and my sincerity will make itself manifest) not only that I mean to submit myself freely and renounce any errors into which I may fall in this discourse through ignorance of matters pertaining to religion, but that I do not desire in these matters to engage in disputes with anyone, even on points that are disputable. My goal is this alone; that if, among errors that may abound in these con-

---

[4] *De Revolutionibus* (Nuremberg, 1543), f. iiii.

siderations of a subject remote from my profession, there is anything that may be serviceable to the holy Church in making a decision concerning the Copernican system, it may be taken and utilized as seems best to the superiors. And if not, let my book be torn and burnt, as I neither intend nor pretend to gain from it any fruit that is not pious and Catholic. And though many of the things I shall reprove have been heard by my own ears, I shall freely grant to those who have spoken them that they never said them, if that is what they wish, and I shall confess myself to have been mistaken. Hence let whatever I reply be addressed not to them, but to whoever may have held such opinions.

The reason produced for condemning the opinion that the earth moves and the sun stands still is that in many places in the Bible one may read that the sun moves and the earth stands still. Since the Bible cannot err, it follows as a necessary consequence that anyone takes an erroneous and heretical position who maintains that the sun is inherently motionless and the earth movable.

With regard to this argument, I think in the first place that it is very pious to say and prudent to affirm that the holy Bible can never speak untruth—whenever its true meaning is understood. But I believe nobody will deny that it is often very abstruse, and may say things which are quite different from what its bare words signify. Hence in expounding the Bible if one were always to confine oneself to the unadorned grammatical meaning, one might fall into error. Not only contradictions and propositions far from true might thus be made to appear in the Bible, but even grave heresies and follies. Thus it would be necessary to assign to God feet, hands, and eyes, as well as corporeal and human affections, such as anger, repentance, hatred, and sometimes even the forgetting of things past and ignorance of those to come. These propositions uttered by the Holy Ghost were set down in that manner by the sacred scribes in order to accommodate them to the capacities of the common people, who are rude and unlearned. For the sake of those who deserve to be separated from the herd, it is necessary that wise expositors should produce the true senses of such passages, together with the special reasons for which they were set down in these words. This doctrine is so widespread and so definite with all theologians that it would be superfluous to adduce evidence for it.

Hence I think that I may reasonably conclude that whenever the Bible has occasion to speak of any physical conclusion (especially those which are very abstruse and hard to understand), the rule has been observed of avoiding confusion in the minds of the common people which would render them contumacious toward the higher mysteries. Now the Bible, merely to condescend to popular capacity, has not hesitated to obscure some very important pronouncements, attributing to God himself some qualities extremely remote from (and even contrary to) His essence. Who, then, would positively declare that this principle has been set aside, and the Bible has confined itself rigorously to the bare and restricted sense of its words, when speaking but casually of the earth, of water, of the sun, or of any other created thing? Especially in view of the fact that these things in no way concern the primary purpose of the sacred writings, which is the service of God and the salvation of souls—matters infinitely beyond the comprehension of the common people.

This being granted, I think that in discussions of physical problems we ought to begin not from the authority of scriptural passages, but from sense-experiences and necessary demonstrations; for the holy Bible and the phenomena of nature proceed alike from the divine Word, the former as the dictate of the Holy Ghost and the latter as the observant executrix of God's commands. It is necessary for the Bible, in order to be accommodated to the understanding of every man, to speak many things which appear to differ from the absolute truth so far as the bare meaning of the words is concerned. But Nature, on the other hand, is inexorable and immutable; she never transgresses the laws imposed upon her, or cares a whit whether her abstruse reasons and methods of operation are understandable to men. For that reason it appears that nothing physical which sense-experience sets before our eyes, or which necessary demonstrations prove to us, ought to be called in question (much less condemned) upon the testimony of biblical passages which may have some different meaning beneath their words. For the Bible is not chained in every expression to conditions as strict as those which govern all physical effects; nor is God any less excellently revealed in Nature's actions than in the sacred statements of the Bible. Perhaps this is what Tertullian meant by these words:

"We conclude that God is known first through Nature, and then again, more particularly, by doctrine; by Nature in His works, and by doctrine in His revealed word."[5]

From this I do not mean to infer that we need not have an extraordinary esteem for the passages of holy Scripture. On the contrary, having arrived at any certainties in physics, we ought to utilize these as the most appropriate aids in the true exposition of the Bible and in the investigation of those meanings which are necessarily contained therein, for these must be concordant with demonstrated truths. I should judge that the authority of the Bible was designed to persuade men of those articles and propositions which, surpassing all human reasoning, could not be made credible by science, or by any other means than through the very mouth of the Holy Spirit.

Yet even in those propositions which are not matters of faith, this authority ought to be preferred over that of all human writings which are supported only by bare assertions or probable arguments, and not set forth in a demonstrative way. This I hold to be necessary and proper to the same extent that divine wisdom surpasses all human judgment and conjecture.

But I do not feel obliged to believe that that same God who has endowed us with senses, reason, and intellect has intended to forgo their use and by some other means to give us knowledge which we can attain by them. He would not require us to deny sense and reason in physical matters which are set before our eyes and minds by direct experi-

[5] *Adversus Marcionem,* ii, 18.

ence or necessary demonstrations. This must be especially true in those sciences of which but the faintest trace (and that consisting of conclusions) is to be found in the Bible. Of astronomy, for instance, so little is found that none of the planets except Venus are so much as mentioned, and this only once or twice under the name of "Lucifer." If the sacred scribes had had any intention of teaching people certain arrangements and motions of the heavenly bodies, or had they wished us to derive such knowledge from the Bible, then in my opinion they would not have spoken of these matters so sparingly in comparison with the infinite number of admirable conclusions which are demonstrated in that science. Far from pretending to teach us the constitution and motions of the heavens and the stars, with their shapes, magnitudes, and distances, the authors of the Bible intentionally forbore to speak of these things, though all were quite well known to them. Such is the opinion of the holiest and most learned Fathers, and in St. Augustine we find the following words:

"It is likewise commonly asked what we may believe about the form and shape of the heavens according to the Scriptures, for many contend much about these matters. But with superior prudence our authors have forborne to speak of this, as in no way furthering the student with respect to a blessed life—and, more important still, as taking up much of that time which should be spent in holy exercises. What is it to me whether heaven, like a sphere, surrounds the earth on all sides as a mass balanced in the center of the universe, or whether like a dish it merely covers and overcasts the earth? Belief in Scripture is urged rather for the reason we have often mentioned; that is, in order that no one, through ignorance of divine passages, finding anything in our Bibles or hearing anything cited from them of such a nature as may seem to oppose manifest conclusions, should be induced to suspect their truth when they teach, relate, and deliver more profitable matters. Hence let it be said briefly, touching the form of heaven, that our authors knew the truth but the Holy Spirit did not desire that men should learn things that are useful to no one for salvation."[6]

The same disregard of these sacred authors toward beliefs about the phenomena of the celestial bodies is repeated to us by St. Augustine in his next chapter. On the question whether we are to believe that the heaven moves or stands still, he writes thus:

"Some of the brethren raise a question concerning the motion of heaven, whether it is fixed or moved. If it is moved, they say, how is it a firmament? If it stands still, how do these stars which are held fixed in it go round from east to west, the more northerly performing shorter circuits near the pole, so that heaven (if there is another pole unknown to us) may seem to revolve upon some axis, or (if there is no other pole) may be thought to move as a discus? To these men I reply that it would require many subtle and profound reasonings to find out which of these things is actually so; but to undertake this and discuss it is consistent neither with my leisure nor with the duty of those whom I desire to instruct in essential matters more directly conducing to their salvation and to the benefit of the holy Church."[7]

From these things it follows as a necessary consequence that, since the Holy Ghost did not intend to teach us whether heaven moves or stands still, whether its shape is spherical or like a discus or extended in a plane, nor whether the earth is located at its center or off to one side, then so much the less was it intended to settle for us any other conclusion of the same kind. And the motion or rest of the earth and the sun is so closely linked with the things just named, that without a determination of the one, neither side can be taken in the other matters. Now if the Holy Spirit has purposely neglected to teach us propositions of this sort as irrelevant to the highest goal (that is, to our salvation), how can anyone affirm that it is obligatory to take sides on them, and that one belief is required by faith, while the other side is erroneous? Can an opinion be heretical and yet

[6] *De Genesi ad literam* ii, 9. Galileo has noted also: "The same is to be read in Peter the Lombard, master of opinions."
[7] *Ibid.*, ii, 10.

have no concern with the salvation of souls? Can the Holy
Ghost be asserted not to have intended teaching us something that does concern our salvation? I would say here
something that was heard from an ecclesiastic of the most
eminent degree: "That the intention of the Holy Ghost is
to teach us how one goes to heaven, not how heaven
goes."[8]

But let us again consider the degree to which necessary
demonstrations and sense experiences ought to be respected
in physical conclusions, and the authority they have enjoyed
at the hands of holy and learned theologians. From among
a hundred attestations I have selected the following:

"We must also take heed, in handling the doctrine of
Moses, that we altogether avoid saying positively and confidently anything which contradicts manifest experiences
and the reasoning of philosophy or the other sciences. For
since every truth is in agreement with all other truth, the
truth of Holy Writ cannot be contrary to the solid reasons
and experiences of human knowledge."[9]

And in St. Augustine we read: "If anyone shall set the
authority of Holy Writ against clear and manifest reason,
he who does this knows not what he has undertaken; for
he opposes to the truth not the meaning of the Bible, which
is beyond his comprehension, but rather his own interpretation; not what is in the Bible, but what he has found in
himself and imagines to be there."[10]

This granted, and it being true that two truths cannot
contradict one another, it is the function of wise expositors
to seek out the true senses of scriptural texts. These will unquestionably accord with the physical conclusions which
manifest sense and necessary demonstrations have previously made certain to us. Now the Bible, as has been re-
marked, admits in many places expositions that are remote

[8] A marginal note by Galileo assigns this epigram to Cardinal Baronius (1538–1607). Baronius visited Padua with
Cardinal Bellarmine in 1598, and Galileo probably met him
at that time.

[9] Pererius on Genesis, near the beginning.

[10] In the seventh letter to Marcellinus.

from the signification of the words for reasons we have already given. Moreover, we are unable to affirm that all interpreters of the Bible speak by divine inspiration, for if that were so there would exist no differences between them about the sense of a given passage. Hence I should think it would be the part of prudence not to permit anyone to usurp scriptural texts and force them in some way to maintain any physical conclusion to be true, when at some future time the senses and demonstrative or necessary reasons may show the contrary. Who indeed will set bounds to human ingenuity? Who will assert that everything in the universe capable of being perceived is already discovered and known? Let us rather confess quite truly that "Those truths which we know are very few in comparison with those which we do not know."

We have it from the very mouth of the Holy Ghost that God delivered up the world to disputations, *so that man cannot find out the work that God hath done from the beginning even to the end.*[11] In my opinion no one, in contradiction to that dictum, should close the road to free philosophizing about mundane and physical things, as if everything had already been discovered and revealed with certainty. Nor should it be considered rash not to be satisfied with those opinions which have become common. No one should be scorned in physical disputes for not holding to the opinions which happen to please other people best, especially concerning problems which have been debated among the greatest philosophers for thousands of years. One of these is the stability of the sun and mobility of the earth, a doctrine believed by Pythagoras and all his followers, by Heracleides of Pontus[12] (who was one of them),

---

[11] Ecclesiastes 3:11.
[12] Heracleides was born about 390 B.C. and is said to have attended lectures by Aristotle at Athens. He believed that the earth rotated on its axis, but not that it moved around the sun. He also discovered that Mercury and Venus revolve around the sun, and may have developed a system similar to that of Tycho.

by Philolaus the teacher of Plato,[13] and by Plato himself according to Aristotle. Plutarch writes in his *Life of Numa* that Plato, when he had grown old, said it was most absurd to believe otherwise.[14] The same doctrine was held by Aristarchus of Samos,[15] as Archimedes tells us; by Seleucus[16] the mathematician, by Nicetas[17] the philosopher (on the testimony of Cicero), and by many others. Finally this opinion has been amplified and confirmed with many observations and demonstrations by Nicholas Copernicus. And Seneca,[18] a most eminent philosopher, advises us in his book on comets that we should more diligently seek to ascertain whether it is in the sky or in the earth that the diurnal rotation resides.

Hence it would probably be wise and useful counsel if, beyond articles which concern salvation and the establish-

[13] Philolaus, an early follower of Pythagoras, flourished at Thebes toward the end of the fifth century B.C. Although a contemporary of Socrates, the teacher of Plato, he had nothing to do with Plato's instruction. According to Philolaus the earth revolved around a central fire, but not about the sun (cf. note 7, p. 34).

[14] "Plato held opinion in that age, that the earth was in another place than in the very middest, and that the centre of the world, as the most honourable place, did appertain to some other of more worthy substance than the earth." (Trans. Sir Thomas North.) This tradition is no longer accepted.

[15] Aristarchus (ca. 310–230 B.C.) was the true forerunner of Copernicus in antiquity, and not the Pythagoreans as was generally believed in Galileo's time.

[16] Seleucus, who flourished about 150 B.C., is the only ancient astronomer known to have adopted the heliocentric system of Aristarchus. After his time this gave way entirely to the system founded by his contemporary Hipparchus.

[17] Nicetas is an incorrect form given by Copernicus to the name of Hicetas of Syracuse. Of this mathematician nothing is known beyond the fact that some of the ancients credited him instead of Philolaus with the astronomy which came to be associated with the Pythagoreans in general.

[18] Seneca (ca. 3–65 A.D.) was the tutor of Nero. He devoted the seventh book of his *Quaestiones Naturales* to comets. In the second chapter of this book he raised the question of the earth's rotation, and in the final chapters he appealed for patience and further investigation into such matters.

ment of our Faith, against the stability of which there is no
danger whatever that any valid and effective doctrine can
ever arise, men would not aggregate further articles unnec-
essarily. And it would certainly be preposterous to introduce
them at the request of persons who, besides not being
known to speak by inspiration of divine grace, are clearly
seen to lack that understanding which is necessary in order
to comprehend, let alone discuss, the demonstrations by
which such conclusions are supported in the subtler sciences. If I may speak my opinion freely, I should say further
that it would perhaps fit in better with the decorum and
majesty of the sacred writings to take measures for preventing every shallow and vulgar writer from giving to his
compositions (often grounded upon foolish fancies) an air
of authority by inserting in them passages from the Bible,
interpreted (or rather distorted) into senses as far from the
right meaning of Scripture as those authors are near to
absurdity who thus ostentatiously adorn their writings. Of
such abuses many examples might be produced, but for the
present I shall confine myself to two which are germane to
these astronomical matters. The first concerns those writings which were published against the existence of the
Medicean planets recently discovered by me, in which
many passages of holy Scripture were cited.[19] Now that
everyone has seen these planets, I should like to know
what new interpretations those same antagonists employ
in expounding the Scripture and excusing their own sim-

---

[19] The principal book which had offended in this regard
was the *Dianoia Astronomica* . . . of Francesco Sizzi (Venice,
1611). About the time Galileo arrived at Florence, Sizzi departed for France, where he came into association with some
good mathematicians. In 1613 he wrote to a friend at Rome
to express his admiration of Galileo's work on floating bodies
and to deride its opponents. The letter was forwarded to
Galileo. In it Sizzi had reported, though rather cryptically,
upon some French observations concerning sunspots, and it
was probably this which led Galileo to his knowledge of the
tilt of the sun's axis (cf. note 14, p. 125). Sizzi was broken
on the wheel in 1617 for writing a pamphlet against the king
of France.

plicity. My other example is that of a man who has lately published, in defiance of astronomers and philosophers, the opinion that the moon does not receive its light from the sun but is brilliant by its own nature.[20] He supports this fancy (or rather thinks he does) by sundry texts of Scripture which he believes cannot be explained unless his theory is true; yet that the moon is inherently dark is surely as plain as daylight.

It is obvious that such authors, not having penetrated the true senses of Scripture, would impose upon others an obligation to subscribe to conclusions that are repugnant to manifest reason and sense, if they had any authority to do so. God forbid that this sort of abuse should gain countenance and authority, for then in a short time it would be necessary to proscribe all the contemplative sciences. People who are unable to understand perfectly both the Bible and the sciences far outnumber those who do understand. The former, glancing superficially through the Bible, would arrogate to themselves the authority to decree upon every question of physics on the strength of some word which they have misunderstood, and which was employed by the sacred authors for some different purpose. And the smaller number of understanding men could not dam up the furious torrent of such people, who would gain the majority of followers simply because it is much more pleasant to gain a reputation for wisdom without effort or study than to consume oneself tirelessly in the most laborious disciplines. Let us therefore render thanks to Almighty God, who in His beneficence protects us from this danger by depriving such persons of all authority, reposing the power of consultation, decision, and decree on such important matters in the high wisdom and benevolence of most prudent

[20] This is frequently said to refer to J. C. Lagalla's *De phaenominis in orbe lunae* . . . (Venice, 1612), a wretched book which has the sole distinction of being the first to mention the word "telescope" in print. A more probable reference, however, seems to be to the *Dialogo di Fr. Ulisse Albergotti . . . nel quale si tiene . . . la Luna esser da sé luminosa . . .* (Viterbo, 1613).

Fathers, and in the supreme authority of those who cannot fail to order matters properly under the guidance of the Holy Ghost. Hence we need not concern ourselves with the shallowness of those men whom grave and holy authors rightly reproach, and of whom in particular St. Jerome said, in reference to the Bible:

"This is ventured upon, lacerated, and taught by the garrulous old woman, the doting old man, and the prattling sophist before they have learned it. Others, led on by pride, weigh heavy words and philosophize amongst women concerning holy Scripture. Others—oh, shame!—learn from women what they teach to men, and (as if that were not enough) glibly expound to others that which they themselves do not understand. I forbear to speak of those of my own profession who, attaining a knowledge of the holy Scriptures after mundane learning, tickle the ears of the people with affected and studied expressions, and declare that everything they say is to be taken as the law of God. Not bothering to learn what the prophets and the apostles have maintained, they wrest incongruous testimonies into their own senses—as if distorting passages and twisting the Bible to their individual and contradictory whims were the genuine way of teaching, and not a corrupt one."[21]

I do not wish to place in the number of such lay writers some theologians whom I consider men of profound learning and devout behavior, and who are therefore held by me in great esteem and veneration. Yet I cannot deny that I feel some discomfort which I should like to have removed, when I hear them pretend to the power of constraining others by scriptural authority to follow in a physical dispute that opinion which they think best agrees with the Bible, and then believe themselves not bound to answer the opposing reasons and experiences. In explanation and support of this opinion they say that since theology is queen of all the sciences, she need not bend in any way to accommodate herself to the teachings of less worthy sciences which are subordinate to her; these others must rather be referred to

[21] *Epistola ad Paulinum*, 103.

her as to their supreme empress, changing and altering their conclusions according to her statutes and decrees. They add further that if in the inferior sciences any conclusion should be taken as certain in virtue of demonstrations or experiences, while in the Bible another conclusion is found repugnant to this, then the professors of that science should themselves undertake to undo their proofs and discover the fallacies in their own experiences, without bothering the theologians and exegetes. For, they say, it does not become the dignity of theology to stoop to the investigation of fallacies in the subordinate sciences; it is sufficient for her merely to determine the truth of a given conclusion with absolute authority, secure in her inability to err.

Now the physical conclusions in which they say we ought to be satisfied by Scripture, without glossing or expounding it in senses different from the literal, are those concerning which the Bible always speaks in the same manner and which the holy Fathers all receive and expound in the same way. But with regard to these judgments I have had occasion to consider several things, and I shall set them forth in order that I may be corrected by those who understand more than I do in these matters—for to their decisions I submit at all times.

First, I question whether there is not some equivocation in failing to specify the virtues which entitle sacred theology to the title of "queen." It might deserve that name by reason of including everything that is learned from all the other sciences and establishing everything by better methods and with profounder learning. It is thus, for example, that the rules for measuring fields and keeping accounts are much more excellently contained in arithmetic and in the geometry of Euclid than in the practices of surveyors and accountants. Or theology might be queen because of being occupied with a subject which excels in dignity all the subjects which compose the other sciences, and because her teachings are divulged in more sublime ways.

That the title and authority of queen belongs to theology in the first sense, I think will not be affirmed by theologians who have any skill in the other sciences. None of these, I think, will say that geometry, astronomy, music, and medicine are much more excellently contained in the Bible than they are in the books of Archimedes, Ptolemy, Boethius, and Galen. Hence it seems likely that regal pre-eminence is given to theology in the second sense; that is, by reason of its subject and the miraculous communication of divine revelation of conclusions which could not be conceived by men in any other way, concerning chiefly the attainment of eternal blessedness.

Let us grant then that theology is conversant with the loftiest divine contemplation, and occupies the regal throne among sciences by dignity. But acquiring the highest authority in this way, if she does not descend to the lower and humbler speculations of the subordinate sciences and has no regard for them because they are not concerned with blessedness, then her professors should not arrogate to themselves the authority to decide on controversies in professions which they have neither studied nor practiced. Why, this would be as if an absolute despot, being neither a physician nor an architect but knowing himself free to command, should undertake to administer medicines and erect buildings according to his whim—at grave peril of his poor patients' lives, and the speedy collapse of his edifices.

Again, to command that the very professors of astronomy themselves see to the refutation of their own observations and proofs as mere fallacies and sophisms is to enjoin something that lies beyond any possibility of accomplishment. For this would amount to commanding that they must not see what they see and must not understand what they know, and that in searching they must find the opposite of what they actually encounter. Before this could be done they would have to be taught how to make one mental faculty command another, and the inferior powers the superior, so that the imagination and the will might be forced to believe the opposite of what the intellect understands. I am referring at all times to merely physical propositions, and not to supernatural things which are matters of faith.

I entreat those wise and prudent Fathers to consider with

great care the difference that exists between doctrines subject to proof and those subject to opinion. Considering the force exerted by logical deductions, they may ascertain that it is not in the power of the professors of demonstrative sciences to change their opinions at will and apply themselves first to one side and then to the other. There is a great difference between commanding a mathematician or a philosopher and influencing a lawyer or a merchant, for demonstrated conclusions about things in nature or in the heavens cannot be changed with the same facility as opinions about what is or is not lawful in a contract, bargain, or bill of exchange. This difference was well understood by the learned and holy Fathers, as proven by their having taken great pains in refuting philosophical fallacies. This may be found expressly in some of them; in particular, we find the following words of St. Augustine: "It is to be held as an unquestionable truth that whatever the sages of this world have demonstrated concerning physical matters is in no way contrary to our Bibles; hence whatever the sages teach in their books that is contrary to the holy Scriptures may be concluded without any hesitation to be quite false. And according to our ability let us make this evident, and let us keep the faith of our Lord, in whom are hidden all the treasures of wisdom, so that we neither become seduced by the verbiage of false philosophy nor frightened by the superstition of counterfeit religion."[22]

From the above words I conceive that I may deduce this doctrine: That in the books of the sages of this world there are contained some physical truths which are soundly demonstrated, and others that are merely stated; as to the former, it is the office of wise divines to show that they do not contradict the holy Scriptures. And as to the propositions which are stated but not rigorously demonstrated, anything contrary to the Bible involved by them must be held undoubtedly false and should be proved so by every possible means.

Now if truly demonstrated physical conclusions need not

[22] *De Genesi ad literam* i, 21.

be subordinated to biblical passages, but the latter must rather be shown not to interfere with the former, then before a physical proposition is condemned it must be shown to be not rigorously demonstrated—and this is to be done not by those who hold the proposition to be true, but by those who judge it to be false. This seems very reasonable and natural, for those who believe an argument to be false may much more easily find the fallacies in it than men who consider it to be true and conclusive. Indeed, in the latter case it will happen that the more the adherents of an opinion turn over their pages, examine the arguments, repeat the observations, and compare the experiences, the more they will be confirmed in that belief. And Your Highness knows what happened to the late mathematician of the University of Pisa[23] who undertook in his old age to look into the Copernican doctrine in the hope of shaking its foundations and refuting it, since he considered it false only because he had never studied it. As it fell out, no sooner had he understood its grounds, procedures, and demonstrations than he found himself persuaded, and from an opponent he became a very staunch defender of it. I might also name other mathematicians[24] who, moved by my latest discoveries, have confessed it necessary to alter the previously accepted system of the world, as this is simply unable to subsist any longer.

If in order to banish the opinion in question from the world it were sufficient to stop the mouth of a single man—as perhaps those men persuade themselves who, measuring the minds of others by their own, think it impossible that this doctrine should be able to continue to find adherents—then that would be very easily done. But things stand otherwise. To carry out such a decision it would be necessary not only to prohibit the book of Copernicus and the writings of other authors who follow the same opinion, but to ban the whole science of astronomy. Furthermore, it would be necessary to forbid men to look at the heavens, in order that

[23] Antonio Santucci (d. 1613).
[24] A marginal note by Galileo here mentions Father Clavius; cf. p. 153.

they might not see Mars and Venus sometimes quite near
the earth and sometimes very distant, the variation being
so great that Venus is forty times and Mars sixty times as
large at one time as another. And it would be necessary to
prevent Venus being seen round at one time and forked at
another, with very thin horns; as well as many other sensory observations which can never be reconciled with the
Ptolemaic system in any way, but are very strong arguments for the Copernican. And to ban Copernicus now that
his doctrine is daily reinforced by many new observations
and by the learned applying themselves to the reading of
his book, after this opinion has been allowed and tolerated
for those many years during which it was less followed and
less confirmed, would seem in my judgment to be a con-
travention of truth, and an attempt to hide and supress her
the more as she revealed herself the more clearly and
plainly. Not to abolish and censure his whole book, but only
to condemn as erroneous this particular proposition, would
(if I am not mistaken) be a still greater detriment to the
minds of men, since it would afford them occasion to see
a proposition proved that it was heresy to believe. And to
prohibit the whole science would be but to censure a hundred passages of holy Scripture which teach us that the
glory and greatness of Almighty God are marvelously discerned in all his works and divinely read in the open book
of heaven. For let no one believe that reading the lofty
concepts written in that book leads to nothing further than
the mere seeing of the splendor of the sun and the stars
and their rising and setting, which is as far as the eyes of
brutes and of the vulgar can penetrate. Within its pages
are couched mysteries so profound and concepts so sublime
that the vigils, labors, and studies of hundreds upon hundreds of the most acute minds have still not pierced them,
even after continual investigations for thousands of years.
The eyes of an idiot perceive little by beholding the external appearance of a human body, as compared with the
wonderful contrivances which a careful and practiced anat-
omist or philosopher discovers in that same body when he
seeks out the use of all those muscles, tendons, nerves, and

bones; or when examining the functions of the heart and the other principal organs, he seeks the seat of the vital faculties, notes and observes the admirable structure of the sense organs, and (without ever ceasing in his amazement and delight) contemplates the receptacles of the imagination, the memory, and the understanding. Likewise, that which presents itself to mere sight is as nothing in comparison with the high marvels that the ingenuity of learned men discovers in the heavens by long and accurate observation. And that concludes what I have to say on this matter.

Next let us answer those who assert that those physical propositions of which the Bible speaks always in one way, and which the Fathers all harmoniously accept in the same sense, must be taken according to the literal sense of the words without glosses or interpretations, and held as most certain and true. The motion of the sun and stability of the earth, they say, is of this sort; hence it is a matter of faith to believe in them, and the contrary view is erroneous.

To this I wish first to remark that among physical propositions there are some with regard to which all human science and reason cannot supply more than a plausible opinion and a probable conjecture in place of a sure and demonstrated knowledge; for example, whether the stars are animate. Then there are other propositions of which we have (or may confidently expect) positive assurances through experiments, long observation, and rigorous demonstration; for example, whether or not the earth and the heavens move, and whether or not the heavens are spherical. As to the first sort of propositions, I have no doubt that where human reasoning cannot reach—and where consequently we can have no science but only opinion and faith—it is necessary in piety to comply absolutely with the strict sense of Scripture. But as to the other kind, I should think, as said before, that first we are to make certain of the fact, which will reveal to us the true senses of the Bible, and these will most certainly be found to agree with the proved fact (even though at first the words sounded otherwise), for two truths can never contradict each other. I take this to be an orthodox and indisputable doctrine, and I find it specifically in St. Augustine when he speaks of the shape of heaven and what we may believe concerning that. Astronomers seem to declare what is contrary to Scripture, for they hold the heavens to be spherical, while the Scripture calls it "stretched out like a curtain."[25] St. Augustine opines that we are not to be concerned lest the Bible contradict astronomers; we are to believe its authority if what they say is false and is founded only on the conjectures of frail humanity. But if what they say is proved by unquestionable arguments, this holy Father does not say that the astronomers are to be ordered to dissolve their proofs and declare their own conclusions to be false. Rather, he says it must be demonstrated that what is meant in the Bible by "curtain" is not contrary to their proofs. Here are his words:

"But some raise the following objection. 'How is it that the passage in our Bibles, *Who stretcheth out the heavens as a curtain,* does not contradict those who maintain the heavens to have a spherical shape?' It does contradict them if what they affirm is false, for that is true which is spoken by divine authority rather than that which proceeds from human frailty. But if, peradventure, they should be able to prove their position by experiences which place it beyond question, then it is to be demonstrated that our speaking of a curtain in no way contradicts their manifest reasons."[26]

He then proceeds to admonish us that we must be no less careful and observant in reconciling a passage of the Bible with any demonstrated physical proposition than with some other biblical passage which might appear contrary to the first. The circumspection of this saint indeed deserves admiration and imitation, when even in obscure conclusions (of which we surely can have no knowledge through human proofs) he shows great reserve in determining what is to be believed. We see this from what he writes at the end of the second book of his commentary on Genesis, concerning the question whether the stars are to be believed animate:

[25] Psalms 103:2 (Douay); 104:2 (King James).
[26] *De Genesi ad literam* [ii,] 9.

"Although at present this matter cannot be settled, yet I suppose that in our further dealing with the Bible we may meet with other relevant passages, and then we may be permitted, if not to determine anything finally, at least to gain some hint concerning this matter according to the dictates of sacred authority. Now keeping always our respect for moderation in grave piety, we ought not to believe anything inadvisedly on a dubious point, lest in favor of our error we conceive a prejudice against something that truth hereafter may reveal to be not contrary in any way to the sacred books of either the Old or the New Testament."

From this and other passages the intention of the holy Fathers appears to be (if I am not mistaken) that in questions of nature which are not matters of faith it is first to be considered whether anything is demonstrated beyond doubt or known by sense-experience, or whether such knowledge or proof is possible; if it is, then, being the gift of God, it ought to be applied to find out the true senses of holy Scripture in those passages which superficially might seem to declare differently. These senses would unquestionably be discovered by wise theologians, together with the reasons for which the Holy Ghost sometimes wished to veil itself under words of different meaning, whether for our exercise, or for some purpose unknown to me.

As to the other point, if we consider the primary aim of the Bible, I do not think that its having always spoken in the same sense need disturb this rule. If the Bible, accommodating itself to the capacity of the common people, has on one occasion expressed a proposition in words of different sense from the essence of that proposition, then why might it not have done the same, and for the same reason, whenever the same thing happened to be spoken of? Nay, to me it seems that not to have done this would but have increased confusion and diminished belief among the people.

Regarding the state of rest or motion of the sun and earth, experience plainly proves that in order to accommodate the common people it was necessary to assert of these things precisely what the words of the Bible convey. Even in our own age, people far less primitive continue to maintain the same opinion for reasons which will be found extremely trivial if well weighed and examined, and upon the basis of experiences that are wholly false or altogether beside the point. Nor is it worth while to try to change their opinion, they being unable to understand the arguments on the opposite side, for these depend upon observations too precise and demonstrations too subtle, grounded on abstractions which require too strong an imagination to be comprehended by them. Hence even if the stability of heaven and the motion of the earth should be more than certain in the minds of the wise, it would still be necessary to assert the contrary for the preservation of belief among the all-too-numerous vulgar. Among a thousand ordinary men who might be questioned concerning these things, probably not a single one will be found to answer anything except that it looks to him as if the sun moves and the earth stands still, and therefore he believes this to be certain. But one need not on that account take the common popular assent as an argument for the truth of what is stated; for if we should examine these very men concerning their reasons for what they believe, and on the other hand listen to the experiences and proofs which induce a few others to believe the contrary, we should find the latter to be persuaded by very sound arguments, and the former by simple appearances and vain or ridiculous impressions.

It is sufficiently obvious that to attribute motion to the sun and rest to the earth was therefore necessary lest the shallow minds of the common people should become confused, obstinate, and contumacious in yielding assent to the principal articles that are absolutely matters of faith. And if this was necessary, there is no wonder at all that it was carried out with great prudence in the holy Bible. I shall say further that not only respect for the incapacity of the vulgar, but also current opinion in those times, made the sacred authors accommodate themselves (in matters unnecessary to salvation) more to accepted usage than to the true essence of things. Speaking of this, St. Jerome writes:

"As if many things were not spoken in the Holy Bible according to the judgment of those times in which they were acted, rather than according to the truth contained."[27] And elsewhere the same saint says: "It is the custom for the biblical scribes to deliver their judgments in many things according to the commonly received opinion of their times."[28] And on the words in the twenty-sixth chapter of Job, *He stretcheth out the north over the void, and hangeth the earth above nothing,*[29] St. Thomas Aquinas notes that the Bible calls "void" or "nothing" that space which we know to be not empty, but filled with air. Nevertheless the Bible, he says, in order to accommodate itself to the beliefs of the common people (who think there is nothing in that space), calls it "void" and "nothing." Here are the words of St. Thomas: "What appears to us in the upper hemisphere of the heavens to be empty, and not a space filled with air, the common people regard as void; and it is usually spoken of in the holy Bible according to the ideas of the common people."[30]

Now from this passage I think one may very logically argue that for the same reason the Bible had still more cause to call the sun movable and the earth immovable. For if we were to test the capacity of the common people, we should find them even less apt to be persuaded of the stability of the sun and the motion of the earth than to believe that the space which environs the earth is filled with air. And if on this point it would not have been difficult to convince the common people, and yet the holy scribes forbore to attempt it, then it certainly must appear reasonable that in other and more abstruse propositions they have followed the same policy.

Copernicus himself knew the power over our ideas that is exerted by custom and by our inveterate way of conceiving things since infancy. Hence, in order not to increase for us the confusion and difficulty of abstraction, after he had

[27] On Jeremiah, ch. 28.
[28] On Matthew, ch. 13.
[29] Job 26:7.
[30] Aquinas on Job.

first demonstrated that the motions which appear to us to belong to the sun or to the firmament are really not there but in the earth, he went on calling them motions of the sun and of the heavens when he later constructed his tables to apply them to use. He thus speaks of "sunrise" and "sunset," of the "rising and setting" of the stars, of changes in the obliquity of the ecliptic and of variations in the equinoctial points, of the mean motion and variations in motion of the sun, and so on. All these things really relate to the earth, but since we are fixed to the earth and consequently share in its every motion, we cannot discover them in the earth directly, and are obliged to refer them to the heavenly bodies in which they make their appearance to us. Hence we name them as if they took place where they appear to us to take place; and from this one may see how natural it is to accommodate things to our customary way of seeing them.

Next we come to the proposition that agreement on the part of the Fathers, when they all accept a physical proposition from the Bible in the same sense, must give that sense authority to such a degree that belief in it becomes a matter of faith. I think this should be granted at most only of those propositions which have actually been discussed by the Fathers with great diligence, and debated on both sides, with them all finally concurring in the censure of one side and the adoption of the other. But the motion of the earth and stability of the sun is not an opinion of that kind, inasmuch as it was completely hidden in those times and was far removed from the questions of the schools; it was not even considered, much less adhered to, by anyone. Hence we may believe that it never so much as entered the thoughts of the Fathers to debate this. Bible texts, their own opinions, and the agreement of all men concurred in one belief, without meeting contradiction from anyone. Hence it is not sufficient to say that because all the Fathers admitted the stability of the earth, this is a matter of faith; one would have to prove also that they had condemned the contrary opinion. And I may go on to say that they left this out because they had no occasion to reflect upon the matter and discuss it; their opinion was admitted only as current, and not as analyzed and determined. I think I have very good reason for saying this.

Either the Fathers reflected upon this conclusion as controversial, or they did not; if not, then they cannot have decided anything about it even in their own minds, and their incognizance of it does not oblige us to accept teaching which they never imposed, even in intention. But if they had reflected upon and considered it, and if they judged it to be erroneous, then they would long ago have condemned it; and this they are not found to have done. Indeed, some theologians have but now begun to consider it, and they are not seen to deem it erroneous. Thus in the *Commentaries on Job* of Didacus à Stunica, where the author comments upon the words *Who moveth the earth from its place* . . . ,[31] he discourses at length upon the Copernican opinion and concludes that the mobility of the earth is not contrary to Scripture.

Besides, I question the truth of the statement that the church commands us to hold as matters of faith all physical conclusions bearing the stamp of harmonious interpretation by all the Fathers. I think this may be an arbitrary simplification of various council decrees by certain people to favor their own opinion. So far as I can find, all that is really prohibited is the "perverting into senses contrary to that of the holy Church or that of the concurrent agreement of the Fathers those passages, and those alone, which pertain to faith or ethics, or which concern the edification of Christian doctrine." So said the Council of Trent in its fourth session. But the mobility or stability of the earth or sun is neither a matter of faith nor one contrary to ethics. Neither would anyone pervert passages of Scripture in opposition to the holy Church or to the Fathers, for those who have written on this matter have never employed scriptural passages. Hence it remains the office of grave and wise theologians to interpret the passages according to their true meaning.

[31] Job 9:6. The commentary was that of Didacus à Stunica, published at Toledo in 1584; cf. p. 219.

Council decrees are indeed in agreement with the holy Fathers in these matters, as may be seen from the fact that they abstain from enjoining us to receive physical conclusions as matters of faith, and from censuring the opposite opinions as erroneous. Attending to the primary and original intention of the holy Church, they judge it useless to be occupied in attempting to get to the bottom of such matters. Let me remind Your Highness again of St. Augustine's reply to those brethren who raised the question whether the heavens really move or stand still: "To these men I reply that it would require many subtle and profound reasonings to find out which of these things is actually so; but to undertake this and discuss it is consistent neither with my leisure nor with the duty of those whom I desire to instruct in essential matters more directly conducive to their salvation and to the benefit of the holy Church."[32]

Yet even if we resolved to condemn or admit physical propositions according to scriptural passages uniformly expounded in the same sense by all the Fathers, I still fail to see how that rule can apply in the present case, inasmuch as diverse expositions of the same passage occur among the Fathers. Dionysius the Areopagite says that it is the *primum mobile*[33] which stood still, not the sun.[34] St. Augustine is of the same opinion; that is, that all celestial bodies would be stopped; and the Bishop of Avila concurs.[35] What is

---

[32] Cf. note 6, p. 185.

[33] The outermost crystalline sphere was known as the *primum mobile*, or prime mover, and was supposed to complete each revolution in twenty-four hours, causing night and day. A part of its motion was imagined to be transmitted to each inner sphere, sweeping along the fixed stars and the planets (which included the sun and moon) at nearly its own speed. The inherent motion of the other spheres was supposed to be eastward at much slower rates. In the case of the sun, this speed would have the same proportion to that of the *primum mobile* as a day has to a year.

[34] In the *Epistola ad Polycarpum*.

[35] In the second book of St. Augustine's *De Mirabilius Sacrae Scripturae*. The Bishop of Avila referred to was Alfonso

more, among the Jewish authors endorsed by Josephus,[36] some held that the sun did not really stand still, but that it merely appeared to do so by reason of the shortness of the time during which the Israelites administered defeat to their enemies. (Similarly, with regard to the miracle in the time of Hezekiah, Paul of Burgos was of the opinion that this took place not in the sun but on the sundial.)[37] And as a matter of fact no matter what system of the universe we assume, it is still necessary to gloss and interpret the words in the text of Joshua, as I shall presently show.

But finally let us grant to these gentlemen even more than they demand; namely, let us admit that we must subscribe entirely to the opinion of wise theologians. Then, since this particular dispute does not occur among the ancient Fathers, it must be undertaken by the wise men of this age. After first hearing the experiences, observations, arguments, and proofs of philosophers and astronomers on both sides—for the controversy is over physical problems and logical dilemmas, and admits of no third alternative —they will be able to determine the matter positively, in accordance with the dictates of divine inspiration. But as to those men who do not scruple to hazard the majesty and dignity of holy Scripture to uphold the reputation of their own vain fancies, let them not hope that a decision such as this is to be made without minutely airing and discussing all the arguments on both sides. Nor need we fear this from men who will make it their whole business to examine most attentively the very foundations of this doctrine, and who will do so only in a holy zeal for the truth, the Bible, and the majesty, dignity, and authority in which every Christian wants to see these maintained.

Anyone can see that dignity is most desired and best secured by those who submit themselves absolutely to the

---

Tostado (1400–55), and the reference is to his twenty-second and twenty-fourth questions on the tenth chapter of Joshua.

[36] Flavius Josephus (ca. 37–95 A.D.), historian of the Jews.

[37] Isaiah 38:8. Paul of Burgos (ca. 1350–1435), also known as Paul de Santa Maria, was a Jewish convert to Christianity who became Bishop of Burgos.

holy Church and do not demand that one opinion or another be prohibited, but merely ask the right to propose things for consideration which may the better guarantee the soundest decision—not by those who, driven by personal interest or stimulated by malicious hints, preach that the Church should flash her sword without delay simply because she has the power to do so. Such men fail to realize that it is not always profitable to do everything that lies within one's power. The most holy Fathers did not share their views. They knew how prejudicial (and how contrary to the primary intention of the Catholic Church) it would be to use scriptural passages for deciding physical conclusions, when either experiments or logical proofs might in time show the contrary of what the literal sense of the words signifies. Hence they not only proceeded with great circumspection, but they left the following precepts for the guidance of others: "In points that are obscure, or far from clear, if we should read anything in the Bible that may allow of several constructions consistently with the faith to be taught, let us not commit ourselves to any one of these with such precipitous obstinacy that when, perhaps, the truth is more diligently searched into, this may fall to the ground, and we with it. Then we would indeed be seen to have contended not for the sense of divine Scripture, but for our own ideas by wanting something of ours to be the sense of Scripture when we should rather want the meaning of Scripture to be ours."[38] And later it is added, to teach us that no proposition can be contrary to the faith unless it has first been proven to be false: "A thing is not forever contrary to the faith until disproved by most certain truth. When that happens, it was not holy Scripture that ever affirmed it, but human ignorance that imagined it."

From this it is seen that the interpretation which we impose upon passages of Scripture would be false whenever it disagreed with demonstrated truths. And therefore we should seek the incontrovertible sense of the Bible with the

[38] This and the ensuing quotations from St. Augustine are referred to *De Genesi ad literam* i, 18 and 19.

assistance of demonstrated truth, and not in any way try to force the hand of Nature or deny experiences and rigorous proofs in accordance with the mere sound of words that may appeal to our frailty. Let Your Highness note further how circumspectly this saint proceeds before affirming any interpretation of Scripture to be certain and secure from all disturbing difficulties. Not content that some given sense of the Bible agrees with some demonstration, he adds: "But when some truth is demonstrated to be certain by reason, it is still not certain whether in these words of holy Scripture the writer intended this idea, or some other that is no less true. And if the context of his words prove that he did not intend this truth, the one that he did intend will not thereby be false, but most true, and still more profitable for us to know." Our admiration of the circumspection of this pious author only grows when he adds the following words, being not completely convinced after seeing that logical proof, the literal words of the Bible, and all the context before and after them harmonize in the same thing: "But if the context supplies nothing to disprove this to be the author's sense, it yet remains for us to inquire whether he may not intend the other as well." Nor even yet does he resolve to accept this one interpretation and reject the other, appearing never to be able to employ sufficient caution, for he continues: "But if we find that the other also may be meant, it may be inquired which of them the writer would want to have stand, or which one he probably meant to aim at, when the true circumstances on both sides are weighed." And finally he supplies a reason for this rule of his, by showing us the perils to which those men expose the Bible and the Church, who, with more regard for the support of their own errors than for the dignity of the Bible, attempt to stretch its authority beyond the bounds which it prescribes to itself. The following words which he adds should alone be sufficient to repress or moderate the excessive license which some men arrogate to themselves: "It often falls out that a Christian may not fully understand some point about the earth, the sky, or the other elements of this world—the motion, rotation, magnitude, and distances of the stars; the known vagaries of the sun and moon; the circuits of the years and epochs; the nature of animals, fruits, stones, and other things of that sort, and hence may not expound it rightly or make it clear by experiences. Now it is too absurd, yea, most pernicious and to be avoided at all costs, for an infidel to find a Christian so stupid as to argue these matters as if they were Christian doctrine; he will scarce be able to contain his laughter at seeing error written in the skies, as the proverb says. The worst of the matter is not that a person in error should be laughed at, but that our authors should be thought by outsiders to hold the same opinions, and should be censured and rejected as ignorant, to the great prejudice of those whose salvation we are seeking. For when infidels refute any Christian on a matter which they themselves thoroughly understand, they thereby evince their slight esteem for our Bible. And why should the Bible be believed concerning the resurrection of the dead, the hope of eternal life, and the Kingdom of Heaven, when it is considered to be erroneously written as to points which admit of direct demonstration or unquestionable reasoning?"

There are men who, in defense of propositions which they do not understand, apply—and in a way commit—some text of the Bible, and then proceed to magnify their original error by adducing other passages that are even less understood than the first. The extent to which truly wise and prudent Fathers are offended by such men is declared by the same saint in the following terms: "Inexpressible trouble and sorrow are brought by rash and presumptuous men upon their more prudent brethren. When those who respect the authority of our Bible commence to reprove and refute their false and unfounded opinions, such men defend what they have put forth quite falsely and rashly by citing the Bible in their own support, repeating from memory biblical passages which they arbitrarily force to their purposes, without knowing either what they mean or to what they properly apply."

It seems to me that we may number among such men those who, being either unable or unwilling to comprehend the experiences and proofs used in support of the new doctrine by its author and his followers, nevertheless expect to bring the Scriptures to bear on it. They do not consider that the more they cite these, and the more they insist that they are perfectly clear and admit of no other interpretations than those which they put on them, the more they prejudice the dignity of the Bible—or would, if their opinion counted for anything—in the event that later truth shows the contrary and thus creates confusion among those outside the holy Church. And of these she is very solicitous, like a mother desiring to recover her children into her lap.

Your Highness may thus see how irregularly those persons proceed who in physical disputes arrange scriptural passages (and often those ill-understood by them) in the front rank of their arguments. If these men really believe themselves to have the true sense of a given passage, it necessarily follows that they believe they have in hand the absolute truth of the conclusion they intend to debate. Hence they must know that they enjoy a great advantage over their opponents, whose lot it is to defend the false position; and he who maintains the truth will have many sense-experiences and rigorous proofs on his side, whereas his antagonist cannot make use of anything but illusory appearances, quibbles, and fallacies. Now if these men know they have such advantages over the enemy even when they stay within proper bounds and produce no weapons other than those proper to philosophy, why do they, in the thick of battle, betake themselves to a dreadful weapon which cannot be turned aside, and seek to vanquish the opponent by merely exhibiting it? If I may speak frankly, I believe they have themselves been vanquished, and, feeling unable to stand up against the assaults of the adversary, they seek ways of holding him off. To that end they would forbid him the use of reason, divine gift of Providence, and would abuse the just authority of holy Scripture—which, in the general opinion of theologians, can never oppose manifest experiences and necessary demonstrations when rightly understood and applied. If I am correct, it will stand them in no stead to go running to the Bible to cover up their inability to understand (let alone resolve) their opponents' arguments, for the opinion which they fight has never been condemned by the holy Church. If they wish to proceed in sincerity, they should by silence confess themselves unable to deal with such matters. Let them freely admit that although they may argue that a position is false, it is not in their power to censure a position as erroneous— or in the power of anyone except the Supreme Pontiff, or the Church Councils. Reflecting upon this, and knowing that a proposition cannot be both true and heretical, let them employ themselves in the business which is proper to them; namely, demonstrating its falsity. And when that is revealed, either there will no longer be any necessity to prohibit it (since it will have no followers), or else it may safely be prohibited without the risk of any scandal.

Therefore let these men begin to apply themselves to an examination of the arguments of Copernicus and others, leaving condemnation of the doctrine as erroneous and heretical to the proper authorities. Among the circumspect and most wise Fathers, and in the absolute wisdom of one who cannot err, they may never hope to find the rash decisions into which they allow themselves to be hurried by some particular passion or personal interest. With regard to this opinion, and others which are not directly matters of faith, certainly no one doubts that the Supreme Pontiff has always an absolute power to approve or condemn; but it is not in the power of any created being to make things true or false, for this belongs to their own nature and to the fact. Therefore in my judgment one should first be assured of the necessary and immutable truth of the fact, over which no man has power. This is wiser counsel than to condemn either side in the absence of such certainty, thus depriving oneself of continued authority and ability to choose by determining things which are now undetermined and open and still lodged in the will of supreme authority. And in brief, if it is impossible for a conclusion to be declared heretical while we remain in doubt as to its truth, then these men are wasting their time clamoring for condemnation of the motion of the earth and stability of the sun, which they have not yet demonstrated to be impossible or false.

Now let us consider the extent to which it is true that the famous passage in Joshua may be accepted without altering the literal meaning of its words, and under what conditions the day might be greatly lengthened by obedience of the sun to Joshua's command that it stand still.

If the celestial motions are taken according to the Ptolemaic system, this could never happen at all. For the movement of the sun through the ecliptic is from west to east, and hence it is opposite to the movement of the *primum mobile*, which in that system causes day and night. Therefore it is obvious that if the sun should cease its own proper motion, the day would become shorter, and not longer. The way to lengthen the day would be to speed up the sun's proper motion; and to cause the sun to remain above the horizon for some time in one place without declining towards the west, it would be necessary to hasten this motion until it was equal to that of the *primum mobile*. This would amount to accelerating the customary speed of the sun about three hundred sixty times. Therefore if Joshua had intended his words to be taken in their pure and proper sense, he would have ordered the sun to accelerate its own motion in such a way that the impulse from the *primum mobile* would not carry it westward. But since his words were to be heard by people who very likely knew nothing of any celestial motions beyond the great general movement from east to west, he stooped to their capacity and spoke according to their understanding, as he had no intention of teaching them the arrangement of the spheres, but merely of having them perceive the greatness of the miracle. Possibly it was this consideration that first moved Dionysius the Areopagite to say that in this miracle it was the *primum mobile* that stood still, and that when this halted, all the celestial spheres stopped as a consequence —an opinion held by St. Augustine himself, and confirmed in detail by the Bishop of Avila. And indeed Joshua did intend the whole system of celestial spheres to stand still, as may be deduced from his simultaneous command to the moon, which had nothing to do with lengthening the day. And under his command to the moon we are to understand the other planets as well, though they are passed over in silence here as elsewhere in the Bible, which was not written to teach us astronomy.

It therefore seems very clear to me that if we were to accept the Ptolemaic system it would be necessary to interpret the words in some sense different from their strict meaning. Admonished by the useful precepts of St. Augustine, I shall not affirm this to be necessarily the above sense, as someone else may think of another that is more proper and harmonious. But I wish to consider next whether this very event may not be understood more consistently with what we read in the Book of Joshua in terms of the Copernican system, adding a further observation recently pointed out by me in the body of the sun. Yet I speak always with caution and reserve, and not with such great affection for my own inventions as to prefer them above those of others, or in the belief that nothing can be brought forth that will be still more in conformity with the intention of the Bible.

Suppose, then, that in the miracle of Joshua the whole system of celestial rotations stood still, in accordance with the opinion of the authors named above. Now in order that all the arrangements should not be disturbed by stopping only a single celestial body, introducing great disorder throughout the whole of Nature, I shall next assume that the sun, though fixed in one place, nevertheless revolves upon its own axis, making a complete revolution in about a month, as I believe is conclusively proven in my *Letters on Sunspots*. With our own eyes we see this movement to be slanted toward the south in the more remote part of the sun's globe, and in the nearer part to tilt toward the north, in just the same manner as all the revolutions of the planets occur. Third, if we consider the nobility of the sun, and the fact that it is the font of light which (as I shall conclusively prove) illuminates not only the moon and the earth but all the other planets, which are inherently dark, then I believe that it will not be entirely unphilosophical to say that the sun, as the chief minister of Nature and in a certain sense the heart and soul of the universe, infuses by its own rotation not only light but also motion into other bodies which surround it. And just as if the motion of the heart should cease in an animal, all other motions of its members would also cease, so if the rotation of the sun were to stop, the rotations of all the planets would stop too. And though I could produce the testimonies of many grave authors to prove the admirable power and energy of the sun, I shall content myself with a single passage from the blessed Dionysius the Areopagite in his book *Of the Divine Name*,[39] who writes thus of the sun: "His light gathers and converts to himself all things which are seen, moved, lighted, or heated; and in a word all things which are preserved by his splendor. For this reason the sun is called HELIOS, because he collects and gathers all dispersed things." And shortly thereafter he says: "This sun which we see remains one, and despite the variety of essences and qualities of things which fall under our senses, he bestows his light equally on them, and renews, nourishes, defends, perfects, divides, conjoins, cherishes, makes fruitful, increases, changes, fixes, produces, moves, and fashions all living creatures. Everything in this universe partakes of one and the same sun by His will, and the causes of many things which are shared from him are equally anticipated in him. And for so much the more reason," and so on.

The sun, then, being the font of light and the source of motion, when God willed that at Joshua's command the whole system of the world should rest and should remain for many hours in the same state, it sufficed to make the sun stand still. Upon its stopping all the other revolutions ceased; the earth, the moon, and the sun remained in the same arrangement as before, as did all the planets; nor in all that time did day decline towards night, for day was miraculously prolonged. And in this manner, by the stopping of the sun, without altering or in the least disturbing the other aspects and mutual positions of the stars, the day

[39] The book *Of the Divine Name*, then attributed to Dionysius the disciple of Paul, actually belongs to the late fifth or early sixth century.

could be lengthened on earth—which agrees exquisitely with the literal sense of the sacred text.

But if I am not mistaken, something of which we are to take no small account is that by the aid of this Copernican system we have the literal, open, and easy sense of another statement that we read in this same miracle, that the sun stood still *in the midst of the heavens*.[40] Grave theologians raise a question about this passage, for it seems very likely that when Joshua requested the lengthening of the day, the sun was near setting and not at the meridian. If the sun had been at the meridian, it seems improbable that it was necessary to pray for a lengthened day in order to pursue victory in battle, the miracle having occurred around the summer solstice when the days are longest, and the space of seven hours remaining before nightfall being sufficient. Thus grave divines have actually held that the sun was near setting, and indeed the words themselves seem to say so: *Sun, stand thou still, stand thou still*.[41] For if it had been near the meridian, either it would have been needless to request a miracle, or it would have been sufficient merely to have prayed for some retardation. Cajetan[42] is of this opinion, to which Magellan[43] subscribes, confirming it with the remark that Joshua had already done too many things that day before commanding the sun to stand still for him to have done them in half a day. Hence they are forced to interpret the words *in the midst of the heavens* a little knottily, saying that this means no more than that the sun stood still while it was in our hemisphere; that is, above our horizon. But unless I am mistaken we may avoid this and all other knots if, in agreement with the Copernican system, we place the sun in the "midst"—that is, in the center—of the celestial orbs and planetary rotations, as it is most necessary to do. Then take

[40] Joshua 10:13.

[41] Joshua 10:12.

[42] Thomas de Vio (1468–1534), Bishop of Gaeta, commenting on the *Summa Theologica* of Thomas Aquinas.

[43] Cosme Magalhaens (1553–1624), a Portuguese Jesuit who in 1612 had published a two-volume treatise on the Book of Joshua.

any hour of the day, either noon, or any hour as close to evening as you please, and the day would be lengthened and all the celestial revolutions stopped by the sun's standing still *in the midst of the heavens;* that is, in the center, where it resides. This sense is much better accommodated to the words, quite apart from what has already been said; for if the desired statement was that the sun was stopped at midday, the proper expression would have been that it "stood still at noonday," or "in the meridian circle," and not "in the midst of the heavens." For the true and only "midst" of a spherical body such as the sky is its center.

As to other scriptural passages which seem to be contrary to this opinion, I have no doubt that if the opinion itself were known to be true and proven, those very theologians who, so long as they deem it false, hold these passages to be incapable of harmonious exposition with it, would find interpretations for them which would agree very well, and especially if they would add some knowledge of astronomical science to their knowledge of divinity. At present, while they consider it false, they think they find in Scripture only passages that contradict it; but if they once entertained a different view of the matter they would probably find as many more that would harmonize with it. And then they might judge that it is fitting for the holy Church to tell that God placed the sun in the center of heaven, and that by rotating it like a wheel gave to the moon and the other wandering stars their appointed courses, when she sings the hymn:

> Most Holy God of Heaven
> Who paints with fiery splendor
> The brilliant center of the pole
> Enriched with beauteous light;
> Who, creating on the fourth day
> The flaming disk of the sun
> Gave order to the moon
> And wandering courses to the stars . . .[44]

[44] From the hymn *God, Creator of All*, attributed to St. Ambrose.

And they could say that the name "firmament" agrees literally quite well with the starry sphere and all that lies beyond the revolutions of the planets, which according to this arrangement is quite firm and immovable. Again, with the earth turning, they might think of its poles when they read *He had not yet made the earth, the rivers, and the hinges of the terrestrial orb*,[45] for hinges would seem to be ascribed in vain to the earth unless it needed them to turn upon.

[45] Proverbs 8:26 (Douay). At present the word in question is translated "poles."

INTRODUCTION: FOURTH PART

XXIV

Shortly before Galileo arrived at Rome, the Holy Office had completed its investigation. His letter to Castelli had been mildly criticized by an officer assigned to report on it, and nothing damaging to Galileo had been established by the three witnesses who had been examined. Of these, two had been called only because Caccini had introduced their names. Caccini himself had not been called at all, but had eagerly volunteered his testimony.

So far as high officials of the church were concerned, the prosecution seems to have been rather half-hearted. Bellarmine had given Foscarini a written opinion without asking for an official ruling, and although he associated Galileo's views with Foscarini's in this, he had not reported the matter to the investigating body. Yet he knew very well that Galileo was under scrutiny.[1] His actions suggest that truly responsible officials did not particularly wish to see an official ruling on the points in dispute. Officious clerics like Caccini, however, behaved very differently. Among them, and particularly among the Dominicans, all sorts of rumors were rife and a great deal of unpleasant gossip had been circulated about Galileo personally.

Galileo's first efforts at Rome were devoted to countering these intrigues. Next he took to debating the merits of the Copernican system at every opportunity. If nobody had been discussing this subject before he came to Rome, everybody was doing so by the end of that year. An unbiased observer who heard many of the debates reported that al-

[1] Bellarmine was one of the Cardinal Inquisitors who had been present at the meetings in which Galileo's case was discussed.

though Galileo had not managed to prove his own side of
the argument, he had conclusively destroyed every argument on the other side.[2] By the beginning of February
1616, Galileo seems to have felt certain that victory was in
sight. He wrote to secure permission from the Grand Duke
for a visit to Naples, probably to see Foscarini (and if possible Campanella) and to organize the campaign in favor
of Copernicus. Even his archenemy Caccini came to visit
him and seems to have tried to establish friendly relations.
Although Galileo recognized duplicity and hypocrisy in
this act, it suggests that his adversaries were close to capit-
ulation.

But Galileo's hopes and his enemies' fears were mistaken.
Pope Paul V, never a friend to the intellectuals of his time,
determined to end the discussion by calling for an official
opinion concerning the motion of the earth and stability of
the sun. Bellarmine was consulted and was still of the
opinion that the teachings of Copernicus were probably
contrary to the Bible. The consultors of the Congregation
of the Index decided accordingly, and the pope instructed
Bellarmine to notify Galileo that he must no longer hold
or defend these ideas. The case was closed. No appeal was
possible. On March 5 the decree was officially published,
and Galileo had the unpleasant task of conveying the news
to the Grand Duke through the Tuscan secretary of state,
Curzio Picchena. Since ostensibly his activities in Rome
had centered upon the protection of his own reputation
while the general issue had been only incidental, he was
able to minimize the degree of his personal defeat:

"I did not write to you in the last post because there
was nothing new to tell you; a decision was awaited on that
matter which I mentioned to you as of public concern and
not related to my own interests except in so far as my enemies have irrelevantly made it so. This was the deliberation
of the holy Church on the book and theory of Copernicus
regarding the motion of the earth and stability of the sun.
Some trouble was made about this last year at the Church

[2] *Opere* xii, 226–27.

of Santa Maria Novella, and then later by the same friar
here in Rome, he calling it heretical and contrary to the
faith. He and his adherents have done their best to persuade people of this orally and in writing; but, as the outcome has shown, his view did not correspond with that of
the holy Church, which has gone no further than to decide
that such an opinion does not concur with the Bible.
Hence they have forbidden only such books as profession-
ally attempt to sustain it as not discordant with the Bible,
and only one such book has been prohibited, published
last year by a Carmelite friar. A thirty-year-old commentary on Job by an Augustinian monk, Didacus à Stunica,[3]
is suspended pending correction for the same reason, but
the correction is merely the removal of a page of exposition
on the words *who moveth the earth from its place*, etc.
From Copernicus's own work ten lines will be taken from
the preface addressed to Pope Paul III, where the author
says that his doctrine does not to him seem contrary to the
Bible, and I hear that here and there a word may be removed where the earth is called a "star." Cardinal Gae-
tano is to correct these two books. No mention is made of
other authors.

"As may be seen from the very nature of the business,
I am not in the least concerned, nor would I have been
involved had it not been for my enemies, as I have said
before. What I have done may always be seen from my
writings (which I keep so that I may always silence the
malevolent), and I can show that my activity in this matter
has been such that not even a saint could have dealt more
reverently or more zealously with the holy Church than I.
This is perhaps not equally true of my foes, who have not
scrupled to scheme, slander, and make diabolical suggestions. . . ."[4]

But despite his pretended detachment, Galileo was sick
at heart. At the end of the above letter he withdrew his
plan to visit Naples, "because of the bad roads." The road
to Naples was a bad one now in more than one sense. The

---

[3] Cf. p. 203. Didacus à Stunica is the Latin form of Diego
de Zuñiga.

[4] *Opere* xii, 243–45.

printer who had published Foscarini's book there was soon to be imprisoned, and the author died that same year under obscure circumstances. The battle Galileo had tackled was simply too big for any individual, and he had received only discouragement from many who might have helped him. Yet he had come within a hairsbreadth of victory, and had still many friends in high places. Before he left Rome he was granted an interview by the pope and was assured that further rumors against him would not be lightly entertained. From Bellarmine he secured a certificate that the gossip already circulating was false. Several Jesuit fathers confided in Cesi that they were astonished and displeased by the decision. Better still, the Grand Duke remained unwaveringly loyal to his court mathematician and philosopher.

For a while Galileo remained out of the public eye. A part of the time he was ill, and otherwise he occupied himself mainly with some inventions and projects of a noncontroversial nature. The one book which he had urgently wished to publish, his treatise on the system of the world, was now forbidden, at least in the form which he had long since promised to his readers. The other works which he had left Padua to bring to a conclusion remained unfinished; he seems to have had no heart for them at this period. But in time he did appear again as an author. His next acknowledged work was a curious one, and in order to account for its production one must rely more upon psychological evidence than upon documented facts. For that reason the ensuing sections contain a large element of conjecture.

XXV

Galileo was not a man who could accept defeat without a struggle. Barred from presenting his views frankly and openly, he soon began to cast around for some means of doing so by indirection. Early in 1618 he revived a paper on the theory of tides, composed at Rome two years before and presented at that time to Cardinal Orsini as an attempted physical proof of the Copernican system. Galileo's theory implied that the tides were caused by the double motion of the earth around its axis and around the sun; he now added to this thesis a preface describing it as merely an ingenious speculation, and sent it to the Archduke Leopold of Austria. Perhaps he hoped that Leopold would publish it for him, as Welser had done with Scheiner's sunspot letters, thus relieving him of any responsibility. But while this trial balloon of his was still in the air, another event occurred which presented a safer if far less direct approach to Galileo's problem.

In the autumn of 1618 three comets appeared in rapid succession, the last one being unusually bright and remaining visible until the following January. At this time Galileo was confined to bed and could not make extensive observations of his own, but the friends who visited him often discussed the comets. Ancient writers had regarded such things as meteorological phenomena and not as heavenly bodies at all. Tycho, however, had established by means of parallax that the comet of 1577 was located far beyond the moon, and had tentatively assigned to comets in general an orbit somewhere in the neighborhood of Venus. Five years before, in the *Letters on Sunspots,* Galileo had endorsed the first part of this opinion. Word now reached him that Tycho's view had been adopted by the mathematician at the Jesuit college in Rome, and that the Jesuits considered this explanation of comets to be the best possible argument against Copernicus.

As a matter of fact Copernicus had never attempted to explain comets, and even if he had it was forbidden for Galileo to defend him. Still, Galileo seems to have seen in this event a pretext for taking up the cudgels again. In May 1619, his friend and former pupil Mario Guiducci delivered two lectures on comets before the Florentine Academy, and these were then printed. It was well known that the ideas set forth were principally Galileo's, as was indeed acknowledged by Guiducci in his opening remarks. The *Discourse on Comets,* truly Galileo's own though published over his pupil's name, opened with a calm appraisal of all previous

theories. Among these the views set forth by the anonymous
Jesuit (Father Horatio Grassi) were examined and criticized.

The nature of this criticism is very interesting. No mention of Copernicus is made. No rival theory to Grassi's is
set forth by Guiducci (that is, by Galileo) as demonstrated.
Instead, a mere hypothesis is presented from which could
be deduced certain damaging objections to the very foundations of Grassi's argument. They were objections which
at that time could not possibly be avoided or removed. In
this way a thoroughly skeptical note was introduced, and
upon that basis Galileo succeeded in presenting to the
public the essential elements of scientific method. He may
well have hoped that the application of this method in astronomy would lead others along the same path, and eventually to the same conclusions, as his own. It was a devious
approach to his goal, but a prudent one; and Galileo himself had never doubted the effectiveness of methodological
considerations in undermining the errors of the past. To
appreciate this fact, let us next review his actions when he
entered the service of the Grand Duke of Tuscany.

XXVI

In 1610, when he was negotiating for his position at
Florence, Galileo had rather oddly insisted upon having the
title of "philosopher" as well as the more customary post of
court mathematician. That he deserved this title, he said,
would become clear to Their Highnesses as soon as he was
given a chance to debate in their presence against the most
esteemed philosophers. The justice of his claim was not
long in becoming apparent to his friends and foes alike. If
it is not equally evident in his early books, that is because
they teemed so richly with new and exciting discoveries
that all strictly philosophical and methodological points
were crowded aside. Galileo's opponents in oral debate,
however, quickly found themselves in trouble on such
points as well as on those of scientific fact. This may be
illustrated by a passage from the opening section of Co-

lombe's dissertation against the motion of the earth, sent to Galileo no later than 1611.

"Some men," wrote Colombe, "despairing to understand Aristotle or to say anything that will gain them celebrity in his philosophy, and yet being unable to deny all his truths and to show off in any ordinary way, oppose against him all sorts of insincere notions, revealing—or rather dreaming of—a new philosophy and a new method of philosophizing. Of this sort were some of the ancients, and in our time the followers of Telesio.[5]

"Other men, having no grounding in philosophy at all, give themselves over to mathematics and preach that it is sovereign over all other disciplines. In Aristotle's time this was considered a schoolboys' science, learned before any other, ... and yet these modern mathematicians solemnly declare that Aristotle's divine mind failed to understand it, and that as a result he made ridiculous mistakes. . . ."[6]

There can hardly be any doubt that this last remark was a personal reproach against Galileo. He indeed not only dreamed of (and did much to reveal) a new philosophy and a new method of philosophizing, but insisted upon the central role of mathematics in this. Telesio had taught, in effect, that the authority of Aristotle and all other theorists should be thrown out, only the evidence of the senses being acceptable as a true source of knowledge. On the other hand some mathematicians indulged in a kind of mysticism which sought to replace ordinary reasoning and observation with causal properties attributed to numbers and to geometric forms; even the great Kepler was prone to such speculations. But Galileo's views were quite different from these; they were less extreme and at the same time even more revolutionary. He agreed that in order to become science, philosophy must throw out blind respect for au-

[5] Bernard Telesio (1508–88), mentioned briefly below.
[6] *Opere* iii:1, 253–54. "And they are right in saying so," noted Galileo in his copy, "for he committed many and serious mathematical blunders, though neither so many nor so silly as does this author every time he opens his mouth on the subject."

thority, but he also saw that neither observation, nor reasoning, nor the use of mathematics could be thrown out along with this. True philosophy had to be built upon the interplay of all three, and no combination could supply the absence of any one of them. He knew very well that the unsupported evidence of the senses might lead a man astray. Finally, he realized that philosophy must learn to be content with pursuing limited objectives, reaching out gradually into the infinity of unknown events and undiscovered laws of nature, without ever achieving complete and exact knowledge of anything at all.

Now this was a method of philosophizing calculated to scandalize all conventional philosophers. They saw things just the other way around. To them, the complex phenomena of nature were to be explained by reference to a few grand principles, and this was precisely what constituted philosophy. They might disagree over the principles to be accepted, but never over the procedure itself. The trouble with Galileo's system was that he was often obliged to say (and taught his pupils to make a habit of saying) "I do not know." This was something that no competent philosopher of the age would dream of doing. Galileo recognized the necessity of a skeptical and undogmatic approach to nature, and at his time such a view was calculated to scandalize nearly everyone—not only philosophers, but theologians and rulers too. In an age when authority was everywhere taken for granted, Galileo's watchword was the rejection of authority of any kind. His entire attitude has been well summed up by the saying that he was never willing to accept any intermediary between himself and nature.

"The difference between philosophizing and studying philosophy," wrote Galileo in his notes on Lagalla's book, "is that which exists between drawing from nature and copying pictures. In order to become accustomed to handling the pen or crayon in good style, it is right to begin by redrawing good pictures created by excellent artists. Likewise in order to stimulate the mind and guide it toward good philosophy, it is useful to observe the things that have already been investigated by others in their philosophizing; especially those which are true and certain, these being chiefly mathematical.

"But men who go on forever copying pictures and never get around to drawing from nature can never become perfect artists, or even good judges of painting. For they remain unpracticed in separating the good from the bad, or the accurately from the poorly drawn, by means of recognizing in nature itself (as a result of countless experiences) the true effects of foreshortening, of backgrounds, of lights and shadows, of reflections, and of the infinite variations in differing viewpoints.

"In the same way a man will never become a philosopher by worrying forever about the writings of other men, without ever raising his own eyes to nature's works in the attempt to recognize there the truths already known and to investigate some of the infinite number that remain to be discovered. This, I say, will never make a man a philosopher, but only a student of other philosophers and an expert in their works. I do not believe that you would esteem as a good painter a man who had made so great a study of the drawings and canvases of all painters that he could promptly identify the style of each one, even if he could also imitate them."[7]

Among other characteristic indications of his philosophical views at this earlier period are these:

"From the statements of this author philosophy might have reached greater perfection if men had been born blind, as then they would be free from many false assumptions that come from our sense of sight."[8]

"You want to convict mathematicians of ignorance for not being aware that the senses deceive us in our ordinary perceptions—as if knowing whether or not one is deceived were some abstruse and profound secret of philosophy. But who has given us better and more accurate observations

---

[7] *Opere* iii:1, 395–96.
[8] *Opere* iii:1, 395.

and notions about optical illusions than these very mathematicians?"[9]

Thus, long before he attempted to present his philosophical views in any book, Galileo was doubtless teaching them to his pupils. When some began to call themselves "Galileists," it was because they recognized in his teachings far more than a repudiation of Aristotle, or an espousal of Archimedes and Copernicus. What they were learning from Galileo later came to be known as "experimental philosophy."[10] It was not appreciably different from what we call scientific method.

XXVII

The criticism of Grassi's views which Galileo offered through the mouth of Guiducci was quite mild. But the Jesuits were not amenable to challenge by outsiders, and Grassi took much offense. Masquerading as a pupil of Grassi's, he immediately replied under the pseudonym of Lothario Sarsi; and, brushing Guiducci aside, he delivered a bitter and slashing attack against Galileo himself. He called his new book *The Astronomical and Philosophical Balance,* punning upon the name of the sign of the zodiac in which he (incorrectly) asserted that the comet had first appeared. In this "balance" Grassi pretended to weigh some of his opponent's arguments.

Galileo's friends were unanimous in urging him not to let this book go by unanswered, for it contained many serious

---

[9] *Opere* iii:1, 397.

[10] This term, which continued in use until the nineteenth century, was an excellent one for the purpose. Modern scientific method is characterized by an inseparable linkage of theory to experiment, in such a way that no theory may properly be called scientific unless it implies experiments or observations capable of supporting or destroying it, while no experiment is scientifically significant except in its relation to some definitely formulated theory. This linkage was stressed in the phrase "experimental philosophy," but it quite disappears in such modern expressions as "experimental science" and "experimental method."

and unjust accusations. But fearing the consequences of a frontal attack upon the powerful Jesuits, they counseled him to reply in some indirect way. Accordingly Galileo wrote his reply in the form of a letter to a friend. He took his time about it, and greatly expanded the philosophical sections of the original *Discourse*. Also he took pains to see that the bitter and personal language which Grassi had adopted should be returned with interest. The result was the greatest polemic ever written in physical science. It was called *The Assayer*,[11] in continuation of Grassi's metaphor. The crude steelyard of Galileo's adversary was to be replaced by the delicate instrument which is employed in the assay of pure gold.

This book has been justly called Galileo's scientific manifesto. To dwell upon the scientific faults of the cometary hypothesis it contains is to miss the main point of the book, which lay not in the hypothesis itself but in its use.[12] The discussions of comets as such have been largely omitted in the excerpts which follow, and the polemic and philosophical aspects of the book are displayed instead. Published when Galileo was sixty years of age, *The Assayer* stands midway between two decade-long silences on the part of its author. The three scientific works which preceded it had consisted largely of isolated discoveries and experimental demonstrations. The two which were to follow would reveal theoretical frameworks into which discoveries and experiments were introduced as integrated components.

The Assayer marked a crucial point in the history of Galileo's thought. Before, he had spoken as the experimental scientist; later he was to speak as a theoretical scientist. In this work he speaks as the philosopher of science.

[11] *Il Saggiatore*. Grassi, in his counterattack, later transformed this into winetaster (*assagiatore*), and implied that Galileo had been drinking when he wrote it (*Opere* vi, 380–81).

[12] Galileo did not contend, as is often asserted, that comets were located close to the earth. He did, however, believe them to originate from terrestrial vapors rising in straight lines and vanishing at immense distances.

THE ASSAYER

In which
with a most just and accurate
balance there are weighed the
things contained in
THE ASTRONOMICAL AND PHILO-
SOPHICAL BALANCE OF LOTHARIO
SARSI OF SIGUENZA

Written in the form of a letter
To the Illustrious and Very Reverend Monsignor
DON VIRGINIO CESARINI
Lincean Academician, and Chamberlain to His Holiness
By Signor
GALILEO GALILEI
Lincean Academician, Gentleman of Florence,
Chief Philosopher and Mathematician to the
Most Serene Grand Duke of Tuscany

ROME
1623

THE ASSAYER
A Letter to the Illustrious and Very Reverend
Don Virginio Cesarini[1]

I have never understood, Your Excellency, why it is that
every one of the studies I have published in order to please
or to serve other people has aroused in some men a certain
perverse urge to detract, steal, or deprecate that modicum
of merit which I thought I had earned, if not for my work,
at least for its intention. In my *Starry Messenger* there were
revealed many new and marvelous discoveries in the heavens that should have gratified all lovers of true science;
yet scarcely had it been printed when men sprang up
everywhere who envied the praises belonging to the discoveries there revealed. Some, merely to contradict what I
had said, did not scruple to cast doubt upon things they
had seen with their own eyes again and again.

My lord the Grand Duke Cosimo II, of glorious memory,
once ordered me to write down my opinions about the
causes of things floating or sinking in water, and in order to
comply with that command I put on paper everything I
could think of beyond the teachings of Archimedes, which
perhaps is as much as may truly be said on this subject.
Immediately the entire press was filled with attacks against
my *Discourse*. My opinions were contradicted without the
least regard for the fact that what I had set forth was supported and proved by geometrical demonstrations; and
such is the strength of men's passion that they failed to

[1] Cesarini (1595–1624) was a brilliant man of letters at
whose house in Rome Galileo had often debated in favor of
Copernicus during his ill-starred visit in 1615–16. He had
served as confidential secretary to Pope Gregory XV and was
appointed chamberlain by Urban VIII in 1623.

notice how the contradiction of geometry is a bald denial of truth.

How many men attacked my *Letters on Sunspots*, and under what disguises! The material contained therein ought to have opened to the mind's eye much room for admirable speculation; instead it met with scorn and derision. Many people disbelieved it or failed to appreciate it. Others, not wanting to agree with my ideas, advanced ridiculous and impossible opinions against me; and some, overwhelmed and convinced by my arguments, attempted to rob me of that glory which was mine, pretending not to have seen my writings and trying to represent themselves as the original discoverers of these impressive marvels.[2]

I say nothing of certain unpublished private discussions, demonstrations, and propositions of mine which have been impugned or called worthless; yet even these have sometimes been stumbled upon by other men who with admirable dexterity have exerted themselves to appropriate these as inventions of their own ingenuity. Of such usurpers I might name not a few. I shall pass over first offenders in silence, as they customarily receive less severe punishment than repeaters. But I shall no longer hold my peace about one of the latter, who has too boldly tried once more to do the very same thing he did many years ago when he appropriated the invention of my geometric compass, after I had shown it to and discussed it with many gentlemen

---

[2] This statement was believed by Scheiner to be unjustly aimed at him, and was probably the source of his disastrous enmity toward Galileo. But Galileo had already spoken of Scheiner in his reference to "attacks under disguises." Here he was probably speaking of another opponent, most likely Jean Tarde, who had published a book on sunspots at Paris while *The Assayer* was being written. Tarde had visited Galileo in 1614 and had discussed sunspots with him personally, yet in his book he completely ignored Galileo's conclusions and appropriated the earlier mistaken ideas of Scheiner. The charge of plagiarism from Galileo's books could not be aimed at Scheiner himself for obvious reasons, but judging from the bitter attack on Galileo in the *Rosa Ursina* and from its author's undoubted role in Galileo's final condemnation, Scheiner believed that to be the intention.

years before, and had finally published a book about it. May I be pardoned if on this occasion—against my nature, my custom, and my present purpose—I show resentment and protest (perhaps too bitterly) about something I have kept to myself all these years.

I speak of Simon Mayr of Guntzenhausen. He it was in Padua, where I resided at the time, who set forth in Latin the uses of my compass and had one of his pupils publish this and sign it. Then, perhaps to escape punishment, he departed immediately for his native land and left his pupil in the lurch. In Simon Mayr's absence I was obliged to proceed against his pupil, in the manner described in the *Defense* which I published at the time.[3]

Now four years after my *Starry Messenger* appeared, this same fellow (in the habit of trying to ornament himself with other people's works) unblushingly made himself the author of the things I had discovered and printed in that book. Publishing under the title of *The World of Jupiter*, he had the gall to claim that he had observed the Medicean planets which revolve about Jupiter before I had. . . . But note his sly way of attempting to establish his priority. I had written of making my first observation on the seventh of January, 1610. Along comes Mayr, and, appropriating my very observations, he prints on the title page of his book (as well as in the opening pages) that he had made his observations in the year 1609. But he neglects to warn the reader that he is a Protestant, and hence had not accepted the Gregorian calendar. Now the seventh day of January, 1610, for us Catholics, is the same as the twenty-eighth day of December, 1609, for those heretics. And so much for his pretended priority of observation.[4]

[3] Little was said in the *Defense* to indicate that Galileo then suspected Mayr, though he had been mentioned with praise by Capra in the preface to his outrageous plagiarism.

[4] Galileo was on absolutely solid ground here, though efforts have been made even in modern times to rob him of this as well as most of his other discoveries. Mayr, like Scheiner, gave his undivided attention to a single topic for several years, and as a result produced some observations and deductions more accurate than Galileo's on these special studies. But

·   ·   ·   ·   ·   ·   ·   ·   ·   ·

After such clear proofs as these, there was no longer any room for doubt in my mind about the ill feeling and stubborn opposition that existed against my works. I considered remaining perfectly silent in order to save myself any occasion for being the unhappy target of such sharpshooting, and to remove from others any material capable of exciting these reprehensible talents. I have certainly not lacked opportunities to put forth other works that would perhaps be no less astonishing to the schools of philosophy and no less important to science than those published previously. But the reason cited above was so cogent that I contented myself merely with the opinion and judgment of a few gentlemen, my real friends, to whom I communicated my thoughts. In discussions with these men I have enjoyed that pleasure which accompanies the opportunity to impart what one's mind brings forth bit by bit, and at the same time I avoided any renewal of those stings which I had previously experienced with so much vexation. Demonstrating in no small degree their approval of my ideas, these gentlemen have managed for a variety of reasons to draw me away from the resolution I had made.

At first they tried to persuade me not to be upset by obstinate attacks, saying that in the end those would rebound upon their authors and merely render my own reasoning more lively and attractive, furnishing as they did clear proof that my essays were of an uncommon nature. They pointed out to me the familiar maxim that vulgarity and mediocrity receive little or no attention and are soon left in the cold, while men's minds turn to the revelation of wonders and transcendent things—though these indeed may give rise in ill-tempered minds to envy, and thereby to slander. Now these and similar arguments, coming to me on the authority of those gentlemen, almost took away my resolve to write no more; yet my desire to live in tran-

Mayr's effrontery in claiming priority is so palpable that one cannot help sympathizing entirely with Galileo in these plaintive opening paragraphs of *The Assayer*.

quillity prevailed. And, fixed in my resolve, I believed that I had silenced all the tongues that once had shown such eagerness to contradict me. But it was in vain that I had reached this frame of mind, and by remaining silent I could not evade the stubborn fate of having to concern myself continually with men who write against me and quarrel with me. It was useless to hold my peace, because those who are so anxious to make trouble for me have now had recourse to attributing to me the works of others. In that way they have stirred up a bitter fight against me, something that I believe never happens without indicating some insane passion.

One might have thought that Sig. Mario Guiducci would be allowed to lecture in his Academy, carrying out the duties of his office there, and even to publish his *Discourse on Comets* without "Lothario Sarsi," a person never heard of before, jumping upon me for this. Why has he considered me the author of this *Discourse* without showing any respect for that fine man who was? I had no part in it beyond the honor and regard shown me by Guiducci in concurring with the opinions I had expressed in discussions with him and other gentlemen. And even if the entire *Discourse* were the work of my pen[5]—a thing that would never enter the mind of anyone who knows Guiducci—what kind of behavior is this for Sarsi to unmask me and reveal my face so zealously? Should I not have been showing a wish to remain incognito?

Now for this reason, forced to act by this unexpected and uncalled-for treatment, I break my previous resolve to publish no more. I am going to do my best to see that this act shall not escape notice, and to discourage those who refuse to let sleeping dogs lie and who stir up trouble with men that are at peace.

I am aware that this name Lothario Sarsi, unheard of in the world, serves as a mask for someone who wants to remain unknown. It is not my place to make trouble for another man by tearing off his mask after Sarsi's own fash-

[5] So it was, to all intents and purposes, and most of the manuscript survives in Galileo's handwriting.

ion, for this seems to me neither a thing to be imitated nor one which could in any way assist my cause. On the contrary, I have an idea that to deal with him as a person unknown will leave me a clearer field when I come to make my reasoning clear and explain my notions freely. I realize that often those who go about in masks are low persons who attempt by disguise to gain esteem among gentlemen and scholars, utilizing the dignity that attends nobility for some purpose of their own. But sometimes they are gentlemen who, thus unknown, forgo the respectful decorum attending their rank and assume (as is the custom in many Italian cities) the liberty of speaking freely about any subject with anyone, taking whatever pleasure there may be in this discourteous raillery and strife. I believe that it must be one of the latter who is hidden behind the mask of "Lothario Sarsi," for if he were one of the former it would indeed be poor taste for him to impose upon the public in this manner. Also I think that just as he has permitted himself incognito to say some things that he might perhaps repress to my face, so it ought not to be taken amiss if I, availing myself of the privilege accorded against masqueraders, shall deal with him quite frankly. Let neither Sarsi nor others imagine me to be weighing every word when I deal with him more freely than he may like.

. . . .

During the entire time the comet was visible I was confined by illness to my bed. There I was often visited by friends. Discussions of the comets frequently occurred, during which I had occasion to voice some thoughts of mine which cast doubt upon the doctrines that have been previously held on this matter. Sig. Guiducci was often present, and one day he told me that he had thought of speaking on comets before the Academy; if I liked, he would include what he had heard from me along with things he had gathered from other authors or had thought himself. Inasmuch as I was in no condition to write, I regarded this courtesy as my good fortune, and I not only accepted but I thanked him and acknowledged my debt.

Meanwhile from Rome and elsewhere there came insistent requests to know whether I had anything to say on this subject, from friends and patrons who perhaps did not know that I was ill. I replied to them that I had only some questions to raise, which I was unable to write down because of my infirmity, but that I hoped these ideas of mine would soon be included in a discourse by a friend who had taken the trouble to collect them. That is all I said, and it has been told in several places by Guiducci. There was no need for Sarsi to pass him off as a mere copyist. But since Sarsi wants it so, let it be; meanwhile let Guiducci accept my defense of his treatise in return for the honor he did me.

. . . .

I have never claimed (as Sarsi pretends) that my opinion was certain to be swiftly carried by the winds to Rome. That usually happens only with the words of great and celebrated men, which really far exceeds the bounds of my ambition. It is true, though, that in reading Sarsi's book I have wondered that what I said never did reach Sarsi's ears. Is it not astonishing that so many things have been reported to him which I never said, nor even thought, while not a single syllable reached him of other things that I have said over and over again? But perhaps the winds that blow the clouds and those chimeras and monsters that tumultuously take shape in them had not the strength to carry solid and weighty things.

. . . .

In Sarsi I seem to discern the firm belief that in philosophizing one must support oneself upon the opinion of some celebrated author, as if our minds ought to remain completely sterile and barren unless wedded to the reasoning of some other person. Possibly he thinks that philosophy is a book of fiction by some writer, like the *Iliad* or *Orlando Furioso*, productions in which the least important thing is whether what is written there is true. Well, Sarsi, that is not how matters stand. Philosophy is written in this grand book, the universe, which stands continually open to our gaze. But the book cannot be understood unless one first learns to comprehend the language and read the letters in which it is composed. It is written in the language of mathematics, and its characters are triangles, circles, and other geometric figures without which it is humanly impossible to understand a single word of it; without these, one wanders about in a dark labyrinth.

Sarsi seems to think that our intellect should be enslaved to that of some other man. . . . But even on that assumption, I do not see why he selects Tycho. . . . Tycho could not extricate himself from his own explanation of diversity in the apparent motion of his comet; but now Sarsi expects my mind to be satisfied and set at rest by a little poetic flower that is not followed by any fruit at all. It is this that Guiducci rejected when he quite rightly said that nature takes no delight in poetry. That is a very true statement, even though Sarsi appears to disbelieve it and acts as if acquainted with neither nature nor poetry. He seems not to know that fables and fictions are in a way essential to poetry, which could not exist without them, while any sort of falsehood is so abhorrent to nature that it is as absent there as darkness is in light.

.   .   .   .

Guiducci wrote that "people who wish to determine the location of a comet by means of parallax must first establish that the comet is a fixed and real object and not a mere appearance, since reasoning by parallax is indeed conclusive for real things but not for apparent ones." . . . Sarsi says that no author worth considering, ancient or modern, has ever supposed a comet to be a mere appearance; hence that his teacher, who was disputing only with such men and did not aspire to victory over any others, did not need to remove comets from the company of mere images. To this I reply in the first place that for the same reason Sarsi might let Guiducci and me alone, as we are outside the circle of those worthy ancient and modern authors against whom his teacher was contending. We meant only to address those men, ancient or modern, who try in all their studies to investigate some truth in nature. We meant to steer clear of those who ostentatiously engage in noisy contests merely to be popularly judged victors over others and pompously praised. . . . Guiducci, in the hope of doing something that would be welcome to men studious of truth, proposed with all modesty that henceforth it would be good to consider the nature of a comet, and whether it might be a mere appearance rather than a real object. He did not criticize Father Grassi or anyone else who had not previously done this. Now Sarsi rises up in arms and passionately strives to prove that this suggestion is beside the point and false to boot. Yet in order to be prepared for anything (lest the idea appear worthy of some consideration), he robs me of any possible credit by calling this "an ancient notion of Cardan[6] and Telesio," which his teacher disparages as a fantasy of feeble philosophers who had no followers. And under this pretense, without the least shame for his disrespect, he robs those men of their reputations in order to cover up a slight oversight of his teacher's. . . . But I must not neglect to show, for his benefit and in their defense, how implausible is his deduction that their science was poor from their having had few followers.

Perhaps Sarsi believes that all the host of good philosophers may be enclosed within four walls. I believe that they fly, and that they fly alone, like eagles, and not in flocks like starlings. It is true that because eagles are rare birds they are little seen and less heard, while birds that fly like starlings fill the sky with shrieks and cries, and wherever they settle befoul the earth beneath them. Yet if true philosophers are like eagles they are not [unique] like the phoenix. The crowd of fools who know nothing, Sarsi, is infinite. Those who know very little of philosophy are numerous. Few indeed are they who really know some part of it, and only One knows all.

To put aside hints and speak plainly, and dealing with science as a method of demonstration and reasoning capa-

---

[6] Jerome Cardan (1501–76) was a noted mathematician and the author of works on philosophy, medicine, astronomy, and nearly every other branch of learning.

ble of human pursuit, I hold that the more this partakes of perfection the smaller the number of propositions it will promise to teach, and fewer yet will it conclusively prove. Consequently the more perfect it is the less attractive it will be, and the fewer its followers. On the other hand magnificent titles and many grandiose promises attract the natural curiosity of men and hold them forever involved in fallacies and chimeras, without ever offering them one single sample of that sharpness of true proof by which the taste may be awakened to know how insipid is the ordinary fare of philosophy. Such things will keep an infinite number of men occupied, and that man will indeed be fortunate who, led by some unusual inner light, can turn from dark and confused labyrinths in which he might have gone perpetually winding with the crowd and becoming ever more entangled.

Hence I consider it not very sound to judge a man's philosophical opinions by the number of his followers. Yet though I believe the number of disciples of the best philosophy may be quite small, I do not conclude conversely that those opinions and doctrines are necessarily perfect which have few followers, for I know well enough that some men hold opinions so erroneous as to be rejected by everyone else. But from which of those sources the two authors mentioned by Sarsi derive the scarcity of their followers I do not know, for I have not studied their works sufficiently to judge.[7]

. . . .

If I accept Sarsi's charge of negligence because various motions that might have been attributed to the comet did not occur to me, I fail to see how he can free his teacher from the same criticism for not considering the possibility of motion in a straight line. . . . There is no doubt whatever that by introducing irregular lines one may save not only the appearance in question but any other. Yet I warn

[7] It was noted by Vincenzio Viviani in his biography of Galileo that he read little of other men's works and owned few books in comparison to other philosophers of the time.

Sarsi that far from being of any assistance to his teacher's case, this would only prejudice it more seriously; not only because he did not mention this, and on the contrary accepted the most regular line there is (the circular), but because it would have been very flippant to propose such a thing. Sarsi himself may understand this if he will consider what is meant by an irregular line. Lines are called regular when, having a fixed and definite description, they are susceptible of definition and of having their properties demonstrated. Thus the spiral is regular, and its definition originates in two uniform motions, one straight and the other circular. So is the ellipse, which originates from the cutting of a cone or a cylinder. Irregular lines are those which have no determinacy whatever, but are indefinite and casual and hence undefinable; no property of such lines can be demonstrated, and in a word nothing can be known about them. Hence to say, "Such events take place thanks to an irregular path" is the same as to say, "I do not know why they occur." The introduction of such lines is in no way superior to the "sympathy," "antipathy," "occult properties," "influences," and other terms employed by some philosophers as a cloak for the correct reply, which would be: "I do not know." That reply is as much more tolerable than the others as candid honesty is more beautiful than deceitful duplicity.

·   ·   ·   ·   ·   ·   ·   ·   ·   ·

Guiducci has written, "Many stars completely invisible to the naked eye are made easily visible by the telescope; hence their magnification should be called infinite rather than nonexistent." Here Sarsi rises up and, in a series of long attacks, does his best to show me to be a very poor logician for calling this enlargement "infinite." At my age these altercations simply make me sick, though I myself used to plunge into them with delight when I too was under a schoolmaster. So to all this I answer briefly and simply that it appears to me Sarsi is showing himself to be just what he wants to prove me; that is, little cognizant of logic, for he takes as absolute that which was spoken relatively.

No one ever seriously claimed that the magnification of fixed stars is infinite. Rather, Father Grassi wrote that it was nil, and Guiducci, having noted that this is not correct inasmuch as many totally invisible stars are brought to visibility, remarked that such enlargment should be called infinite rather than nil. Now who is so simple-minded as not to understand that if we call a profit of one thousand ducats on a capital of one hundred "large," and not "nil," and the same upon a capital of ten "very large," and not "nil," then the acquisition of one thousand upon no capital at all should be called "infinite" rather than "nil"? . . . And even if Guiducci called the magnification "infinite" without any relative term, I should not have expected such carping criticism as this, for the word "infinite" in place of the phrase "extremely large" is a way of talking that is used every day. Here, indeed, Sarsi has a large field in which to show himself a better logician than all the other authors in the world; for I assure him that he will find the word "infinite" chosen in place of "extremely large" nine times out of ten. Nor is that all, Sarsi. If the Preacher should confront you and say: *Stultorum infinitus est numerus* ("the number of fools is infinite"),[8] what would you do? Would you argue with him and maintain his proposition to be false? You could prove on equal scriptural authority that the world is not eternal, and that having been created in time there cannot have been and cannot be an infinite number of men; and since foolishness reigns only among men, the above proposition could never be true even if all men—past, present, and future—were fools. For there could never be an infinite number of human beings even if the world were to endure eternally.

.   .   .   .

I did not mean to spend so many words on this trifling, Your Excellency, but since the more has been done, the less remains to do. Now for this other charge of violating

[8] Ecclesiastes 1:15 (Douay). The translators of the King James version render this passage in an entirely different sense; namely, as "that which is wanting cannot be numbered."

the laws of logic. Guiducci, in his discussion of the telescope, is said either to have included an effect which does not exist or to have left out one that should be given. He said, "The telescope renders stars visible either by enlarging their images or by illuminating them," whereas Sarsi will have it that he should have said, "by enlarging them or by uniting the images and the rays." I reply that Guiducci had no intention of dividing what is one, and so far as he and I are concerned there is but one operation of the telescope in representing objects. What he said was, to be exact, "If the telescope does not render stars visible by enlarging them, then by some unheard-of means it must illuminate them." He did not introduce "illumination" as an effect that he believed in, but counterpoised it against the other as an obvious impossibility, intending in this way to make the truth of the alternative still more evident. This is quite a common figure of speech, as when one says: "If our enemies did not scale the fortress, they must have rained here from the sky." Now if Sarsi thinks he can win acclaim by condemning this idiom, then in addition to his animadversions on the word "infinite" he has another road open to him for winning a battle of logic against all the other writers on earth. But in trying to show himself off as a great logician, let him beware lest he make himself appear a still greater sophist.— I seem to see Your Excellency grin, but what can I do? It is Sarsi who has taken it into his head to write against Guiducci's treatise, and in the process he has been forced to grasp at skyhooks. For my part I do not merely excuse him, I praise him; for to me it appears he has accomplished the impossible.

* * * * * * * * *

Immediately after this, though perhaps not very appositely, Sarsi is induced to call the telescope my "foster child," and to disclose that it is not my offspring in any other way. Now how is this, Sig. Sarsi? First you try to place me under great obligations by showering new virtues upon this supposed child of mine, and next you tell me it is only an adopted one. Is this rhetorically sound? I should have thought that on such an occasion you would have tried to make me believe it was my very own child, even if you had been certain it was not.

Well, my part in the discovery of this instrument (and whether I may reasonably claim to be its parent) was long ago set forth in my *Starry Messenger*. There I wrote that in Venice, where I happened to be at the time, news arrived that a Fleming had presented to Count Maurice [of Nassau] a glass by means of which distant objects might be seen as distinctly as if they were nearby. That was all. Upon hearing this news I returned to Padua, where I then resided, and set myself to thinking about the problem. The first night after my return I solved it, and on the following day I constructed the instrument and sent word of this to those same friends at Venice with whom I had discussed the matter the previous day. Immediately afterward I applied myself to the construction of another and better one, which six days later I took to Venice, where it was seen with great admiration by nearly all the principal gentlemen of that republic for more than a month on end, to my considerable fatigue. Finally, at the suggestion of one of my patrons, I presented it to the Doge at a meeting of the Council. How greatly it was esteemed by him, and with what admiration it was received, is testified by ducal letters still in my possession. These reveal the munificence of that serene ruler in compensation for the invention presented to him, for I was reappointed and confirmed for life in my professorship at the University of Padua with double my previous salary, which was already three times that of some of my predecessors. These acts did not take place in some forest or desert, Sig. Sarsi; they happened in Venice, and if you had been there you would not be dismissing me thus as a simple schoolmaster. But most of those gentlemen are still living there, by the grace of God, and you may be better informed by them.

Yet perhaps some will say that in the discovery and solution of a problem it is of no little assistance first to be conscious in some way that the goal is a real one, and to be sure that one is not attempting the impossible, and hence that my knowledge and certainty of the telescope having already been made was of so much help to me that without this I should never have made the discovery. To this I shall reply by making a distinction. I say that the aid afforded me by the news awoke in me the will to apply my mind to the matter, and that without this I might never have thought about it, but beyond that I do not believe any such news could facilitate the invention. I say, moreover, that to discover the solution of a stated and fixed problem is a work of much greater ingenuity than to solve a problem which has not been thought of and defined, for luck may play a large part in the latter, while the former is entirely a work of reasoning. Indeed, we know that the Fleming who was first to invent the telescope was a simple maker of ordinary spectacles who, casually handling lenses of various sorts, happened to look through two at once, one convex and the other concave, and placed at different distances from the eye. In this way he observed the resulting effect and thus discovered the instrument. But I, incited by the news mentioned above, discovered the same thing by means of reasoning. And this reasoning, easy as it is, I wish to reveal to Your Excellency, for if set forth where it is to the purpose it may by its simplicity reduce the incredulity of those who (like Sarsi) try to diminish whatever praise there may be in this that belongs to me.

My reasoning was this. The device needs either a single glass or more than one. It cannot consist of one glass alone, because the shape of this would have to be convex (that is, thicker in the middle than at the edges) or concave (that is, thinner in the middle), or bounded by parallel surfaces. But the last-named does not alter visible objects in any way, either by enlarging or reducing them; the concave diminishes them; and the convex, though it does enlarge them, shows them indistinctly and confusedly. Passing then to two, and knowing as before that a glass with parallel faces alters nothing, I concluded that the effect would still not be achieved by combining such a glass with either of the other two. Hence I was restricted to discovering what would be done by a combination of the convex and the concave.[9] You see how this gave me what I sought; and such were the steps in my discovery, in which I was assisted not at all by the received opinion that the goal was a real one.

If Sarsi and others think that certainty of a conclusion extends much assistance in the discovery of some means for realizing it, let them study history. There they may learn that Archytas[10] made a dove that flew, that Archimedes made a mirror which kindled fires at great distances and many other remarkable machines, that other men have kindled perpetual fires, and a hundred more inventions no less amazing. By reasoning about these they may easily discover, to their great honor and profit, how to construct such things. Or, if they do not succeed, at least they will derive some benefit in the form of a clarification of their ideas about the help which they expect from a foreknowledge of the effects. That help will be a good deal less than they have imagined.

.   .   .   .

Sarsi now prepares with admirable boldness to maintain, by means of acute syllogisms, that objects seen through the telescope are the more enlarged the closer they are, and he is so confident that he practically promises I shall come to admit this to be true, though at present I deny it. Now I make a very different forecast. I believe that in the weaving of this cloth, Sarsi is going to get himself so entangled—far more than he supposes now, while he is laying the warp—that in the end he will voluntarily admit himself defeated. This will become apparent to anyone

[9] The reasoning is of course entirely *post hoc,* and in fact a combination of two convex lenses is much more satisfactory for astronomical purposes. Such telescopes were described by Kepler in 1611, and are said to have been first constructed and used by Scheiner some years later.

[10] Archytas was the teacher of Eudoxus (note 3, p. 11); he flourished at Tarentum in the fourth century B.C. Numerous stories are told of his skill as a mathematician and statesman, but he is best remembered in the tradition that he constructed an automaton in the form of a wooden dove which could fly.

who will notice that he ends by saying precisely the same things that Guiducci wrote, though he disguises this and fits it in piecemeal among such a variety of wordy ornaments and arabesques that those who merely glance at his statements may take them to be something different from what they really are.

Meanwhile I say, in order not to discourage him, that if what he is attempting turns out to be correct, then this reasoning which his teacher and his astronomer friends use to determine the location of the comet is not only the most ingenious argument of all, but such an employment of the telescope far transcends all others in the importance of its consequences. I cannot help being astonished that Sarsi and his teacher, thinking it to be true, should have regarded it less highly than their others—which, if I may say so, are not fit to hold a candle to this one. Your Excellency, if this thing is true, Sarsi has a clear road to the most admirable inventions ever thought of. Not only may any distance on earth be measured from a single place, but the distances of the heavenly bodies may also be established exactly. For once we have observed a circle through a telescope at a distance of one mile and found it to be thirty times as large as when viewed with the naked eye, we need only find a tower that is magnified ten times and we may be sure that it is three miles distant. If this telescope merely triples the moon's diameter, we may say that the moon is ten miles away, and the sun would be fifteen if its diameter is but doubled. Conversely, if the moon is tripled by some excellent telescope when it is more than one hundred thousand miles away (as Father Grassi says), then the ball on a cupola at a distance of one mile would be enlarged more than a million times. Now to add what I can to so astounding a venture, I shall set forth some trifling questions which arose in me as Sarsi proceeded. Your Excellency may, if you like, show them to him some time so that he may by replying establish his position more solidly.

Sarsi wishes to persuade me that the fixed stars receive no appreciable enlargement from the telescope. He begins with objects in my room, and asks me whether I need to

lengthen my telescope very much in order to view them.[11]
I answer, yes. Now, letting the objects pass out the window
to a great distance, he tells me that in order to look at
them it is necessary to shorten the telescope a good deal;
and I affirm this. Next I concede to him that this comes
about from the very nature of the instrument, which must
be made longer for observing nearby objects and shorter
for those that are more distant. Moreover, I confess that the
longer tube shows the objects larger than the shorter; and
finally I grant him for the present his whole syllogism, the
conclusion being that in general nearby objects are
enlarged and farther ones less so. This implies that the fixed
stars, which are remote objects, are less enlarged than
things within a room or a courtyard, for it appears to me
that Sarsi includes things which he calls "nearby" within
those limits, he not having specifically removed this boundary to any greater distance.

But the statement made thus far is still a long way from
proving Sarsi's point. For next I ask him whether he places
the moon in the class of "nearby" objects, or in that of "distant" ones? If he puts it with distant objects, then he must
conclude for it the same thing he concludes for the fixed
stars; namely, slight enlargement. But this is in direct contradiction to his teacher, who, in order to situate the comet
beyond the moon, requires that the moon be one of those
objects which are greatly magnified. He even wrote that
the moon viewed through the telescope is much enlarged,
and the comet was but little. On the other hand if Sarsi
places the moon among nearby objects, then I shall reply
to him that he should not have restricted such objects to
the walls of a room at the outset; he should have extended

[11] Grassi's queries may have been responsible for Galileo's
having taken up again his interest in the use of lenses to
magnify very small objects. In the early days of the telescope
he had experimented with such an application of it, but it
was only when writing *The Assayer* that he altered the lens
system and produced a manageable compound microscope. The
invention is, of course, contested in favor of several other men
about this time.

this boundary at least as far as the moon. But having extended it that far, let Sarsi return again to his original questions, and ask me whether I need to lengthen my telescope very much in order to see "nearby" objects—that is, objects which are not beyond the orbit of the moon. I answer no, and the archer's bow is broken and the shooting of syllogisms is over.

If we go back to examine his argument more closely, we find it to be defective because it takes as absolute that which must be understood relatively, or as bounded that which is unbounded. In a word, Sarsi has created an incomplete dichotomy (as logicians call this error) when he divided visible objects into "far" and "near" without assigning limits and boundaries between these. He has made the same mistake as a person who should say, "Everything in the world is either large or small." This proposition is neither true nor false, and neither is the proposition "objects are either near or far." From indeterminacy of this sort it will come about that the same objects may be called "quite close" and "very remote"; that the closer may be called "distant" and the farther "close"; that the larger may be called "small" and the smaller "large." Thus one may say "This is a very small hill," and "this is a very large diamond." A courier calls the trip from Rome to Naples very short, while a great lady grieves that her house is so far from the church.

In order to avoid equivocation Sarsi needed to give his classification at least three parts, and say: "Of visible objects, some are near, some far, and others are situated at a medium distance." Nor should he even stop there; he should give an exact determination of this limit, saying for example: "I call 'medium' a distance of one league; 'far,' that which is more than one league; and 'near,' that which is less." I fail to see why he did not do this, unless it was that he realized his case would be stronger if he advanced it by cleverly juggling equivocations in front of the simpleminded than by reasoning it soundly for the more intelligent. Well, it truly is a great advantage to have one's bread buttered on both sides, and to be able to say: "Because the fixed stars are distant, they are not much magnified, whereas the moon is, because it is close," and then to say, if necessity arises, "Objects in a room, being close, are magnified a great deal, but the moon, because it is distant, is little enlarged."

. . . .

Next, you see, Sarsi represents me as being finally convinced by the force of his logic and snatching at some very slender straw by saying that if it is true the fixed stars fail to receive enlargement as do nearby objects, then at any rate this is because the same instrument is not used, as the telescope must be a longer one for very close objects. He adds, with a "get thee hence," that I am seizing at trifles. But it is you, Sig. Sarsi, and not I who take refuge in these minutiae and in "at any rate." It was you who had to say that in the very subtle concepts of geometry "at any rate", the fixed stars require more shortening of the telescope than does the moon. Later it turned out that if the moon were magnified one thousand times, the fixed stars would be magnified nine hundred and ninety-nine, whereas to support your position they could not be allowed to be enlarged by even one-half. This is indeed resorting to "at any rate." It is like insisting that something is still a serpent when, scotched and trampled, it has no longer any life left outside the tip of its tail, which goes on twitching to fool the passersby into thinking it is still healthy and strong.

It is perfectly true that the lengthened telescope is a "different" instrument from what it was before, and this was essential to our point. Sarsi would not have thought otherwise if he had not equivocated from the subject matter of our meaning to the form of our argument, as may easily be shown from the very example he himself uses. I ask Sarsi why it is that some organ pipes produce deep tones and some high. Will he say that this comes about because they are made of different materials? Surely not; they are all of lead. They sound different tones because they are of different lengths; and as to the material, this plays no part whatever in the formation of the sound. Some pipes are made of wood, some of pewter, some of lead, some of silver, and some of paper, but all will sound in unison when their lengths and sizes are equal. But on the other hand one may make now a larger and now a smaller tube with the same quantity of material, say the same five pounds of lead, and form different notes from it. With regard to the production of sound those instruments are different which are of different sizes, not those which are of different materials. Now if by melting down one pipe and remolding the same lead we make a new tube that is longer, and therefore of lower pitch, will Sarsi refuse to grant that this is a different pipe from the first? I think he will not. And if we find a way to make this longer tube without melting down the shorter, would not this come to the same thing? Surely it would. The method will be to make the tube in two pieces, one inserted in the other. This may be lengthened and shortened at will, making diverse pipes which will produce different notes; and such is the construction of the trombone. The strings of a harp are all of the same material, but they produce different sounds because they are of various lengths. On a lute, one string will do what many strings on a harp will do; for in fingering the lute the sound is drawn now from one part of the string and now from another, which is the same as lengthening and shortening it, and making of it different strings so far as relates to the production of sound. The same may be said of the tube of the throat, which, varying in length and breadth, accommodates itself to the formation of various notes and may be said to become various tubes. Now since a greater or less enlargement depends not upon the material of a telescope but upon its shape, the tube constitutes different instruments when the same material is used but the separation of the lenses is altered. . . .

At the end of this argument Sarsi says that a telescope which is now long and now short may be called "the same instrument, but differently applied." If I am not mistaken, this is a quibble, and it seems to me that matters stand quite the opposite—the instrument is altered while its application remains the same. The same instrument is said to be differently applied when it is employed for different uses without any alteration; thus the anchor was the same when used by the pilot to secure the ship and when employed by Orlando to catch a whale,[12] but it was differently applied. In our case the reverse is true, for the use of a telescope is always the same, being invariably applied to looking at things, whereas the instrument is varied in an essential respect by altering the interval between its lenses. This makes Sarsi's quibble apparent.

· · · · · · · · · ·

Next Sarsi patches together an argument out of various fragments of propositions designed to prove that the comet was situated between the moon and the sun. Guiducci and I may concede the whole thing to him without prejudice, as we have never said anything about the location of the comet, nor have we denied that it might have been beyond the moon. We merely said that the proofs thus far set forth by other authors are not free from objections. Sarsi would fail to remove these objections no matter how many new proofs of his own he added, even if they were themselves conclusive. . . . Still, since I like to see mysterious things brought to light, and since I wish to discover the truth, I shall consider his argument; and for a clearer understanding let me first reduce it to as few words as possible.

Sarsi says he has it from my *Starry Messenger* that the fixed stars are widely irradiated with a fulgor which is not real but only apparent, as they shine with their own light; that the planets, having no light of their own, are not similarly irradiated—especially the moon, Jupiter, and Saturn, which are seen to be almost devoid of any such splendor; and that Venus, Mercury, and Mars, though they have no light of their own, are nevertheless irradiated by reason of their proximity to the sun and their consequent bright illumination by it. He goes on to say that in my

[12] *Orlando Furioso*, c. xi, 37–38. The translation here is deliberately free. Orlando did not employ the anchor as a fishhook, but used it to prop open the mouth of a sea monster while he entered to kill it.

opinion a comet receives its light from the sun, and he adds that he himself and other reputable authors for a while regarded the comet as a planet. Hence they reasoned about it as about the other planets, to the effect that the closer of these to the sun are the more irradiated and consequently are less enlarged when observed through the telescope. Now, since the comet was enlarged little more than Mercury and much less than the moon (he says), it might be very reasonably concluded that it was not much farther from the sun than Mercury is, and very much closer to the sun than to the moon. This is his argument, which so smoothly fits his needs and so neatly assists him that it almost looks as if his conclusion had been made before his premises, and the latter depended upon the former instead of vice versa. It is as if the premises had been prepared not by the bounty of nature but by the precision of the subtlest art. But let us see how conclusive they are.

First of all, it is quite false that I said in my *Starry Messenger* that Jupiter and Saturn have little or no irradiation, while Mars and Venus and Mercury are grandly crowned with rays. It was the moon alone that I sequestered from the rest of the stars and planets.

Second, I am not so sure that in order to make a comet a quasi-planet, and as such to deck it out in the attributes of other planets, it is sufficient for Sarsi or his teacher to regard it as one and so name it. If their opinions and their voices have the power of calling into existence the things they name, then I beg them to do me the favor of naming a lot of old hardware I have about my house, "gold." But names aside, what attribute induced them to regard the comet as a quasi-planet for a time? That it shone like other planets? But what cloud, what smoke, what wood, what wall, what mountain, touched by the sun does not shine equally? Sarsi has seen it proved in my *Starry Messenger* that the earth itself shines more brightly than the moon. And why should I speak of the comet as shining like a planet? I myself believe that the light of a comet may be so weak and its material so thin and rare that if anyone could get close enough to it he would completely lose it from view, as happens with some fires which glow on earth and are seen only at night and from afar, being lost when close at hand. Thus also we see distant clouds as sharply bounded, but later, from close by, they show no more than a misty shadowiness, so indefinitely bounded that a person entering within them will fail to distinguish their limits or to separate them from the surrounding air. . . . Comets may be dissolved in a few days, and they are not of a circular and bounded shape, but confused and indistinct—indicating that their material is thinner and more tenuous than fog or smoke. In a word, a comet is more like a toy planet than the real thing.

.   .   .   .

Up to this point Sarsi has gone along arbitrarily shaping his premises to fit the conclusions he meant to prove; now it seems to me that he proceeds to shape conclusions for the purpose of opposing them to Guiducci's and mine, for they are certainly different from those set forth in the *Discourse,* or at least they are differently construed. That the comet was a mere image and appearance was never positively affirmed by us; it was merely raised as a question and offered for the consideration of philosophers, along with various arguments and conjectures that appeared suitable to show them this possibility. Here are Guiducci's words: "I do not say positively that a comet is formed in this way, but I do say that just as doubts exist concerning this, so doubts exist concerning the origins suggested by other authors; and if they claim to have established their ideas beyond doubt, they are under an obligation to show that this (and any other theory) is vain and foolish."

Once more distorting things, Sarsi represents us as having definitely declared that the motion of a comet must necessarily be straight and perpendicular to the earth's surface —a thing which was not said in that way at all, but was merely brought under consideration as explaining the observed changes in position of the comet more simply and in better agreement with the appearances. The notion was put forth so temperately by Guiducci that at the end he said,

"Hence we must content ourselves with what little we can conjecture thus among shadows." Sarsi, however, has attempted to represent me as firmly believing these opinions, and himself as being able to annihilate them. Well, if he succeeds I shall be the more obliged to him, as in the future I shall have one less theory to worry about when I set my mind to philosophizing on such matters. But since it seems to me that there is still some life left in Guiducci's conjectures, I shall make a few remarks upon the strength of Sarsi's refutations.

Attacking the first conclusion with great boldness, he says that to anyone who once looked at the comet, no other argument is necessary to prove the nature of its light, for by comparison with other true lights it clearly showed itself to be real and not spurious. Your Excellency will note the great confidence which Sarsi places in the sense of sight, deeming it impossible for us to be deceived by a spurious object whenever that may be set beside a real one. I confess that I do not possess such a perfect faculty of discrimination. I am more like the monkey that firmly believed he saw another monkey in a mirror, and the image seemed so real and alive to him that he discovered his error only after running behind the glass several times to catch the other monkey.

Assuming that what Sarsi sees in his mirror is not a true and real man at all, but just an image like those which the rest of us see there, I should like to know the visual differences by which he so readily distinguishes the real from the spurious. I have often been in some room with closed shutters and seen on the wall a reflection of sunlight coming through some tiny hole; and so far as vision could determine, it seemed to be a star no less bright than Venus. When we walk over a field into the sunlight, thousands of straws and pebbles that are smooth or moistened will reflect the sun in the aspect of the most brilliant stars. Sarsi has but to spit upon the ground and undoubtedly he will see the appearance of a natural star when he looks from the point toward which the sun's rays are reflected. And any object placed at a great distance and struck by the sun will appear as a star, particularly if it is placed so high as to be visible at nightfall when other stars appear. Who could distinguish between the moon seen in daylight and a cloud touched by the sun, were it not for differences of shape and size? If simple appearance can determine the essence of a thing, Sarsi must believe that the sun, the moon, and the stars seen in still water are true suns, real moons, and veritable stars.

.   .   .   .

Long experience has taught me this about the status of mankind with regard to matters requiring thought: the less people know and understand about them, the more positively they attempt to argue concerning them, while on the other hand to know and understand a multitude of things renders men cautious in passing judgment upon anything new.

Once upon a time, in a very lonely place, there lived a man endowed by nature with extraordinary curiosity and a very penetrating mind. For a pastime he raised birds, whose songs he much enjoyed; and he observed with great admiration the happy contrivance by which they could transform at will the very air they breathed into a variety of sweet songs.

One night this man chanced to hear a delicate song close to his house, and being unable to connect it with anything but some small bird he set out to capture it. When he arrived at a road he found a shepherd boy who was blowing into a kind of hollow stick while moving his fingers about on the wood, thus drawing from it a variety of notes similar to those of a bird, though by quite a different method. Puzzled, but impelled by his natural curiosity, he gave the boy a calf in exchange for this flute and returned to solitude. But realizing that if he had not chanced to meet the boy he would never have learned of the existence of a new method of forming musical notes and the sweetest songs, he decided to travel to distant places in the hope of meeting with some new adventure.

The very next day he happened to pass by a small hut

within which he heard similar tones; and in order to see whether this was a flute or a bird he went inside. There he found a small boy who was holding a bow in his right hand and sawing upon some fibers stretched over a hollowed piece of wood. The left hand supported the instrument, and the fingers of the boy were moving so that he drew from this a variety of notes, and most melodious ones too, without any blowing. Now you who participate in this man's thoughts and share his curiosity may judge of his astonishment. Yet finding himself now to have two unanticipated ways of producing notes and melodies, he began to perceive that still others might exist.

His amazement was increased when upon entering a temple he heard a sound, and upon looking behind the gates discovered that this had come from the hinges and fastenings as he opened it. Another time, led by curiosity, he entered an inn expecting to see someone lightly bowing the strings of a violin, and instead he saw a man rubbing his fingertip around the rim of a goblet and drawing forth a pleasant tone from that. Then he observed that wasps, mosquitoes, and flies do not form single notes by breathing, as did the birds, but produce their steady sounds by swift beating of their wings. And as his wonder grew, his conviction proportionately diminished that he knew how sounds were produced; nor would all his previous experiences have sufficed to teach him or even allow him to believe that crickets derive their sweet and sonorous shrilling by scraping their wings together, particularly as they cannot fly at all.

Well, after this man had come to believe that no more ways of forming tones could possibly exist—after having observed, in addition to all the things already mentioned, a variety of organs, trumpets, fifes, stringed instruments, and even that little tongue of iron which is placed between the teeth and which makes strange use of the oral cavity for sounding box and of the breath for vehicle of sound—when, I say, this man believed he had seen everything, he suddenly found himself once more plunged deeper into ignorance and bafflement than ever. For having cap in his hands a cicada, he failed to diminish its strident noise either by closing its mouth or stopping its wings, yet he could not see it move the scales that covered its body, or any other thing. At last he lifted up the armor of its chest and there he saw some thin hard ligaments beneath; thinking the sound might come from their vibration, he decided to break them in order to silence it. But nothing happened until his needle drove too deep, and transfixing the creature he took away its life with its voice, so that he was still unable to determine whether the song had originated in those ligaments. And by this experience his knowledge was reduced to diffidence, so that when asked how sounds were created he used to answer tolerantly that although he knew a few ways, he was sure that many more existed which were not only unknown but unimaginable.

I could illustrate with many more examples Nature's bounty in producing her effects, as she employs means we could never think of without our senses and our experiences to teach them to us—and sometimes even these are insufficient to remedy our lack of understanding. So I should not be condemned for being unable to determine precisely the way in which comets are produced, especially in view of the fact that I have never boasted that I could do this, knowing that they may originate in some manner that is far beyond our power of imagination. The difficulty of comprehending how the cicada forms its song even when we have it singing to us right in our hands ought to be more than enough to excuse us for not knowing how comets are formed at such immense distances. Let us therefore go no further than our original intention, which was to set forth the questions that appeared to upset the old theories, and to propose a few new ideas.

.   .   .   .

Sarsi should not have undue trouble in understanding that even if all the material involved in a comet is equally illuminated, sunlight might be reflected to the eyes of one particular observer only from some particular part of it. . . . In order to explain a point that is of the utmost importance, and perhaps to give someone (I shall not say Sarsi) a new idea, imagine yourself to be at the seashore when the sun is descending in the west. You will see a bright reflection of the sun on the surface of the sea near the line passing vertically through the solar disk. It will not spread over a large area; indeed, if the water is quite calm you will see a pure image of the sun as sharply bounded as in a mirror. Now let a slight breeze spring up and ruffle the surface of the water, when you will see the image of the sun begin to break up into many pieces and extend into a wider area. If you were close by, you might be able to distinguish the broken pieces of this image from one another. But from a greater distance you would not see that separation because of the narrow gaps between the pieces, or because the great brilliance of the shining parts would cause them to intermingle and behave as do several fires close together which from afar seem to be one. If the ruffling goes on to form greater and greater waves, the multitude of mirrors from which the image of the sun will be reflected will extend over wider and wider spaces. Now withdraw to a greater distance and climb some hill or other prominence in order to see the water better; the lighted field will now appear to be one and continuous. From a very high mountain about sixty miles from the Bay of Leghorn, on a clear and windy day about an hour before sunset, I have seen a very bright strip spreading out on both sides of the sun and extending for tens or perhaps hundreds of miles, this being a reflection of sunlight identical with those just described.

Now let Sarsi imagine most of the sea on both sides to be removed, leaving only a breadth of two or three miles in the center, pointing toward the sun. This would surely all be illuminated, but it would not change place with every motion of the observer to one side, unless perhaps he were to move several miles. . . . Even then the image would not move with the same motion as the observer, but the whole of it would move so that its center would always be in line with the sun. . . .

Here I should like to suggest something that

curred to me as a solution of a problem that concerns
sailors. When they are experienced, they sometimes recognize that a wind will approach before long from a certain
direction, and they say that a sure sign of this is to see the
air brighter in that direction than it would normally be.
Might this not come about from a wind in that quarter
disturbing the waves at a distance? From such waves, as
from many mirrors extending over a wide area, would result a much brighter reflection of the sunlight than would
occur if the sea were calm. In turn, that region of the vapor-
laden air would be made brighter by this new light and
by the diffusion of that reflection. Such air, being high,
would send some reflection of light to the sailors' eyes while
they, being low and far off, would be unable to catch the
primary reflection from that part of the sea that is already
being ruffled by a wind some twenty or thirty miles away.
Thus they might perceive and predict this wind from a
distance.

.   .   .   .

It is true that smooth and polished surfaces such as those
of mirrors send a strong reflection of the sun's light to us,
so much so that we can hardly look at these without injury
to the eyes; but it is also true that surfaces which are not so
smooth make some reflection, less powerful in inverse ratio to the smoothness. Now Your Excellency may decide
whether the brilliance of a comet belongs among things
which dazzle the vision, or among those so feeble as not to
offend the eyes; then you may judge whether a mirrorlike
surface is required for its production or whether one much
less smooth will suffice.

I want to teach Sarsi a method of representing a reflection very like a comet. Take a clean carafe and hold a
lighted candle not far from it, and you will see in its surface
a tiny image of the light, very sharp and bright. Next with
the tip of your finger take a small quantity of any oily material that will adhere to the glass, and spread a thin coat-
ing where the image appears, dimming the surface a little.
The image will promptly be dimmed too. Now turn the

carafe so that the image emerges from the oiled spot and just touches its edge, and rub your finger once right across the oiled part. Instantly you will see a ray formed in imitation of the tail of a comet, cutting right across the place where you rubbed your finger. If you rub across this again, the ray will be led off in another direction. This happens because the skin on the ball of the finger is not smooth, but is marked with certain twisted lines which we use in sensing the slightest irregularity of objects by touch. These leave some tracks in moving over the oily surface, and the reflection of light takes place in their edges, and since they are numerous and regularly arranged this forms a light stripe. The image may be placed at the head of this stripe by moving the carafe, and will then appear brighter than the tail. The same effect may be produced by fogging the glass with the breath instead of using oil. But if you ever suggest this little game to Sarsi, and if he protests at great length, then I beg Your Excellency to tell him that I do not mean to imply by this that there is in the sky a huge carafe, and someone oiling it with his finger, thus forming a comet; I merely offer this as an example of Nature's bounty and variety of methods for producing her effects. I could offer many, and doubtless there are still others that we cannot imagine.

. . . .

Only too clearly does Sarsi show his desire to strip me completely of any praise. Not content with having disproved our reasoning set forth to explain the fact that the tails of comets sometimes appear to be bent in an arc, he adds that nothing new was achieved by me in this, as it had all been published long ago, and then refuted, by Johann Kepler. In the mind of the reader who goes no more deeply than Sarsi's account, the idea will remain that I am not only a thief of other men's ideas, but a petty, mean thief at that, who goes about pilfering even what has been refuted. And who knows; perhaps in Sarsi's eyes the pettiness of the theft does not render me more blameworthy than I would be if I had bravely applied myself to greater

thefts. If, instead of filching some trifle, I had more nobly
set myself to search out books by some reputable author
not as well known in these parts, and had then tried to
suppress his name and attribute all his labors to myself,
perhaps Sarsi would consider such an enterprise as grand
and heroic as the other seems to him cowardly and abject.
Well, I lack the stomach for this and I freely confess this
cowardice. But poor as I am in courage and power, I am
at least upright. I will not carry this undeserved wound,
and I shall write frankly what you, Sarsi, have left out; and
since I cannot divine what passion gave rise to the omission,
I leave it to you to explain that later in your apology. . . .

Kepler tried to give a reason for the tail being really
curved; Guiducci supposes it to be really straight, and
seeks a cause for its bent appearance. Kepler reduced his
reason to a diversity in refraction of the sun's rays occurring
in the material from which the comet's tail is formed. . . .
Guiducci introduces a refraction not of the sun's rays, but
of the comet's image, and not in the material of the comet
but in the vaporous sphere which surrounds the earth.
Hence the cause, the material, the place, and the method
all differ between the two, and no correspondence exists
except in both authors' use of the word "refraction." . . .
Kepler has always been known to me as a man no less frank
and honest than intelligent and learned. I am sure that he
would admit our statement to be entirely different from the
one which he refuted.[13]

.   .   .   .

Before I proceed let me tell Sarsi that it is not I who

[13] So far as this goes, it is quite correct. Grassi had referred
to the views which Kepler had set forth in an early optical
work, and Galileo rightfully objected to the implication that
these views were similar to his own. In 1619, however, Kepler
had published a book on comets in which he changed his
previous notion and foreshadowed the modern view that the
tails of comets consist of material driven from their bodies by
the sun's rays, and that their curvature arises from a composition of motions. See *Ad Vitellionem paralipomena* . . .
(Frankfort, 1604), pp. 264 ff., and *De cometis libelli tres*
(Augsburg, 1619) bk. ii.

want the sky to have the noblest shape because of its being the noblest body; it is Aristotle himself, against whose views Sig. Guiducci is arguing. For my own part, never having read the pedigrees and patents of nobility of shapes, I do not know which of them are more and which are less noble, nor do I know their rank in perfection. I believe that in a way all shapes are ancient and noble; or, to put it better, that none of them are noble and perfect, or ignoble and imperfect, except in so far as for building walls a square shape is more perfect than the circular, and for wagon wheels the circle is more perfect than the triangle.

Sarsi says that abundant arguments have been supplied by me for proving the roughness of the interior surface of the sky, since I will have it that the moon and other planets —bodies which are also celestial, and even more noble and perfect than the sky itself—are mountainous and rough. And if that is so, he asks, why shouldn't irregularity exist also in the shape of the sky? For an answer to this let him put down whatever it is that he would reply to a man who argued that the surface of the ocean should be bony and scaly, since the fish which inhabit it are.

As to his question why the moon is not smooth, I reply that it and all the other planets are inherently dark and shine by light from the sun. Hence they must have rough surfaces, for if they were smooth as mirrors no reflection would reach us from them and they would be quite invisible to us. . . . On the other hand almost equal disorder would ensue if the celestial orbs were of a solid substance and had surfaces not perfectly smooth, since then refractions would be disturbed and the movements, shapes, and projections of rays from the planets would be most confused and irregular.

.   .   .   .

Sarsi tries to attribute to me something quite false; namely, that the water in a bowl remains as motionless as air when the bowl is rotated. Well, I am not surprised that he says this, for any man who is constantly reversing the sense of things that others have written and published will think it even more permissible to alter things he admits he has only on hearsay. Just the same, I do not consider it within the bounds of good breeding to print something that a man has merely heard from his neighbors, and the more so when (either deliberately or as a result of misunderstanding) his report is quite different from what was actually said. It is my affair to print my ideas for the world to read, Sarsi, not yours. And if in the course of an argument a man has said something foolish, as indeed does happen sometimes, why must you rush into print with it, and thus deprive him of the opportunity to think it over more carefully and amend his own error, preserving mastery over his own mind and pen?

What Sarsi may have heard—but, from what I see, did not understand very well—was a certain experiment which I exhibited to some gentlemen there at Rome, and perhaps at the very house of Your Excellency, in partial explanation and partial refutation of the "third motion"[14] attributed by Copernicus to the earth. This extra rotation, opposite in direction to all other celestial motions, appeared to many a most improbable thing, and one that upset the whole Copernican system. . . . I used to remove the difficulty by showing that such a phenomenon was far from improbable, and indeed would be in accordance with Nature and practically forced to occur. For any body resting freely in a thin and fluid medium will, when transported along the circumference of a large circle, spontaneously acquire a rotation in a direction contrary to the larger move-

[14] Copernicus ascribed to the earth what he called a "motion in declination" in addition to the annual and diurnal motions. The purpose of this was to maintain the axis of the earth parallel to itself throughout the year in order to account for the seasons. Galileo, who had discovered the principle of inertia, saw that this did not require a special motion at all, but was a direct consequence of his principle. At first he used his discovery in support of Copernicus. After the theory was banned he utilized it to smuggle in the truth by pretending (as here) that Copernicus had spoken falsely in attributing a nonexistent motion to the earth. Resourcefulness of this sort made him a very hard man to silence.

ment. The phenomenon was seen by taking in one's hands a bowl of water and placing in it a floating ball. Then turning about on the toe with this hand extended, one sees the ball turn on its axis in the opposite direction, and complete this revolution in the same time as one's own. In this way the wonder was removed, and in place of it one would be astonished if the earth were not to acquire a contrary rotation when assumed to be a body suspended in a fluid medium and going around a large circle in a period of one year. What I said was designed to remove a difficulty attributed to the Copernican system, and I later added that anyone who would reflect upon the matter more carefully would see that Copernicus had spoken falsely when he attributed his "third motion" to the earth, since this would not be a motion at all, but a kind of rest. It is certainly true that to the person holding the bowl such a ball appears to move with respect to himself and to the bowl, and to turn upon its axis. But with respect to the wall (or any other external thing) the ball does not turn at all, and does not change its tilt, and any point upon it will continue to point toward the same distant object.

That is what I asserted, and you see it is very different from what Sarsi relates. This experiment, and perhaps others, may have induced someone who was present at our discussions to attribute to me what Sarsi mentions next—that is, a certain natural talent of mine for explaining by means of simple and obvious things others which are more difficult and abstruse. He does not deny me praise for this, but I think this comes from courtesy rather than from his true feelings, for so far as I can see he is not easily persuaded of any talent on my part.

. . . .

Well, now you have seen a great expenditure of words on the part of Sarsi and myself to determine whether the solid hollow of the lunar orb[15] (which does not exist in

[15] This expression refers not to the moon but to the imaginary crystalline sphere that was supposed to transport it around the earth. The inner surface of that sphere was ~~~

Nature), moving around (as it never has), sweeps along with it the element of fire (which is not proved to exist) and along with this the exhalations which in turn kindle the material of comets—a material whose location we cannot establish with certainty, and which we are positive is not combustible. Sarsi here puts me in mind of the saying of a very witty poet:

> By Orlando's sword, which they have not
> And perhaps which they never shall have
> These blows of blind men have been given. . . .[16]

Sarsi next wants to make Guiducci agree with Aristotle, and to show that they have both stated the same conclusion when one of them says that motion is the cause of heat, and the other says that the cause is not motion but the brisk rubbing of two hard bodies. And since it is Guiducci's statement that is correct, Sarsi interprets the other one by saying that if indeed motion, as motion, is not the cause of heat, nevertheless friction is not created without motion, so that at least derivatively we may say that motion is the cause. But if that is what Aristotle meant, why didn't he say "friction"? When a man can say definitely what he means by using a simple and appropriate word, why employ an inappropriate one that requires qualification and ultimately becomes transformed into something quite different? But assuming that this was Aristotle's meaning, it still differs from Guiducci's; for to Aristotle any rubbing of bodies would suffice, even of tenuous ones or of the air itself, whereas Guiducci requires two solid bodies, for he considers that trying to pulverize the air is as great a waste of time as grinding water in the proverbial mortar.

It is my opinion that the original proposition may be quite true, taken in the simplest sense of the words it contains, and that perhaps it came from some good philosophical school of antiquity, but that Aristotle failed to fathom

---

posed to be the boundary between the four terrestrial elements (fire, air, water, and earth) and the special fifth substance (aether) which composed all heavenly bodies.

[16] Boiardo, *Orlando Innamorato* iii, c. vi, 50, 3–5.

the minds of the ancients who propounded it, and deduced his false conception accordingly. Nor would this be the only proposition that is inherently true but is understood by the Peripatetics in a false sense. Of this I shall say more some other time. . . .

Really, I do not believe that Guiducci would say (as Sarsi pretends) that in order to become hot, bodies must first be rarefied, and that rarefaction diminishes them, and that the thinner parts fly away. . . . In the process under discussion one must consider on the one hand the body that is to produce the heat, and on the other hand the body which is to receive heat. Sarsi thinks Guiducci would require the excitation and the consumption of parts to take place in the body receiving the heat, whereas I believe the body that is diminished would be the one that generates heat. . . .

When Sarsi heated his bit of copper by pounding it many times, I can well believe that he detected no diminution in its weight even by the most delicate balance. But I do not think on that account that none can have taken place; it may have been too minute to be perceptible in any balance whatever. Let me ask Sarsi whether he thinks any difference of weight could be detected in a silver button before and after it is gilded. He must say no, as we see gold reduced to such thin leaf that it will sustain itself upon the quiet air and drop with extreme slowness; and with such gold any metal may be gilded. Now this button may be used two or three months before the gilding will wear off, and yet since the gilt is ultimately consumed it must be diminishing every day and even every hour.

Or take a ball of musk and carry it with you for a fortnight; it will fill with odor a thousand rooms and streets, which cannot happen without some diminution of material; yet you will find none by weighing it. Thus Sarsi may see that insensible reductions of weight do occur from consumption over a period of months on end, let alone the few minutes he may have persisted in hammering away at his bit of copper. And precisely by this difference we may measure the sensitivity of the assayer's balance in comparison with that of the philosopher's steelyard. And note that the tenuous material which produces heat is even more subtle than that which causes odor, for the latter cannot leak through a glass container, whereas the material of heat makes its way through any substance.

Here Sarsi objects, saying, "If testing with the balance is insufficient to reveal so small a consumption, how will you have it shown?" The objection is ingenious, though not so profound as to be incapable of solution by a little physical logic. Here are the steps of the argument. Of bodies that are rubbed together, some are certainly not consumed, others are quite perceptibly consumed, and still others are indeed consumed, but insensibly. Our senses show us that those which are not consumed at all by rubbing, such as two polished mirrors, are not heated by rubbing, either. We know that those are heated which are perceptibly consumed, as iron when it is being filed. Therefore when we are in doubt whether things are consumed by rubbing we may believe that they are if they are sensibly heated, while those which are not heated may be said not to be consumed.

Before going on I wish to add something for Sarsi's instruction. To say, "This body has not lost weight in the balance, and hence no part of it has been consumed," is fallacious reasoning. It is possible for part of something to be consumed and yet for it to gain weight instead of losing it. This will happen when the specific gravity of that which is consumed is less than that of the medium in which it is being weighed. For instance a very knotty piece of wood taken from near the root may sink when placed in water. Under water let it weigh four ounces. Now cut away some of the lighter parts and leave the knotty portions; the former, being of less specific gravity than the water, gave some support to the entire mass. Hence I say it may happen that the parts left will weigh more in water than the entire piece of wood did. Now it may be that in filing or rubbing together pieces of iron, sticks, or stones, some particles of material less dense than air become separated from them; if nothing else is removed, this would leave the body heavier than before. What I say is not entirely improbable, or merely a refuge which will leave the adversary some trouble in refuting it. For if you carefully observe what happens in breaking glass or stones, you will see some perceptible fumes emerge and rise high in the air, which must be lighter than air. I first noticed this when breaking the corners off a piece of glass and rounding it with a key or some other piece of iron. Besides the little pieces of various sizes which flew off and fell to the ground, I saw a subtle smoke always arising. And apart from what we see, what we smell is a clear sign that some sulfurous or bituminous parts may be ascending which remain invisible but make themselves known by their odor.

Let Sarsi see from this how superficial his philosophizing is, except in appearance. But let him not think he can reply with additional limitations, distinctions, logical technicalities, philosophical jargon, and other idle words, for I assure him that in sustaining one error he will commit a hundred others that are more serious, and produce always greater follies in his camp. . . . Why must I attribute lightning to vehement motion when I see that fire is not excited without the rubbing of solid bodies which do not exist among the clouds? And heat lightning occurs when no commotion is perceived in the air or in clouds. This theory of his, I think, is no more inherently true than the statements of these same philosophers when they attribute the rumbling of thunder to the tearing apart of clouds, or to their knocking together. Actually in the brilliance of the brightest flashes of lightning not the slightest movement or change of shape is discerned in the clouds, and this is just when thunder is being formed. I pass over in silence the fact that these philosophers say that no noise is produced by the striking of wool or hemp, and require the percussion of solid bodies to make sound; and then again when it suits their purposes they assert that mists and clouds striking together will render the loudest of all sounds. Tractable and benign indeed is such philosophy, so pleasantly and readily adapting itself to men's needs and wishes!

Now let us go on to examine the arrows in flight and the

lead balls hurled by catapults which are supposed to be set
afire and melted in the air, according to the authority of
Aristotle, many famous poets, other philosophers, and historians. But it is wrong to say, as Sarsi does, that Guiducci
and I would laugh and joke at the experiences adduced by
Aristotle. We merely do not believe that a cold arrow shot
from a bow can take fire in the air; rather, we think that
if an arrow were shot when afire, it would cool down more
quickly than it would if it were held still. This is not derision; it is simply the statement of our opinion.

Sarsi goes on to say that since this experience of Aristotle's has failed to convince us, many other great men also
have written things of the same sort. To this I reply that if
in order to refute Aristotle's statement we are obliged to
represent that no other men have believed it, then nobody
on earth can ever refute it, since nothing can make those
who have believed it not believe it. But it is news to me
that any man would actually put the testimony of writers
ahead of what experience shows him. To adduce more
witnesses serves no purpose, Sarsi, for we have never denied
that such things have been written and believed. We did
say they are false, but so far as authority is concerned yours
alone is as effective as an army's in rendering the events true
or false. You take your stand on the authority of many poets
against our experiments. I reply that if those poets could
be present at our experiments they would change their
views, and without disgrace they could say they had
been writing hyperbolically—or even admit they had been
wrong.

Well, if we cannot have the presence of your poets (who,
as I say, would yield to experience), we do have at hand
archers and catapultists, and you may see for yourself
whether citing your authorities to them can strengthen
their arms to such an extent that the arrows they shoot and
the lead balls they hurl will take fire and melt in the air.
In that way you will be able to find out just how much
force human authority has upon the facts of Nature, which
remains deaf and inexorable to our wishes. You say there

is no longer an Acestes or a Mezentius[17] or other mighty paladin? I shall be content to have you shoot an arrow not with a simple longbow, but with the stoutest steel crossbow, or use a catapult drawn by levers and windlasses that could not be managed by thirty of your ancient heroes. Shoot ten arrows, or a hundred; and if it ever happens that on one of them the feathers so much as slightly tan—let alone its shaft taking fire or its steel tip melting—I shall not only concede the argument but forfeit your respect, which I regard so highly. . . .

I cannot but be astonished that Sarsi should persist in trying to prove by means of witnesses something that I may see for myself at any time by means of experiment. Witnesses are examined in doubtful matters which are past and transient, not in those which are actual and present. A judge must seek by means of witnesses to determine whether Peter injured John last night, but not whether John was injured, since the judge can see that for himself. But even in conclusions which can be known only by reasoning, I say that the testimony of many has little more value than that of few, since the number of people who reason well in complicated matters is much smaller than that of those who reason badly. If reasoning were like hauling I should agree that several reasoners would be worth more than one, just as several horses can haul more sacks of grain than one can. But reasoning is like racing and not like hauling, and a single Arabian steed can outrun a hundred plowhorses. So when Sarsi brings in this multitude of authors it appears to me that instead of strengthening his conclusion he merely ennobles our case by showing that we have outreasoned many men of great reputation.

---

[17] Two powerful warriors of Virgil's *Aeneid:* "Acestes . . . discharged his shaft . . . ; the arrow, flying among the watery clouds, took fire and with flames marked out its path, till being quite consumed it vanished." (v, 525 ff.) "Mezentius himself, having laid aside his arms, thrice whirling about his head the thong, discharged a hissing sling, and with the half-melted lead clove asunder the temples of the son of Arcens." (ix, 585 ff.)

If Sarsi wants me to believe with Suidas[18] that the Babylonians cooked their eggs by whirling them in slings, I shall do so; but I must say that the cause of this effect was very different from what he suggests. To discover the true cause I reason as follows: "If we do not achieve an effect which others formerly achieved, then it must be that in our operations we lack something that produced their success. And if there is just one single thing we lack, then that alone can be the true cause. Now we do not lack eggs, nor slings, nor sturdy fellows to whirl them; yet our eggs do not cook, but merely cool down faster if they happen to be hot. And since nothing is lacking to us except being Babylonians, then being Babylonians is the cause of the hardening of eggs, and not friction of the air." And this is what I wished to discover. Is it possible that Sarsi has never observed the coolness produced on his face by the continual change of air when he is riding post? If he has, then how can he prefer to believe things related by other men as having happened two thousand years ago in Babylon rather than present events which he himself experiences? . . .

Sarsi says he does not wish to be numbered among those who affront the sages by disbelieving and contradicting them. I say I do not wish to be counted as an ignoramus and an ingrate toward Nature and toward God; for if they have given me my senses and my reason, why should I defer such great gifts to the errors of some man? Why should I believe blindly and stupidly what I wish to believe, and subject the freedom of my intellect to someone else who is just as liable to error as I am? . . .

Finally Sarsi is reduced to saying with Aristotle that if the air ever happened to be abundantly filled with warm exhalations in the presence of various other requisites, then leaden balls would melt in the air when shot from muskets or thrown by slings. This must have been the state of the air when the Babylonians were cooking their eggs, . . . and at such times things must go very pleasantly for people who are being shot at. But, Sarsi says, since to find such

---

[18] Suidas was a Greek lexicographer of the tenth century.

conditions is a matter of chance, and one that does not occur too frequently, we must not resort to experiments for settling such questions. So, Sarsi, if experiments are performed thousands of times at all seasons and in every place without once producing the effects mentioned by your philosophers, poets, and historians, this will mean nothing and we must believe their words rather than our own eyes? But what if I find for you a state of the air that has all the conditions you say are required, and still the egg is not cooked nor the lead ball destroyed? Alas! I should be wasting my efforts, . . . for all too prudently you have secured your position by saying that "there is needed for this effect violent motion, a great quantity of exhalations, a highly attenuated material, and whatever else conduces to it." This "whatever else" is what beats me, and gives you a blessed harbor, a sanctuary completely secure.

What I had in mind, though, was to suspend our argument and wait quietly until some new comet came along. I imagined that while this lasted you and Aristotle would grant me that since the air was then properly disposed for kindling the comet, it would likewise be suitable for melting lead balls and cooking eggs, inasmuch as you seem to require the same condition for both effects. It was then that I would have had us set to work with our slings, eggs, bows, muskets, and cannons so that we might clear up this matter for ourselves. And even without waiting for a comet we might find an opportune time when in midsummer the air flashes with heat lightning, as you assign all these "burnings" to a single cause. But I suppose that when you failed to behold a melting of lead balls or even the cooking of eggs under such conditions you would still fail to give in; you would say that this "whatever else conduces to the effect" was lacking. If you would only tell me what this "whatever else" is, I should endeavor to provide it. But if not I shall have to abandon my little scheme, though I do believe it would turn out against you. . . .

It now remains for me to tell Your Excellency, as I promised, some thoughts of mine about the proposition "motion is the cause of heat," and to show in what sense this may be true. But first I must consider what it is that we call heat, as I suspect that people in general have a concept of this which is very remote from the truth. For they believe that heat is a real phenomenon, or property, or quality, which actually resides in the material by which we feel ourselves warmed.[19] Now I say that whenever I conceive any material or corporeal substance, I immediately feel the need to think of it as bounded, and as having this or that shape; as being large or small in relation to other things, and in some specific place at any given time; as being in motion or at rest; as touching or not touching some other body; and as being one in number, or few, or many. From these conditions I cannot separate such a substance by any stretch of my imagination. But that it must be white or red, bitter or sweet, noisy or silent, and of sweet or foul odor, my mind does not feel compelled to bring in as necessary accompaniments. Without the senses as our guides, reason or imagination unaided would probably never arrive at qualities like these. Hence I think that tastes, odors, colors, and so on are no more than mere names so far as the object in which we place them is concerned, and that they reside only in the consciousness. Hence if the living creature were removed, all these qualities would be wiped away and annihilated. But since we have imposed upon them special names, distinct from those of the other and real qualities mentioned previously, we wish to believe that they really exist as actually different from those.

[19] The ensuing passages are generally considered to entitle Galileo to credit for anticipating the fundamental concepts of the empiricist philosophy developed chiefly by John Locke at the close of the seventeenth century. The basic tenets are of course much older, belonging to the atomism of Democritus (b. 460 B.C.), a doctrine which was particularly repugnant to Aristotle. While this exposition is of no little philosophical and scientific interest (inasmuch as empiricism, rightly or wrongly, has been closely associated with the development of modern science), Galileo was no philosophical empiricist. He attached no less importance to reason than to experiment, and he had no doubt about the independent truth of mathematical propositions, the denial of which has always involved empiricist philosophers in serious difficulty with the best logicians.

I may be able to make my notion clearer by means of some examples. I move my hand first over a marble statue and then over a living man. As to the effect flowing from my hand, this is the same with regard to both objects and my hand; it consists of the primary phenomena of motion and touch, for which we have no further names. But the live body which receives these operations feels different sensations according to the various places touched. When touched upon the soles of the feet, for example, or under the knee or armpit, it feels in addition to the common sensation of touch a sensation on which we have imposed a special name, "tickling." This sensation belongs to us and not to the hand. Anyone would make a serious error if he said that the hand, in addition to the properties of moving and touching, possessed another faculty of "tickling," as if tickling were a phenomenon that resided in the hand that tickled. A piece of paper or a feather drawn lightly over any part of our bodies performs intrinsically the same operations of moving and touching, but by touching the eye, the nose, or the upper lip it excites in us an almost intolerable titillation, even though elsewhere it is scarcely felt. This titillation belongs entirely to us and not to the feather; if the live and sensitive body were removed it would remain no more than a mere word. I believe that no more solid an existence belongs to many qualities which we have come to attribute to physical bodies—tastes, odors, colors, and many more.

A body which is solid and, so to speak, quite material, when moved in contact with any part of my person produces in me the sensation we call touch. This, though it exists over my entire body, seems to reside principally in the palms of the hands and in the finger tips, by whose means we sense the most minute differences in texture that are not easily distinguished by other parts of our bodies. Some of these sensations are more pleasant to us than others. . . . The sense of touch is more material than the other senses; and, as it arises from the solidity of matter, it seems to be related to the earthly element.

Perhaps the origin of two other senses lies in the fact

that there are bodies which constantly dissolve into minute particles, some of which are heavier than air and descend, while others are lighter and rise up. The former may strike upon a certain part of our bodies that is much more sensitive than the skin, which does not feel the invasion of such subtle matter. This is the upper surface of the tongue; here the tiny particles are received, and mixing with and penetrating its moisture, they give rise to tastes, which are sweet or unsavory according to the various shapes, numbers, and speeds of the particles. And those minute particles which rise up may enter by our nostrils and strike upon some small protuberances which are the instrument of smelling; here likewise their touch and passage is received to our like or dislike according as they have this or that shape, are fast or slow, and are numerous or few. The tongue and nasal passages are providently arranged for these things, as the one extends from below to receive descending particles, and the other is adapted to those which ascend. Perhaps the excitation of tastes may be given a certain analogy to fluids, which descend through air, and odors to fires, which ascend.

Then there remains the air itself, an element available for sounds, which come to us indifferently from below, above, and all sides—for we reside in the air and its movements displace it equally in all directions. The location of the ear is most fittingly accommodated to all positions in space. Sounds are made and heard by us when the air—without any special property of "sonority" or "transonority" —is ruffled by a rapid tremor into very minute waves and moves certain cartilages of a tympanum in our ear. External means capable of thus ruffling the air are very numerous, but for the most part they may be reduced to the trembling of some body which pushes the air and disturbs it. Waves are propagated very rapidly in this way, and high tones are produced by frequent waves and low tones by sparse ones.

To excite in us tastes, odors, and sounds I believe that nothing is required in external bodies except shapes, numbers, and slow or rapid movements. I think that if ears, tongues, and noses were removed, shapes and numbers and motions would remain, but not odors or tastes or sounds. The latter, I believe, are nothing more than names when separated from living beings, just as tickling and titillation are nothing but names in the absence of such things as noses and armpits. And as these four senses are related to the four elements, so I believe that vision, the sense eminent above all others in the proportion of the finite to the infinite, the temporal to the instantaneous, the quantitative to the indivisible, the illuminated to the obscure—that vision, I say, is related to light itself. But of this sensation and the things pertaining to it I pretend to understand but little; and since even a long time would not suffice to explain that trifle, or even to hint at an explanation, I pass this over in silence.

Having shown that many sensations which are supposed to be qualities residing in external objects have no real existence save in us, and outside ourselves are mere names, I now say that I am inclined to believe heat to be of this character. Those materials which produce heat in us and make us feel warmth, which are known by the general name of "fire," would then be a multitude of minute particles having certain shapes and moving with certain velocities. Meeting with our bodies, they penetrate by means of their extreme subtlety, and their touch as felt by us when they pass through our substance is the sensation we call "heat." This is pleasant or unpleasant according to the greater or smaller speed of these particles as they go pricking and penetrating; pleasant when this assists our necessary transpiration, and obnoxious when it causes too great a separation and dissolution of our substance. The operation of fire by means of its particles is merely that in moving it penetrates all bodies, causing their speedy or slow dissolution in proportion to the number and velocity of the fire-corpuscles and the density or tenuity of the bodies. Many materials are such that in their decomposition the greater part of them passes over into additional tiny corpuscles, and this dissolution continues so long as these continue to meet with further matter capable of being so resolved. I do not believe that in addition to shape, number, motion, penetration, and touch there is any other quality in fire corresponding to "heat"; this belongs so intimately to us that when the live body is taken away, heat becomes no more than a simple name. . . .

Since the presence of fire-corpuscles alone does not suffice to excite heat, but their motion is needed also, it seems to me that one may very reasonably say that motion is the cause of heat. . . . But I hold it to be silly to accept that proposition in the ordinary way, as if a stone or piece of iron or a stick must heat up when moved. The rubbing together and friction of two hard bodies, either by resolving their parts into very subtle flying particles or by opening an exit for the tiny fire-corpuscles within, ultimately sets these in motion; and when they meet our bodies and penetrate them, our conscious mind feels those pleasant or unpleasant sensations which we have named heat, burning, and scalding. And perhaps when such attrition stops at or is confined to the smallest quanta, their motion is temporal and their action calorific only; but when their ultimate and highest resolution into truly indivisible atoms is arrived at, light is created.[20] This may have an instantaneous motion, or rather an instantaneous expansion and diffusion,[21] rendering it capable of occupying immense spaces by its—I know not whether to say its subtlety, its rarity, its immateriality, or some other property which differs from all these and is nameless.

[20] This lucky guess should entitle Galileo to consideration as having anticipated many modern scientific discoveries—in about the same sense as that in which medieval philosophers anticipated Galileo in the discovery of the principle of inertia. At present it is customary to praise their happy conjectures and to overlook his. But perhaps that is because they made so many unsupported guesses, and he so few.

[21] The erroneous view that light is transmitted instantaneously was later withdrawn by Galileo, and in the *Discourses* of 1638 he even proposed an experiment for determining the speed of light. It was, of course, too crude to succeed. Yet Galileo's discoveries played a part in its successful measurement, for this was eventually accomplished by means of observations of eclipses of the satellites of Jupiter.

I do not wish, Your Excellency, to engulf myself inadvertently in a boundless sea from which I might never get back to port, nor in trying to solve one difficulty do I wish to give rise to a hundred more, as I fear may have already happened in sailing but this little way from shore. Therefore I shall desist until some more opportune occasion.

.   .   .   .

Finally I cannot resist speaking about Sarsi's amazement at my hopeless ineptitude in the employment of experiments, inasmuch as he himself errs as badly as a man can in that same activity. You, Sarsi, must show us that an interposed flame would not suffice to hide the stars. In order to convince us by experiments, you say that if we look through flames at people, firebrands, coals, printed pages, and candles, we shall see all these quite plainly. Did it never enter your head to tell us to try looking at stars? Why did you not say to us at the outset, "Interpose a flame between the eye and some star, and the star will be made neither more nor less visible"? Surely there is no lack of stars in the sky. Now is this to be a skillful and prudent experimentalist?

I ask you whether the comet's flame is like our flames, or whether it has a different nature. If its nature is different, experiments made with our flames are not conclusive. If it is like our flames, then you might have made us look at stars through our flames and left out firebrands, candlesnuffs, and such things. Instead of saying that print may be read through a candle flame, you might have said that a star may be so perceived. . . . You are obliged to kindle a very distant flame as large as a comet and to make us see stars through it. . . . But in order to put you at your ease and give you every advantage, I shall be content with much less. Instead of placing the fire as far away as a comet, I am satisfied with a distance of one hundred yards. In place of the thickness of a comet, merely ten yards will suffice. And since you say the object to be seen gains an advantage from being bright, let it be one of the stars which was visible through the tail of the last comet—for you maintain that stars are brighter than any flame.

And now, with all these conditions so advantageous to your cause, if you can make the star visible through the bonfire, I shall admit defeat and place you among the most prudent and expert experimenters in the whole world. But if you fail, I ask no more from you than silence, by which an end will be put to this dispute. And truly that is what I hope will now take place.

.   .   .   .

EPILOGUE

The Assayer enjoyed an immense success. Then, as now, people loved a fighting spirit and applauded a victorious comeback. Just as the printing was completed, Galileo's old friend Maffeo Barberini was elected Pope. Since he was a noted patron of literature, the Linceans redesigned the title page and dedicated the book to him. He was delighted with it, and the official censor had already hailed the book and its author as wonders of the age.

Galileo, who had been hoping for some relaxation of the ban against Copernicus, now revisited Rome and discussed the matter with the new and friendly Pope. It was agreed that the forbidden topic could be discussed hypothetically and impartially, together with the Ptolemaic system. Thus Galileo's treatise on the system of the world, promised as long ago as 1610, finally took shape as the *Dialogue* published in 1632. If this turned out to be not quite impartial, it was at least technically within the bounds agreed upon as understood by the author. But in the face of powerful enemies, and with no hope of support any longer from the Jesuits at the Roman College, that was not enough. The Pope was persuaded that Galileo had ridiculed him personally in the *Dialogue*, and had also broken a previous promise never to discuss the Copernican system again. At his command Galileo was summoned to Rome, tried by the Inquisition, condemned to perpetual arrest, forced to abjure, and forbidden ever to publish anything further.

Five years later Galileo's last and greatest book—the *Discourses on Two New Sciences*—was published in Holland. By that time he was seventy-five years old and totally blind, but four more years went by before, in January, 1642, his indomitable spirit succumbed to death.

APPENDIX I:
CHRONOLOGICAL SUMMARY
OF GALILEO'S LIFE

1564   Galileo born at Pisa on February 15

1574   Is at Florence with his family

1575
to   Receives education at Florence and at Monastery of
1578   Sta. Maria of Vallombrosa

1581   Matriculates at the University of Pisa

1583   Discovers uniformity of pendulum vibrations

1586   Gives public and private instruction at Siena and Florence

1587   Makes first visit to Rome and meets Father Christopher Clavius

1589   Begins teaching at the University of Pisa

1592   Appointed Professor of Mathematics at the University of Padua

1594   Suffers severe chill resulting in permanent arthritic afflictions

1600   Birth of daughter, Virginia (later Sister Maria Celeste)

1601   Birth of daughter, Livia (later Sister Arcangela)

1602   Commences experiments on magnetism

1604   Announces law of falling bodies, correct in result but defective in theory

1605   Instructor of Cosimo, Prince of Tuscany, during summer vacation from Padua

1606   Birth of son, Vincenzio. Publishes first book (on compass of his invention)

1607 Brings successful action against Baldassar Capra for plagiarism of compass

1609 *February:* Prince Cosimo becomes Grand Duke. Galileo makes overtures for employment at the Tuscan court

   June: Arrives at correct theory of falling bodies. Hears first report of telescope made in Belgium

   July–August: Constructs the first astronomically useful telescope

1610 *March:* Publishes first telescopic discoveries in the *Sidereus Nuncius*

   June: Resigns from the University of Padua

   September: Returns to Florence as Chief Mathematician and Philosopher to the Grand Duke

1611 *March to June:* Visits Rome second time. Hailed as discoverer, elected to Lincean Academy, and feted by Jesuit mathematicians at the Roman College

   July: Enters dispute over floating bodies with Peripatetics at Florence

1612 Publishes book on floating bodies. Writes letters on sunspots. Early in November hears that he has been opposed by Fra Niccolo Lorini, a Dominican professor, in certain conversations at Florence

1613 *March:* Galileo's *Letters on Sunspots* published by the Lincean Academy

   December: Warned by Castelli of attacks at Court in Pisa. Writes letter to Castelli concerning science and religion

1614 *July:* Both daughters enter convent of San Matteo at Arcetri

   December: Is publicly attacked from the pulpit by Fra Tommaso Caccini, a Dominican firebrand

1615 *February:* Copy of Galileo's letter to Castelli sent by Lorini to Rome, with denunciation of the views of the "Galileists"

   December: Galileo goes once more to Rome, to answer his enemies and if possible prevent banning of the Copernican theory

1616   *February:* Copernican theory condemned and Galileo told to abandon it

    May: Galileo returns to Florence after receiving from Cardinal Bellarmine a certificate answering various hostile rumors

    November: Turns attention to negotiations with Spain for navigational uses of astronomical discoveries

1617   Works to perfect a telescope for use at sea, and continues negotiations with Spain

1618   Afflicted with serious illness. Holds discussions of comets with friends

1619   Drafts book (published by a pupil) criticizing a work on comets by a Jesuit professor at the Roman College, to which an angry reply is printed

1620   Congregation of the Index decides on minor "corrections" to be made in Copernicus's book, with which it becomes permissible reading

1621   Cosimo II dies and is succeeded by Ferdinand II under regency of Maria Madeleine and Christina.

1622   Completes his devastating answer to the Jesuit attack of 1619

1623   Cardinal Maffeo Barberini becomes Pope Urban VIII, and Galileo's new book is dedicated to him. Galileo once more bedridden

1624   *April to June:* Visits Rome for fourth time; is warmly welcomed and granted six audiences with the Pope

    July–August: Perfects the compound microscope

1625   Begins work on the *Dialogue* in which Copernicus is to be covertly supported

1626   Undertakes new studies in magnetism and interrupts writing of *Dialogue*

1627   Friends urge completion of *Dialogue*, but work is not resumed

1628 Serious illness threatens Galileo's life

1629 *Autumn:* Resumes composition of *Dialogue*
December: Birth of grandson

1630 *January: Dialogue* completed
May: Galileo arrives at Rome with manuscript, seeking license to print; leaves in June with "complete satisfaction"
August: Federico Cesi, head of Lincean Academy, who was to oversee the printing at Rome, dies suddenly

1631 Permission to print *Dialogue* at Florence instead of Rome secured after much delay; printing begun in June

1632 *February: Dialogue* published
August: Printer of *Dialogue* ordered by Rome to suspend sales
October: Galileo ordered to Rome to stand trial

1633 *February:* Galileo arrives at Rome, protests of Grand Duke and certificates of doctors proving of no avail
April: Galileo twice examined by Inquisitors
June: Pope orders rigorous examination; Galileo capitulates and is sentenced to indefinite imprisonment after humiliating abjuration
July: Allowed to leave Rome for Siena in custody of archbishop there
December: Returned to Arcetri, near Florence, for permanent house arrest

1634 Death of eldest daughter brings on illness feared to be mortal for Galileo

1635 Latin translation of *Dialogue* published at Strasbourg. First English translation of *Dialogue* made, but not published

1636 Italian and Latin versions of *Letter to Christina* published at Strasbourg

1637 Right eye blinded by inflammation. By end of year sight of both eyes irretrievably lost

1638   Galileo permitted to move to Florence for medical
       care, under heavy restrictions

       July: Publication at Leyden of the *Two New Sci-
          ences,* first great work of modern physics

       September: John Milton visits Galileo at Arcetri

1639   Pope flatly refuses to free the sightless man, now
       seventy-five years old

1641   Galileo dictates additions to the *Two New Sciences*

1642   Galileo dies at Arcetri, January 8. Pope forbids the
       Grand Duke to erect a monument in Galileo's honor
       if any word on it would "offend the reputation of
       the Holy Office"

APPENDIX II:
BIBLIOGRAPHICAL NOTES

1. Other English translations of works by Galileo.

1590. *De motu* (unpublished ms.)
  1. Translation by I. E. Drabkin:
    On Motion. (Pages 13–114 in *Galileo on Motion and on Mechanics*. Madison, 1960.)
1610. *Sidereus Nuncius* . . . (Venice)
  1. Translation by Edward Stafford Carlos:
    The Sidereal Messenger of Galileo Galilei and a Part of the Preface to Kepler's Dioptrics. London, 1880.
1612. *Discorso . . . intorno alle cose, che stanno in sù l'acqua, ò che in quella si muovono* . . . (Florence)
  1. Translation by Thomas Salusbury:
    A. A Discourse . . . Concerning the Natation of Bodies upon, and Submersion in, the Water. London, 1663.
      (Pages 400–76 in Salusbury's *Mathematical Collections and Translations, The Second Tome*. London, 1665.)
    B. Discourse on Bodies in Water, with Introduction and Notes by Stillman Drake. Urbana, 1960.
1623. *Il Saggiatore* . . . (Rome)
  1. Translation by Stillman Drake:
    The Assayer. (Pages 151–336 in *The Controversy on the Comets of 1618*. Philadelphia, 1960.)
1632. *Dialogo . . . sopra i due Massimi Sistemi del Mondo; Tolemaico, e Copernicano* . . . (Florence)
  1. Translation by Thomas Salusbury:
    A. The Systeme of the World . . . Wherein the Two Grand Systemes of Ptolomy and

Copernicus are largely discoursed of . . .
London, 1661.

 (Pages 1–424 *op. cit., The First Tome.*
London, 1661.)

B. Dialogue on the Great World Systems. In
the Salusbury translation. Revised . . . by
Giorgio de Santillana. Chicago, 1953.

2. Translation by Stillman Drake:
Dialogue Concerning the Two Chief World
Systems—Ptolemaic and Copernican. Berkeley,
1953. Reprinted with revised notes, 1962.

1634. *Les Méchaniques de Galilée . . . traduites de l'italien par* . . . M[arin] M[ersenne]. Paris. (First
published edition of this work, which had long circulated in manuscript.)

1. Translation by Thomas Salusbury:
Galileus His Mechanics. [London, 1662.]

 (Pages 271–302 in the second tome.)

2. Translation by Stillman Drake:
On Mechanics. (Pages 147–82 in *Galileo on
Motion and on Mechanics.* Madison, 1960.)

1636. *Nova-antiqua sanctissimorum patrum . . . doctrina,
de sacrae scripturae testimoniis in conclusionibus
mere naturalibus.* . . . Strasbourg. (First published
edition of the *Letter to the Grand Duchess Christina.*)

1. Translation by Thomas Salusbury:
The Ancient and Modern Doctrine of Holy Fathers . . . Concerning the rash Citation of the
Testimony of Sacred Scripture, in Conclusions
merely Natural. . . . London, 1661.

 (Pages 427–60 in the first tome.)

1638. *Discorsi e dimostrazioni matematiche intorno a due
nuove scienze.* . . . Leyden.

1. Translation by Thomas Salusbury:
Mathematical Discourses and Demonstrations,
Touching Two New Sciences. . . . London,
1665. [1662]

 (Pages 1–270 in the second tome. The date
on the title page is given as 1665, but internal evidence shows this part of the volume
to have been printed in 1662.)

2. Translation by Thomas Weston:

Mathematical Discourses Concerning Two New Sciences. . . . London, 1730.

(Weston undertook this new translation because even at that time the Salusbury work was almost unobtainable.)

3. Translation by Henry Crew and Alfonso De Salvio:

Dialogues Concerning Two New Sciences. New York, 1914.

(This work has been reprinted many times and is currently available. The translation cannot be too highly praised, though by using the word "Dialogues" in place of "Discourses," the translators have introduced some confusion in English references to Galileo's works.)

1644. *Discorso . . . detto dall'autore, bilancetta.* Palermo. In: G. B. Hodierna, *Archimede redivivo.* . . . (First published edition.)

1. Translation by Thomas Salusbury:

The Ballance of Signeur Galileo Galilei. [London, 1662.]

(Pages 303–10 in the second tome.)

2. Translation by L. Fermi and G. Bernardini:

The Little Balance. (Appendix to *Galileo and the Scientific Revolution.* New York, 1961.)

In addition to the published translations listed above, several exist in manuscript only. Of these the most interesting is an English translation of the *Dialogue* probably completed about 1635. The translator has never been positively identified, but was probably Dr. Joseph Webbe of London, who was graduated in medicine at Padua in 1612.

The Thomas Salusbury who did so much to present Galileo in English dress has only recently been identified, through the researches of Mr. Jacob Zeitlin, as the writer of several letters to the Earl of Huntingdon in the years 1664–66, now in the Huntingdon Library. Salusbury then resided in Highgate, where he died in 1666, and was employed as political observer in London and mentor to the young earl. He was probably born about 1630 and lived abroad during the Civil Wars. As a translator he was conscientious and enthusiastic. Apart from the *Mathematical Collections,* his translations include a book by the Jesuit Father Daniel Bartoli, and a moralizing romance called *Arnaldo.*

2. Selected works in English relating to Galileo's life and discoveries.

   1. [John Wilkins], *The Discovery of a New World . . . in the Moon.* London, 1638.

      This was the first book to popularize Galileo's discoveries in England.

   2. Giuseppe Baretti, *The Italian Library.* London, 1757.

      Speaking of Galileo (p. 52) Baretti says: "The moment he was set at liberty, he looked up to the sky and down to the ground, and, stamping with his foot, in a contemplative mood, said, *Eppur si move;* that is, still it moves, meaning the earth." It is curious that this famous story should have first appeared so late and in an English book. It was quickly picked up by other writers, who generally made it appear that Galileo had said these words as he rose from his knees after abjuring before the Inquisition. This preposterous version caused most serious writers to reject the whole story as a myth created to fit Galileo's personality rather than the truth. But in 1911 the same Italian words (correctly spelled, however) were discovered on a painting ascribed to Murillo and dating no more than a decade after Galileo's death.

      It is not impossible to construct a rational basis for this old tradition, in view of Baretti's words "set free." Galileo was never literally set free, but he was allowed to return to Florence after a period in the custody of his friend and former pupil Ascanio Piccolomini, then Archbishop of Siena. It is quite possible that when he set out for Florence, Galileo uttered the famous words either in the presence of the archbishop or in circumstances which permitted them to reach his ears. Piccolomini, it may be supposed, discreetly kept them from the authorities in Rome. But within the family the story was too good to keep. Ascanio's brother, the illustrious soldier Octavio, was in Spain about the time this painting was commissioned. The coincidence is suggestive.

3. [John Elliot Drinkwater (-Bethune)], *The Life of Galileo Galilei*. . . . London, 1829.

Although this is one of the earliest extensive biographies of Galileo it is still one of the best, despite the fact that it was written before the documents of Galileo's trial were made public. Drinkwater was the last writer who had read Salusbury's *Life of Galileo,* and he quotes a few interesting passages from it.

4. David Brewster, *The Martyrs of Science.* London, 1841.

A rather elementary presentation. The otherwise cautious Brewster, himself a noted scientist, represented Galileo as having been subjected to torture, and thereby created a good deal of controversy.

5. Richard Robert Madden, *Galileo and the Inquisition.* London, 1863.

A moderate Catholic appraisal, answering various statements made by Brewster, Drinkwater (whose book Madden mistakenly attributed to Lord Brougham), and several foreign authors. The work is scrupulously written but not entirely accurate. It supplies a good deal of information about the Inquisition generally.

6. [Mary Allan-Olney], *The Private Life of Galileo.* . . . London, 1870.

A charming, competent, and readable account of Galileo's life with particular emphasis upon the letters of his elder daughter. It is valuable also for its translations and extracts from other letters which reveal much about Galileo and his correspondents.

7. Karl von Gebler, *Galileo Galilei and the Roman Curia.* London, 1879.

Translated from the German by Mrs. George Sturge, whose work is particularly valuable in presenting to the English reader accurate translations of the important documents of Galileo's trial, as well as many of his letters. Gebler's is probably the best single book on Galileo yet published in English, especially with regard to the controversial aspects of some of the official documents.

8. F. R. Wegg-Prosser, *Galileo and his Judges*. London, 1889.

Essentially a defense of the Catholic Church in its proceedings against Galileo. It is of interest only to those who may wonder what defense there can possibly be.

9. J. J. Fahie, *Galileo, his Life and Work*. London, 1903.

This attempt to provide a definitive portrayal of Galileo is lacking in a great many respects. It has, however, the advantage of being written after Professor Favaro began the labors which uncovered so much new material.

10. J. J. Fahie, *Memorials of Galileo*. London, 1921.

A specialized work of great value in its field, being the most complete compilation to have been made in any language describing portraits, busts, medallions, and monuments depicting Galileo.

11. Emile Namer, *Galileo*. New York, 1931.

Translated from the French by Sibyl Harris. This is a popularized story of Galileo's life and work, not limited strictly to historical facts.

12. Lane Cooper, *Aristotle, Galileo, and the Leaning Tower of Pisa*. Ithaca, 1935.

An attempt to disprove several commonly accepted views relating to the subjects mentioned in the title.

13. Thomas Campanella, *The Defense of Galileo*. Smith College, 1937.

Translated from the Latin and annotated by Grant McColley. Originally written in 1616 as a result of the events described in the present book, this essay of Campanella's was first published in 1622.

14. F. Sherwood Taylor, *Galileo and the Freedom of Thought*. London, 1938.

A highly readable treatment of Galileo's life and work from the standpoint that is today the most interesting and significant of all.

15. Erwin Panofsky, *Galileo as a Critic of the Arts*. The Hague, 1954.

An illuminating commentary upon a little-known phase of Galileo's interests. The author also establishes the authenticity of a famous letter from Galileo to Cigoli which was long looked upon with suspicion. An abridged reprint of this work appeared in *Isis*, vol. 147, pt. 1 (March 1956).

16. Giorgio de Santillana, *The Crime of Galileo*. New York, 1955.

17. Pasquale M. D'Elia, S.J., *Galileo in China* (tr. R. Suter and M. Sciascia). Cambridge, 1960.

18. Laura Fermi and Gilberto Bernardini, *Galileo and the Scientific Revolution*. New York, 1961.

3. Selected general works (edition cited is the latest rather than the first):

    A. Relating to Copernicus.
        1. Armitage, Angus. *World of Copernicus*. New York, 1951.
        2. Kesten, Herman. *Copernicus and his World*. New York, 1945.
    B. Relating to the astronomical background of Galileo's work.
        1. Dreyer, J. L. E. *A History of Astronomy from Thales to Kepler*. New York, 1954.
    C. Relating to Galileo on philosophical questions.
        1. Burtt, E. A. *The Metaphysical Foundations of Modern Science*. New York, 1954.
        2. Strong, E. A. *Procedures and Metaphysics*. Berkeley, 1937.
    D. Relating to Galileo's role in the origin of modern science.
        1. Hall, A. R. *The Scientific Revolution, 1500–1800*. London, 1954.
        2. Singer, Charles A. *A Short History of Science*. Oxford, 1943.

INDEX

ANCHOR BOOKS

SCIENCE AND MATHEMATICS

ANCHOR BOOKS

Science Study Series (continued)

ANCHOR BOOKS

HISTORY

THE PURITAN REVOLUTION: A Documentary History—Stuart E. Prall, ed., A602
QUEEN ELIZABETH I—J. E. Neale, A105
THE RUSSIAN REVOLUTION—Leon Trotsky, F. W. Dupee, ed., A170
SEVENTEENTH CENTURY BACKGROUND—Basil Willey, A19
SEVENTEENTH CENTURY FRANCE—Geoffrey Treasure, A592
THE SIX HUNDRED DAYS OF MUSSOLINI—F. W. Deakin, A508b
THE SPLENDID CENTURY—W. H. Lewis, A122
STATES AND NATIONS—Benjamin Akzin, A493
THIRTY YEARS WAR—C. V. Wedgwood, A249
TODAY'S LATIN AMERICA—Robert J. Alexander, A327
TO THE FINLAND STATION—Edmund Wilson, A6
THE WANING OF THE MIDDLE AGES—John Huizinga, A42
THE YORKIST AGE: Daily Life During the Wars of the Roses—Paul Murray Kendall, A466